Preface

This laboratory manual has been planned to accompany the textbook Basic Foods, and the units in the manual parallel the chapters in the text with a few exceptions. However, the manual can easily be used with a different text simply by assigning the units out of order.

Both the laboratory manual and the textbook are intended for use in beginning foods classes at the college level. They do not require a knowledge of chemistry or physics, although the principles of these sciences are applied in explaining the principles of food preparation.

It is intended that the students will read the textbook assignments accompanying each laboratory unit for the background needed to work in the laboratory. This manual is unique in that a wide variety of similar recipes are included so that each student or pair of students can prepare a similar yet different product. Thus, students learn, for example, that there are many kinds of muffins but all require the same techniques for preparation. They also can learn ways to vary the recipes and can themselves become creative.

Another unique feature of this laboratory manual is its inclusion of virtually all types of food products, from "soup to nuts." Dishes of many different origins or cultures are sampled —not only the typical American standbys from the West, South, East, and North, but also Oriental, Mexican, Italian, Spanish, French, German and many other cuisines. The author hopes thus to intrigue the student and encourage further ventures into the exciting and satisfying field of food preparation. Beyond question there is great adventure in learning to prepare and eat many kinds of foods.

Emphasis in the laboratory manual and text has also been on nutritional value and economical preparation of foods. Alternate procedures for minimizing the use of fats in food preparation, cooking procedures that preserve nutrients in foods, and the use of some of our more nutritious and perhaps less popular foods and ingredients are presented.

This second edition of the laboratory manual has been expanded to include the adaptation of many of the recipies for microwave oven cooking. Lack of space did not permit the adaptation of all recipes; in fact, many are not suitable for that method of preparation. As the students learn how to use the microwave oven for various cooking procedures, they will learn to make these adaptations for themselves.

Sufficient material is supplied in this manual for a full year of work; for one semester courses the instructor can emphasize those subject areas judged most important for the students. The rest of the material will be there for the student to investigate on his or her own time. If students can be aroused and challenged to practice these principles of food preparation throughout their lives, this author will be gratified. We will all have accomplished something very worthwhile.

J. C. G.

Contents

PREFACE   iii

INTRODUCTION   v

UNIT 1   Introductory Principles of Food Preparation   1
UNIT 2   Comparison of Fats and their Use as a
                 Cooking Medium   8
UNIT 3   Fruit Preparation   19
UNIT 4   Vegetable Cookery   28
UNIT 5   Salad Dressings   43
UNIT 6   Salads   49
UNIT 7   Cereal Products   62
UNIT 8   Sauces and Puddings   70
UNIT 9   Flour and Leavening   82
UNIT 10   Quick Breads   86
UNIT 11   Pastry and Pies   107
UNIT 12   Yeast-Leavened Products   121
UNIT 13   Gelatin Cookery   134
UNIT 14   Milk and Milk Products   141
UNIT 15   Eggs   150
UNIT 16   Food Foams   161
UNIT 17   Angel, Sponge, and Chiffon Cakes   172
UNIT 18   Shortened Cakes   180
UNIT 19   Frostings and Fillings   186
UNIT 20   Cookies and Fruit-Nut Breads   193
UNIT 21   Meat Preparation   207
UNIT 22   Poultry and Seafood   223
UNIT 23   Vegetable Proteins Cookery   243
UNIT 24   Soups and Casseroles   249
UNIT 25   Sandwiches   266
UNIT 26   Hors d'Oeuvres and Canapés   270
UNIT 27   Candies   278
UNIT 28   Frozen Desserts   283
UNIT 29   Beverages   289
UNIT 30   Meal Planning   297

APPENDIX I   Abbreviations   307
APPENDIX II   Seasoning Mixtures   308
APPENDIX III   Ingredients: Description and Sources   309

INDEX   310

Introduction

This laboratory manual has been prepared in order that you, the student:

- can apply the scientific theories of chemistry, physics, and nutrition in the preparation of food.
- will have supervised practice in the preparation of a wide variety of food products.
- will develop habits in food preparation that maintain the sanitary quality of foods and that conserve both time and money by efficient work techniques and economical use of foods and resources.
- will learn to recognize the quality characteristics of various food products and the techniques and ingredients that promote high quality.

To aid in accomplishing these goals, you will be expected to do the following:

1. Read the text assignment and the laboratory manual before coming to class.
2. Upon arriving in the laboratory, store wraps, purses, books, and other gear in the assigned location. They should not be allowed to clutter up the laboratory work area, for this would reduce efficiency.
3. Be sure that you are wearing a clean apron, smock, or lab coat; that your hair is arranged so that it will not get into the food, and that your hands and nails are clean.
4. Wash your hands before starting to prepare foods; avoid touching your hair or face while preparing food. If it is necessary to use a handkerchief, leave the food preparation area and wash hands with soap and water before returning. Do not dry hands on dish towels.
5. Assemble all supplies and equipment needed to carry out your assigned task. Plan ahead so that the job can be done with as few trips as possible; use a tray if a number of items have to be carried from one location to another.
6. Develop good working habits. Wash all the foods that require it at one time; then do all the paring, coring, or trimming and remove and discard all trimmings and waste before proceeding. Some foods, such as potatoes, often need to be washed again after peeling them. Some, such as leafy greens, are trimmed before they are washed. Do not chop foods on a chopping board that also has waste trimmings on it, since this is often unsanitary, wasteful, and inefficient.
7. When using heat for cooking on the surface unit or when baking, do not depend on the times given in the recipes. Pay attention to the product the first time you prepare it so that it does not become overcooked. Ranges and cooking pans vary and can alter cooking time.
8. Clean up as you go along. Put dishes to soak, wipe up counters, clean up spills,

discard waste paper and trimmings, and clean the range top and oven as soon as you are finished using them.

9. Wipe fat or grease from dishes and pans with paper towels before washing them. Scrape food from dishes and rinse before washing them.

10. Wash dishes in hot, soapy water. Change the water as needed; dirty water will not clean dishes. Rinse in hot, running water, not in a pan of cold, murky water.

11. Dry dishes with clean towels. Do not use towels to clean counters, table tops, or range tops.

12. Learn the correct location for all dishes and equipment, and return each item to its correct location. It is inefficient to have to search through cupboards and drawers to find needed utensils. If each student will accept this responsibility, it will simplify the food preparation tasks immeasurably.

13. Clean sinks. Do not leave food debris in the sink strainer, and dry the sink and faucet area.

14. Dispose of used dish towels and dishcloths as directed by the instructor.

WHAT YOU SHOULD KNOW ABOUT USE OF THE MICROWAVE OVEN
(See Basic Foods, pp. 50-52, 66.)

1. The wattage and cavity size of microwave ovens vary considerably; consequently it is impossible to state the exact timing. You may need to use more or less time and use some judgment in determining when a product is properly cooked.

2. Large containers, such as casseroles and those used for layer cakes, tend to cook more quickly on the outer edges than in the middle. With many such foods the outer edges become overcooked by the time the center is adequately cooked. The use of round dishes is preferable to square or rectangular ones. Shielding the outer edges with a strip of aluminum foil during the first half of cooking will further prevent overcooking of the outer edges. Foods that can be stirred, such as macaroni casseroles, should be, to more evenly distribute the heat.

3. The rotation of dishes at intervals during cooking in the microwave oven also helps to distribute the heat; some brands of microwave ovens have spots that do not receive any microwave heat so that foods cook unevenly. The dish will cook more evenly if it is rotated a quarter turn every minute or two.

4. Some of the cooking effect results from the conduction of heat from food at the outer edges to food in the middle, but conduction is a slow method of heat transfer; it takes time. This needs to be allowed for by discontinuing the heating of food in the microwave oven before the food is completely cooked and by allowing the food to stand for a few minutes after cooking.

5. Covers help to retain heat during cooking and speed cooking. If evaporation is needed or desirable, then cook uncovered or cover with a paper towel to prevent spattering.

UNIT 1   INTRODUCTORY PRINCIPLES OF FOOD PREPARATION

Suggested reading: Basic Foods, Chapter 3

Objectives

- To learn the correct use of utensils and techniques in measuring food ingredients
- To learn equivalent weights and measures in the English and metric systems
- To learn the use of the thermometer and temperature relationships in various cooking media and methods

MEASUREMENT OF FOOD INGREDIENTS (BF,* 56-63)

A. Measuring Flour

Different methods of measuring flour are compared by obtaining the weight of the flour per cup. Place a clean, dry, fractional 1-cup measure on the scale and tare it or discount its weight by setting the scale at zero. If the type of scale being used does not permit either of these techniques, get the exact weight of the cup and record it in Table 1-1.

1. Dip the cup into the container of flour until it is filled to overflowing; level it off with the edge of the spatula (Fig. 1-1); wipe the flour off the outside of the cup. Weigh and record the weight of the flour in Table 1-1. Return the flour to the container.

2. Stir the flour in the container and lightly spoon it into the cup until it overflows; level; clean flour from outside of cup. Weigh and record weight. Return the flour to the container.

3. Place several cups of flour in the sifter or strainer and sift the flour onto a piece of waxed, brown, or parchment paper. If using a strainer, sift the flour by gently tapping the rim of the strainer with the hand (BF, 60, Fig. 3.3). Lightly spoon the sifted flour into the measure; level; clean outside of cup. Weigh and record weight. Return the flour to the container.

Fig. 1-1: Level the top of the measure with the edge of the spatula; the flat side will pack the ingredients into the cup.

4. Place several cups of flour in the strainer or sifter. Place the empty cup on the piece of paper and sift the flour directly into the cup until it overflows; level; clean outside of cup. Weigh and record weight. Return the flour to the container.

---

*Throughout this manual, BF refers to Gates, Basic Foods (New York: Holt, Rinehart and Winston, 1981).

Table 1-1   Weight of Flour Measured in Different Ways

Variation	Empty cup(g)	Filled cup(g)	Flour (g)	Standard[1] (g)
Cup dipped into flour	102	$5\frac{3}{4}$	$4\frac{3}{4}$	—
Flour stirred and spooned into cup	102	$5\frac{1}{4}$	$4\frac{1}{4}$	125
Flour sifted and spooned into cup	102	$5\frac{1}{4}$	$4\frac{1}{4}$	115
Flour sifted into cup	102	$5\frac{1}{4}$	$4\frac{1}{4}$	

[1]Standard weights for all-purpose flour.

Questions

1. Does the method used to measure flour affect the amount obtained? Why?
2. Compare weight per cup of flour for each method obtained by different class members; which method gives the most consistent and predictable results?
3. What measuring utensil(s) should be used for measuring (a) 3/4 cup flour; (b) 2/3 cup flour; (c) 1/2 cup flour?

B. Measuring Sugars

1. Use the same cup used for the measurement of flour. Fill the cup to overflowing with granulated white sugar; level. Weigh and record the weight in Table 1-2. Return the sugar to the container.
2. Spoon brown sugar into the cup without pressing it into the cup; level. Weigh and record weight.
3. Press the brown sugar down into the cup with a rubber scraper and fill the cup; level. Weigh and record weight. Return the sugar to the container.
4. Spoon unsifted confectioners' (powdered) sugar into the cup; level. Weigh and record weight. Return the sugar to the container.
5. Place several cups of confectioners' sugar into a sifter or strainer and sift the sugar directly into the cup (placed on a piece of paper). Level. Weigh and record weight. Return the sugar to the container.

Questions

1. What are the recommended methods for measuring granulated, brown, and confectioners' sugars? Explain.
2. Would you conclude that brown sugar and granulated sugar could be used interchangeably in many recipes? Explain.

Table 1-2   Effect of Measurement Method and Type of Sugar on the
Weight of 1 Cup of Sugar

Variation	Empty cup(g)	Filled cup(g)	Sugar (g)	Standard (g)
Granulated sugar	1 oz	7 3/4	6 3/4	200
Brown sugar, not packed	1 oz	5 1/2	4 1/2	——
Brown sugar, packed into cup	1 oz	7	6	220
Confectioners' sugar, unsifted	1 oz	4 3/4	3 3/4	——
Confectioners' sugar, sifted	1 oz	4	3	120

C. Measurement of Fats (BF, 61-62, 82-83)

Obtain the tare or weight of, or set the scale to zero for, a 1/2-cup fractional measure. It
will be filled with different fats to be weighed. The cup can be wiped out with paper towels
between uses.

1. Fill the cup with hydrogenated shortening, packing shortening into cup to eliminate air
    pockets (BF, 61, Fig. 3.4). Level the top with a metal spatula and clean the outside of
    the cup. Weigh and record weight in Table 1-3. Return the shortening to the container.
2. Repeat step 1 using lard instead of hydrogenated shortening.
3. Place the empty cup on the balance or scale pan and fill it with melted hydrogenated
    shortening. Weigh and record weight. Return the shortening to the container and wipe
    out the cup with a paper towel.
4. Repeat step 3 using oil instead of melted hydrogenated shortening.

Table 1-3   Comparison of Weights of 1/2-cup Amounts of
Various Types and Forms of Fats

Variations	Empty cup (g)	Filled cup (g)	1/2 c fat (g)	Standard 1/2 c (g)
Hydrogenated shortening	1/2 oz	4	3.5	94
Lard	1/2 oz	4 1/4	3 1/2	110
Melted shortening	1 3/2 oz	5	3 1/4	——
Oil	1/2 oz	5.5	4.5	105

1 3/4

Questions

1. Account for the difference in weights between solid hydrogenated shortening (1) and lard
    (2) and between solid (1) and melted (3) hydrogenated shortening.
2. Would you conclude that oil can be used interchangeably with melted hydrogenated short-
    ening? Explain.

3. What volume, in cups or Tbsp, of table fat is in one cube, two cubes, and four cubes of margarine or butter (BF, 63, Table 3.6)?

D. Measuring Liquid Ingredients

To measure water and similar liquids, fill the graduated, transparent cup so that the meniscus of the liquid coincides with the desired line on the cup when viewed at eye level (Fig. 1-2). The meniscus curves up on the side of the cup if the liquid is water-based and curves down if fat-based. The cup should be placed on a level surface or held so that it is level when making measurements.

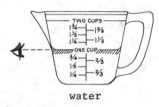

water

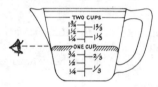

1. Fill a 1-cup liquid measure to the 1-cup line with water and then transfer the water to a 250-ml graduated cylinder. Record the millilitre measurement in Table 1-4. Empty the cylinder.
2. Fill the cup to the 1/2-cup line and transfer the water to the 250-ml graduate; repeat with another 1/2 cup of water. Record the millilitres for the two 1/2 cups combined.
3. Fill a tablespoon with water and pour the water into the measuring cup. Repeat until there is a total of 4 Tbsp of water in the cup. Measure the volume of the 4 Tbsp of water in a 100-ml graduated cylinder and record.

Fig. 1-2: Align the bottom of the meniscus of water-based liquids with the desired line on the cup or graduated cylinder. Align the top of the meniscus of fat-based liquids.

Table 1-4   Comparison of Methods of Measuring Liquids

Variations	Measurement (ml)	Standard (ml)
1 cup water		237
1/2 cup water X 2		237
4 Tbsp water		59.5

Questions

1. Compare the volume of one cup of water (1) to the standard, and account for discrepancies.
2. Compare the volume of one cup of water measured in two 1/2-cup increments to the standard, and of the 1/4 cup measured in four increments to the standard. What can you conclude about the type of measuring utensil to use for accurate measurements?

E. Measuring Small Amounts

Leavening, salt, and spices are called for in small amounts in food preparation; therefore, measuring spoons are used. Stir the ingredient, dip in the spoon, fill it to overflowing, and level off the top. Most sets of measuring spoons have 1/4 tsp as the smallest measure. For amounts smaller than this, it is necessary to divide the 1/4 tsp amount.

Practice measuring 1/8 and 1/16 tsp, as described in Basic Foods, p. 62, using baking soda and then table salt.

EQUIVALENT MEASURES

Fill in the blanks in Table 1-5 with equivalent measures in the English and metric systems of measurement. These measures should be memorized.

Table 1-5   Equivalents in the English and Metric Systems
            of Measurement

English measure		Metric		English measure
1 teaspoon	= _____	milliliters		
1 Tablespoon	= _____	milliliters	= _____	teaspoons
1 fluid ounce	= _____	milliliters	= _____	Tablespoons
1 cup	= _____	milliliters	= _____	Tablespoons
			= _____	fluid ounces
1 ounce	= _____	grams		
1 pound	= _____	grams	= _____	ounces (avoirdupois)

Questions

1. Explain the difference between avoirdupois and fluid ounces.
2. List the weight (in grams) per cup of the following food ingredients:

    all-purpose flour, unsifted, stirred _____ g

    granulated sugar   _____ g

    lard   _____ g

    water   _____ g (BF, 58-59)

    milk   _____ g (BF, Appendix, Table 9)

    applesauce   _____ g (BF, Appendix, Table 9)

3. On the basis of answers given in Question 2, is it correct to conclude that fluid and avoirdupois ounces are the same? Why? For what substance are the two types of ounces equal?

TEMPERATURES AND USE OF THERMOMETERS   (BF, 59, 64)

A. Using a Thermometer

When obtaining the temperature of a substance, be sure that the bulb of the thermometer is immersed in the substance. The thermometer should be held so that the top of the column of mercury is at eye level when being read (Fig. 1-3). The bulb of the thermometer should <u>not</u> touch the sides of the container. If boiling points are being determined, then the liquid must be boiling (bubbling).

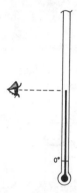

Fig. 1-3: The thermometer must be held so that the top of the mercury is at eye level when the temperature is being read.

1. Place one c of cold water in a 1-qt saucepan. Place the pan on a small surface unit. Use high heat while timing with a stopwatch to determine the exact time required to reach the boiling point. Measure the temperature of the boiling water. Record in Table 1-6 the time required to reach the boiling point and the temperature of the boiling water.

2. Reduce the heat under the saucepan to maintain a simmer (small, occasional bubbles breaking the top surface of the water). Measure and record the temperature.

3. Place the hot water in the bottom of a double boiler with the level of the water low enough so that the top of the double boiler will not be in the water (Fig. 1-4). Place 1 cup of hot tap water in the top of the double boiler and heat until the water in the bottom starts to boil. Allow the water in the bottom to boil for 10 minutes. Measure and record the temperature of the water in the top of the double boiler.

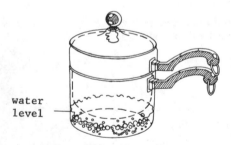

Fig. 1-4: The water level should be below the bottom of the top part of the double boiler when cooking over boiling water.

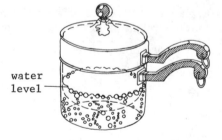

Fig. 1-5: The water should surround the bottom of the top part of the double boiler when higher cooking temperatures are desired.

4. Allow the water in the bottom of the double boiler to boil another 10 minutes (a total of 20 minutes). Measure and record the temperature of the water in the top part.

5. Add enough hot water to the bottom part of the double boiler so that the lower part of the top is immersed in the water in the bottom of the double boiler (Fig. 1-5). Bring the water in the bottom to a boil and let boil for 15 minutes. Measure and record the temperature in the top part.

6. Remove the top part of the double boiler and cover the lower part with aluminum foil, with water still boiling. Place a thermometer in the steam above the water and under the foil. Measure and record the highest temperature reached by the steam.

7. Fill a 1-c liquid measuring c to the 1-c line. Place it in the microwave oven and set it 2-1/4 minutes, using full power. Note whether boiling starts before the time is up. If not boiling at the end of the time, add additional time in 1/4-minute increments. Boiling is indicated when bubbles rise to the top.

Questions

1. Compare temperatures of boiling and simmering water and of water in the top of the double boiler when the top is either above or surrounded by boiling water. Discuss what effect these temperatures might have on the cooking time of foods.
2. Compare the temperature of steam to that of boiling water. Why are steam burns usually more severe than those from boiling water (BF, 48)?
3. Compare the time required to bring one c of water to a boil on the surface unit to the time to reach boiling in a microwave oven.

Table 1-6   Comparison of Temperatures in Different Methods of Cooking

Variations	°F	°C
Boiling water in saucepan		
Simmering water in saucepan		
Top of double boiler above boiling water, after 10 min.		
Top of double boiler above boiling water, after 20 min.		
Top of double boiler in the boiling water, after 15 min.		
Steam		
Microwave oven—boil water		

B. Comparison of Thermometers

1. Examine various types of thermometers—ones used for meat, deep-fat frying, and candy- and jelly-making. Note the upper and lower temperatures of their scales and the subdivisions on the scales. Discuss the reasons for variations in these thermometers.
2. List the temperatures in a pressure cooker at 5, 10, and 15 pounds pressure. What is the advantage in use of a pressure cooker (BF, 53)?

UNIT 2   COMPARISON OF FATS AND THEIR USE

AS A COOKING MEDIUM

Suggested reading: Basic Foods, Chapter 4

Objectives

- To learn the correct use of fat as a cooking medium
- To observe the physical characteristics of various fats
- To become familiar with the composition and labeling of various fats
- To compare nutrient content and cost of foods cooked in fats with those of the same foods cooked by other methods

USE OF FAT AS A COOKING MEDIUM (BF, 7-8, 86-90)

A. Pan-Frying (BF, 66)

- Foods can be pan fried in a regular frying pan on a surface unit or in an electric frying pan.
- To reduce calories and cost, it is preferable to use the minimum amount of fat to coat the pan—just enough to allow the food to brown and crisp properly without sticking to the pan and burning.
- Fat for pan-frying should be heated before food is placed in it.

Pan-Fried Potatoes
_____

    2 or 3 potatoes that have been boiled
        or baked in their skin and cooled
    2-3 Tbsp oil for frying

1. Heat oil in frying pan with medium heat.
2. Slice unpeeled potatoes crosswise or lengthwise, 1/8 to 1/4" thick.
3. Carefully place a single layer of potato slices in the hot pan with tongs or turner.
4. Brown the slices on one side, turn, sprinkle with salt and pepper (optional), and brown the second side. Do not allow the fat to become so hot that it smokes.
5. Remove the browned slices with slotted turner or fork and place on a pan or plate lined with absorbent paper.
6. If necessary, keep warm for serving in oven set at 175°F (79.5°C), but potatoes are better if eaten as soon as cooked.

Note: Pan-frying of meats is included in Unit 21.

B. Deep-Fat Frying

The order of the following steps will depend on the preparation requirements of the food being fried. If preparation time is lengthy, the fat should not be heated until near the time it is to be used.

1. Read the do's and don'ts pertaining to the use of fat as a cooking medium, <u>Basic Foods,</u> p. 48.
2. Fill deep pot about 1/3 full of cooking oil and clip a deep-fat thermometer to the side of the pot so that the bulb is immersed.
3. Place the pot on the surface unit so that it rests firmly on the unit. Turn handle so that the pot will not be easily tipped over and the thermometer can be easily read.
4. Heat the fat using medium heat. Since most foods are fried at temperatures between 350-400°F (177-204.5°C), do not allow the fat temperature to exceed this range.
5. Arrange equipment for draining fried foods. Do not permit towels or paper to touch the hot surface unit or pot of fat.
6. Prepare the food as specified in the recipes for frying (below), using the temperature range suggested for each product.
7. Have fat at the higher end of the temperature range when food is added, and avoid adding so much food at one time that it cools the fat to below the lower end of the range.
8. Add batter-dipped foods cautiously to prevent excessive spattering and foaming; all other foods should be dry when added to the fat.
9. Large pieces of food should be cooked until brown on the underside and then turned over to brown on the second side.
10. Small pieces of food require occasional stirring for even browning.
11. Remove large pieces of food from fat with tongs or with slotted fork or spoon. Drain a few seconds over the pot, then place on baking sheet or tray lined with absorbent paper to finish draining. Do not use an implement that has been dipped in batter to remove food from the fat.
12. A wire frying basket is useful for removing small pieces of food from hot fat. It, too, should be drained over the fat before the fried food is placed on absorbent paper.
13. Continually during the frying, remove stray particles of batter and crumbs, as these cause breakdown of the fat.
14. As soon as the fried food is properly browned and removed from the fat, check it for doneness. Foods started raw, like French-fried potatoes, can be broken or cut to determine if the interior is properly cooked. Batter-dipped foods or foods containing batter, like fritters and doughnuts, can be broken open to determine if the batter is cooked. Croquettes can be checked by inserting the tip of a meat thermometer into the center to be sure the temperature is at least 150°F (65.5°C).

Desirable Characteristics of Fried Foods

- Crisp outer surface, not soggy, limp, or greasy
- Evenly browned outside, neither too dark nor too light
- Properly cooked or sufficiently hot interior (no raw potatoes or cold croquettes)

French-Fried Potatoes   385-395°F (196-201.5°C)

1/2 to 1 lb white potatoes (unrefrigerated)
1 Tbsp salt
1 qt water

1. Wash potatoes, peel, remove eyes, and wash again.
2. Cut into pieces with a French-fry cutter, or slice into 1/3 to 1/2" thick slices and then cut slices into strips of the same width.
3. Soak the strips in salt water for 20 to 30 minutes.
4. Drain the potatoes in a colander and dry them with towels; then fry according to instructions.

Potato Chips   390–400°F (199–204°C)

    1/2 lb white potatoes (unrefrigerated)   1 qt water
    1 Tbsp salt

1. Wash potatoes, peel, remove eyes, and wash again.
2. Slice into very thin slices with a potato peeler or with the slit on the grater.
3. Follow steps 3 and 4 under French-Fried Potatoes, dropping the slices of potato into the hot fat one at a time to prevent them from sticking to each other.

Batter-Fried Foods (Tempura)

Batter

1/2 c cold water	1/4 tsp baking powder
1/2 c all-purpose flour	1 Tbsp nonfat dry milk
1/4 c cornstarch	1/4 tsp monosodium glutamate
1/4 tsp salt	1/8 tsp turmeric

1. Place the water in a blender, add all of the dry ingredients, and blend. If necessary, scrape down the inside of the blender with a rubber scraper and pulsate to obtain a smooth batter.
2. Roll seasoned pieces of food in cornstarch and then place them in a colander and shake vigorously to remove the excess cornstarch.
3. Dip the prepared pieces of food into the batter one at a time, allowing each piece to drain a few seconds before easing it gently into the heated fat.
4. Remove drops of batter from the fat at intervals to prevent the deterioration of the fat.
5. Fry at the specified temperature for each food listed below.

Seafood

Prawns   380–390°F (194–199°C)

Remove the shells from raw prawns and devein. Leave the tails on to use as handles for dipping prawns in batter. Season lightly with seafood salt.

Scallops

Use whole, or if large, cut in half. Season lightly with seafood salt.

Sole

Cut into pieces 1" x 2". Season with seafood salt.

Meats   375–385°F (191–196°C)

Chicken

Remove the skin, fat, and bones; be sure the meat is clean. Cut the chicken into pieces of the desired size. Season lightly with poultry seasoning salt.

Veal

Remove the connective tissues and fat from veal round steak and cut into pieces of the desired size. Season lightly with savory salt.

Vegetables

Asparagus

Wash the asparagus thoroughly and trim off the tough lower stalks. Slice the stalks diagonally into 1/2" thick slices. Place the sliced stalks into a saucepan with 1/4 c of water and 1/4 tsp salt and bring to a boil. Drain well. After coating with cornstarch and dipping in batter, fry at 375-385°F (191-196°C).

Carrots

Wash and peel carrots, cut into 3" lengths, and cut each length into strips about 1/2" wide and 1/4" thick. Place the strips of carrot in a saucepan with 1/4 c water and 1/4 tsp salt and bring to a boil. Drain well. After coating with cornstarch and dipping in batter, fry at 375-385°F (191-196°C).

Zucchini

Wash, trim off ends and discolored spots of zucchini. Cut into diagonal slices about 1/2" thick. Season lightly with savory salt. After coating with cornstarch and dipping in batter, fry at 375-385°F (191-196°C).

Eggplant

Wash and cut the eggplant into slices about 1/2" thick. Peel each slice and cut it into strips about 1/2" wide. Place the strips into a salt solution of 1 Tbsp salt to a q of water. Remove 8-10 strips at a time; drain and dry them. After coating with cornstarch and dipping in batter, fry them at 380-390°F (194-199°C).

Onion Rings

Peel a large white or yellow onion and cut it into slices about 1/4" thick. Separate the slices into rings and sprinkle lightly with savory salt. After coating with cornstarch and dipping in batter, fry at 380-390°F (194-199°C).

Fruits

Raw apples and bananas can be dipped into pineapple or orange juice to prevent enzymatic browning.

Apples

Wash, peel, and core apples with an apple corer so that the apples are left whole with a hole in the center. Slice the apple crosswise in slices about 1/4" to 1/3" thick. Sprinkle the slices of apple with cinnamon sugar. After rolling in cornstarch and dipping in batter, fry at 380-390°F (194-199°C). After frying, drain well and sprinkle with powdered sugar.[1]

Bananas

Peel bananas and cut into 2" lengths. After coating with cornstarch and dipping in batter, fry at 390-400°F (199-204°C). Drain well and sprinkle with powdered sugar.

Pineapple

Use whole or half slices of canned pineapple; drain well and dry. After coating in cornstarch and dipping in batter, fry at 390-400°F (199-204°C).

---

[1]Powdered sugar is easily applied by sprinkling from a tea strainer.

Rosettes (Timbales)

1/2 c milk
1 egg
1/2 c all-purpose flour
1/4 tsp salt

1. Put egg and milk in a small, deep bowl and combine with a French whip.
2. Add flour and salt and mix only until batter is smooth.
3. Heat fat and rosette iron (Fig. 2-1) to 375°F (190.5°C).

Fig. 2-1:   Rosette iron

4. Drip drain the iron over the pot of fat for a few seconds, then dip the hot iron into the batter to about 3/4 the depth of the iron. The batter should not cover the iron completely or it will be impossible to remove the rosette from the iron.
5. Return the batter-coated iron to the hot fat and cook for a few seconds. Use a pointed knife or fork to ease the rosette off the iron into the fat.
6. Fry the rosette until lightly browned. After draining, sprinkle with sugar.

Cake Doughnuts   370-380°F (188-193.5°C)

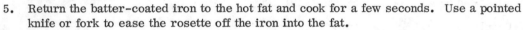

2 Tbsp margarine	3 c stirred all-purpose flour
1/2 c sugar	1 Tbsp SAS (double-acting) baking powder
2 eggs	1/2 tsp salt
1/2 c milk	1/8 tsp each nutmeg and cinnamon

1. With electric mixer, cream together the margarine, eggs, and sugar until light and fluffy.
2. Mix together the dry ingredients and add half the dry mixture to the creamed mixture; mix about 5 seconds.
3. Add the milk; mix 5 seconds, then add the rest of the dry ingredients. Mix only until batter is smooth.
4. Turn dough out onto lightly floured bread board covered with pastry cloth.
5. Round dough into a smooth ball and roll out with a rolling pin to 1/2" thickness.
6. Cut with floured doughnut cutter.
7. Fry both doughnuts and holes until browned and cooked inside.
8. After draining, sprinkle with sugar.

Salmon Croquettes   375-385°F (190.5-196°)

3/4 c milk	1 lb well-drained salmon (or other cooked meat)
1/4 c flour	1 egg white
1/4 tsp salt	1 Tbsp milk
1/8 tsp pepper	1/8 tsp salt
1 tsp seafood seasoning	bread crumbs
1 egg yolk	

1. Combine the milk, flour, and salt in a saucepan, mixing with a spring stirrer until smooth.

2. Cook over moderate heat with constant stirring until the sauce starts to boil.
3. Remove from the heat and add the seasonings, salmon, and egg yolk. Chill the mixture to make it easier to handle; it chills more quickly in a freezer.
4. Shape the salmon mixture into elongated shapes about an inch in diameter and 1-1/2" long.
5. Mix together the egg white, salt and tablespoon of milk. Dip each croquette into the milk mixture and then into the crumbs. Chill another 20 minutes.
6. Cook several croquettes at a time until lightly browned and heated through.

Hush Puppies

1 c corn meal
1 Tbsp all-purpose flour
3/4 tsp savory salt
3 Tbsp finely minced onion

1/2 tsp double acting baking powder
1 egg
1/4 c milk

1. Combine all ingredients and mix well.
2. Using about 1/2 Tbsp of the mixture, shape the mixture into a finger shape.
3. Fry in deep fat at 370-380°F (188-193°C).

Yield: About 2 dozen hush puppies

Fried Won Ton   375-385°F (190.5-196°C)

Wrappers

1 package of won ton wrappers (about 6 dozen)

Sausage Filling

1/4 lb bulk sausage, fried until crumbly and brown and well drained
1 4-1/2 oz can tiny shrimp, well drained
2 Tbsp finely chopped water chestnuts, fresh or canned
2 Tbsp finely chopped green onion, including tops
1 egg yolk
1 Tbsp soy sauce

Chicken Filling

1 c finely chopped cooked chicken
2 Tbsp finely chopped water chestnuts
2 Tbsp finely chopped green onion, including tops
1/2 tsp curry powder
1 Tbsp soy sauce
1 egg yolk

1. Combine all ingredients of sausage or chicken filling.
2. Place about 1/2 teaspoon of filling near the center of each won ton wrapper. Moisten the edges of upper half of the wrapper with water (use finger dipped in water).
3. Fold the top third of the wrapper over the filling to seal the filling in an envelope using about two-thirds of the wrapper. Be sure that it is well sealed on all three edges so that the filling will not leak out during frying.
4. Moisten the ends of the fold and fold it over tightly once more.
5. Moisten one end and bring the ends together.

(See Basic Foods, Figs. 4.4 (p. 93) and 23.2 (p. 447) for illustrations of folding techniques. The won ton can also be folded into triangles and the points brought together.)

6. Fry until golden brown.

(Note: Uncooked, filled won tons, won ton fillings, and won ton wrappers all freeze well if packaged in freezer wrappings or containers.)

C. Care of Used Fat

1. Cool fat to about room temperature, or a little warmer.
2. Place a funnel into the oil bottle from which the fat came.
3. Line the funnel with 6 to 8 thicknesses of cheesecloth. Several pieces of paper towel under the bottle helps to catch spills.
4. Pour the oil through the cheesecloth to remove food particles.
5. Do not try to save badly discolored oil, oil that is overly viscous, or oil containing dregs from the bottom of the pan.
6. Fill the bottle to the top to reduce the air space in the bottle.
7. Store used oil in the refrigerator or freezer between uses to retard development of rancidity.
8. Oil used for frying fish can be deodorized by frying a potato in it, preferably after it has been strained.

Questions

1. If fried food is properly browned on the outside and still raw inside, what change in cooking method is indicated?
2. If fried food is too lightly browned on the outside but well done inside, what change in cooking method is indicated?
3. Excess fat absorption is to be avoided in frying foods. List procedures to follow that will minimize fat absorption.

PHYSICAL CHARACTERISTICS OF VARIOUS FATS

Observe the consistency and appearance of the fats listed in Table 2-1 after holding at room temperature, 70-80°F (21-26.5°C), and after storing in the refrigerator overnight or longer. Record observations.

Table 2-1 Comparison of the Physical Characteristics of Various Fats[1]

Fat	At room temperature	Refrigerated
Lard		
Hydrogenated shortening		
Margarine with liquid oil as first ingredient		
Margarine with partially hardened oil as first ingredient		
Butter		
Oil, salad (winterized)		
Oil, general purpose		

[1]Indicate whether the fat is hard, soft, liquid, solid, plastic (pliable), brittle, transparent, opaque.

Questions

1. Shortened cakes require a highly plastic fat; which ones would be suitable?
2. Pastry requires a solid, brittle, or hard fat; which ones would be suitable?
3. Oil-and-vinegar salad dressings require an oil that remains liquid when refrigerated; which oils would qualify?

NUTRITION LABELING AND INGREDIENTS IN FATS

A. Margarines

Examine the labels on various brands and types of margarine to compare composition and cost. Usually the margarines with the highest content of polyunsaturated fatty acids (PUFA) —5 g or more per Tbsp—are the most expensive, while those with the lowest content of PUFA are the least expensive. Unless one's physician has recommended a very high intake of PUFA for medical reasons, the margarines with moderate levels (2-4 g PUFA per Tbsp) will meet the nutritional needs of most people. The amount of PUFA in the margarine depends on the kind of oil used and the amount of liquid oil in proportion to hydrogenated oil, as well as on the method of manufacture.

In comparing margarines, group them according to high, moderate, and low levels of PUFA and compare costs within these three groups. If the PUFA content is not listed, assume it to be low or nil. Enter data in Table 2-2.

Table 2-2 Comparison of Costs and Ingredients of Margarines

Brand	Cost per lb ($)	First Ingredient		Grams per Tablespoon			Emulsifiers[1]	Anti-oxidants[2]	Kinds of	
		Liquid oil	Partially Hydrogenated oil	Total fat(g)	Saturated fat (g)	Polyun-saturated fat (g)			Oils	Color[3]

[1]Identify kinds of emulsifiers by number: (1) lecithin, (2) mono- and diglycerides.

[2]Identify antioxidants by small letter: (a) citric acid, (b) calcium disodium EDTA, (c) isopropyl citrate, (d) potassium sorbate, (e) sodium benzoate.

[3]Identify color by capital letter: (C) carotene, (A) artificial.

Questions

1. Why are Vitamins A and D added to margarines?
2. How does the cost of diet margarine, based on grams of fat per Tbsp (from label), compare with that of regular margarine?
3. Which margarine with moderate levels of PUFA is least expensive?

B. Hydrogenated Shortenings

It is not required that shortenings be labeled according to the kinds of oil they contain or as to the inclusion of emulsifiers; however, some do carry this information. Check labels of different brands of hydrogenated shortening for presence of emulsifiers. Contact manufacturers of those products that do not list this information on the label. Why is it important to know whether a shortening contains added emulsifiers?

C. Oils

Many brands of oils now use nutritional labeling. Check brands available in your area and fill in the data from the labels in Table 2-3. Contact the manufacturer for the information when it is not listed on the bottle or container.

Table 2-3 Comparison of Essential Fatty Acids in Oils and their Costs

| Brands | Sources[1] of oils | Grams per tablespoon | | | Anti-oxidants | Cost per quart ($) |
		Total fat (g)	Saturated fat (g)	Polyun-saturated fat (g)		

[1]Sources include cottonseed, corn, soy, peanut, olive, palm, safflower, and others.

Questions

1. Which sources of oil are considered to be poor sources of essential fatty acids (PUFA)?
2. Do brands containing these sources of oil appear to have a lower content of essential fatty acids?
3. Why is it necessary to use antioxidants (preservatives) in oils and margarines?

NUTRIENT CONTENT OF FRIED FOODS

It is not possible to determine the fat content of fried food by obtaining its weight before and after frying, because the water content also changes with frying. Also, the amount of fat absorbed by foods during frying is highly variable and depends on the conditions of frying. The amount of fat absorbed affects the caloric content of the food, but not much specific data is available. There is, however, farily good information on potatoes prepared in various ways, so that the effect of frying on fat absorption and increase in calories can be compared.

Fill in Table 2-4 with data from Table 7.1 in Basic Foods (p. 123, or from USDA Handbook No. 8, for 100-gram amounts).

From this data it is apparent that potatoes cooked in these ways are hard to compare because they vary in water content from 1.8% to 79.8%. To compare the true effect of frying on fat content, potatoes must be compared on a water-free, or dry-weight, basis. The calculations for raw potatoes are as follows:

```
  100.0 g  (total weight of raw potatoes)
- 79.8 g  (water)
  20.2 g  (dry weight of potatoes)
```

$$\left[\frac{0.1 \text{ g} \quad (\text{weight of fat in raw p.})}{20.2 \text{ g} \quad (\text{dry weight})} \right] \times 100 = 0.5\% \text{ fat in raw potatoes, dry-weight basis}$$

Table 2-4   Composition of Potatoes Cooked by Different Methods, per 100 grams

Method of preparation	Water(g)	Calories	Protein(g)	Fat(g)
Potatoes, white, raw	79.8	76	2.1	0.1
Potatoes, baked in skin				
Potatoes, boiled in skin				
Potatoes, French-fried				
Potato chips				

$$\left[\frac{2.1 \text{ g} \text{ (weight of protein in raw p.)}}{20.2 \text{ g} \text{ (dry weight)}} \right] \text{ x } 100 = 12.9\% \text{ protein in raw potatoes, dry-weight basis}$$

These calculations, as well as those for baked potatoes, French-fried potatoes, and potato chips, are shown in Table 2-5.

Table 2-5 Composition of Potatoes Cooked by Different Methods on a Dry-Weight Basis

Method of preparation	Dry weight (g)	Dry-weight basis	
		Protein %	Fat %
Potatoes, white, raw	20.2	12.9	0.5
Potatoes, baked in skin	24.9	10.4	0.4
Potatoes, French-fried	55.3	7.8	23.9
Potato chips	98.2	5.4	40.5

Question

What conclusions can you draw about use of fried foods in meals by persons of normal body weight and also by those who carry excessive body weight?

UNIT 3   FRUIT PREPARATION

Suggested reading: Basic Foods, Chapter 6

Objectives

- To learn methods of preventing enzymatic browning in susceptible fruits
- To practice preparing a variety of fresh and cooked fruits
- To learn how to rehydrate and use dried fruits
- To practice preparing fruit purées
- To compare fresh and processed fruits in terms of cost and nutrient retention

PREVENTING ENZYMATIC BROWNING OF RAW FRUITS (BF, 69-70)

1. Prepare about 1/2 c of each of the following solutions and place in a glass or small bowl:
    a) orange juice (fresh, canned, or frozen)
    b) pineapple juice (canned, or from canned pineapple)
    c) lemon juice (canned, bottled, frozen, or fresh)
    d) ascorbic acid solution: 1/2 tsp ascorbic acid powder in 1/2 c water
2. Peel a banana and place two slices in each solution. Remove one slice of banana from each solution and place it beside the container from which it was removed on a piece of wax paper or on a plate.
3. Peel and core an apple. Place two slices of apple in each solution; then remove one slice from each and lay beside the banana.
4. Expose several slices of untreated apple and banana to the air.
5. After one or two hours, compare the treated and untreated fruits for evidence of enzymatic browning.

Questions

1. Is it necessary to "soak" raw fruit in these solutions to prevent enzymatic browning?
2. With what type of food mixtures would the use of lemon juice to prevent enzymatic browning be unacceptable because of the effect of the high acidity of lemons on the flavor?

PREPARATION OF FRUITS

A. Fresh Fruits

Besides preventing the enzymatic browning of raw fruits, fruits require preparation that makes them attractive to serve and easy to eat. (For characteristics to look for in selection of individual fruits, see Basic Foods, pp. 104-115.)

Citrus Fruits
_____

Grapefruit Halves

1. Wash and dry the grapefruit; cut in half.
2. Remove the center core of each half by cutting around it with a sharp knife or kitchen shears.
3. Cut around the rind to separate the fruit from the rind; slide the knife under the fruit, next to the rind, to loosen the fruit from the bottom (Fig. 3-1).
4. Remove the membranes between each section by cutting along each side of the membrane with a sharp knife. Remove all seeds.

   Raw Chilled Grapefruit: Sprinkle prepared grapefruit half with 2 to 3 tsp sugar, if desired. Chill. Top with maraschino cherry before serving.

   Broiled Grapefruit: Sprinkle the prepared grapefruit half with 2 to 3 tsp sugar; dot with with 1 tsp table fat. Broil 5 to 10 minutes or until heated. Serve hot, topped with maraschino cherry.

Sectioning Citrus Fruits

1. Wash and dry fruit.
2. Peel with a sharp knife, removing all of the white rind (Fig. 3-2).
3. Cut along each side of each membrane to separate the sections of fruit.

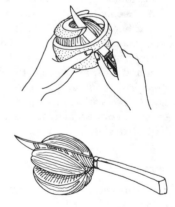

Fig. 3-1: After removing the core from a grapefruit half, cut around the rind to separate the fruit, then cut on each side of the membranes and remove them.

Fig. 3-2: Peel citrus fruit to remove all the white rind; remove sections of fruit by slicing on each side of the membranes.

Sliced Oranges

1. Wash and dry orange; peel with a sharp knife.
2. Cut into "cartwheels" by slicing the whole, peeled orange into slices 1/4 to 1/2" thick (Fig. 3.3), or cut peeled orange into halves or quarters and slice (Fig. 3-4).

Fig. 3-3: Prepare "cartwheels" by slicing a whole, peeled orange.

Fig. 3-4: Half and quarter slices can also be prepared.

Note: See Basic Foods, Figs. 6.4-6.6 (pp. 110-111) for ways citrus fruits can be shaped for use as garnishes or as baskets made of rind.

Other Fresh Fruits

Berries

1. Wash berries under running water and drain in a colander or strainer.
2. Remove stems with a sharp, pointed knife and cut off small bruises and blemishes; discard berries with large decayed spots.
3. Small berries like raspberries may be left whole; large berries may be halved or sliced.
4. Sprinkle with sugar, and refrigerate until ready to serve. The amount of sugar needed will depend on the natural sweetness of the fruit.

Melons

1. Wash and dry the melon before cutting it.
2. Small melons like cantaloupe can be cut in half, crosswise or lengthwise, and the seeds scooped out. When melon is cut in half crosswise, serrated edges can be made by cutting up and down between the natural lines on the rind of the melon.
3. Melons may be served in the half shell or in slices with or without the rind.
4. The center of melons can be filled with sherbet, ice cream, ricotta or cottage cheese, or a mixture of fruits.
5. Melon balls prepared from a variety of melons can be used in fruit mixtures or as garnishes.

Pineapple

1. Wash the pineapple and pat dry with paper towels.
2. See Basic Foods, Fig. 6.7 (p. 114) for illustrations for peeling and cutting fresh pineapple.
3. Fruit may or may not require sugaring, depending on its natural sweetness.

Pineapple Boats

1. Leaving the top and bottom on the pineapple, cut it in half lengthwise, starting at the bottom and slicing through the leaves at the top.
2. Cut sections of the fruit out of the rind to form a hollow shell (BF, 168, Fig. 8.9).

Fresh Fruit Mixtures
___

✶ Fruit Cup

1/4 c banana slices	1/4 c pineapple juice
1/4 c fresh strawberries, halved	1 Tbsp sugar
1/4 c seedless grapes, whole	mint leaves
1/4 c pineapple wedges (fresh, or	
drained canned)	

1. Wash, peel, and prepare fruit as indicated.
2. Heat pineapple juice and sugar together enough to dissolve the sugar.
3. Pour the sweetened pineapple juice over the prepared fruit and mix lightly to coat fruit. Chill.
4. Serve fruit in compote or sauce dishes; garnish with mint leaves.

Yield: Two 1/2-cup servings

✶ Ambrosia

1 large orange, peeled, sectioned
1 large banana, peeled, sliced
1 Tbsp confectioners' sugar
1/2 c sweetened coconut flakes or shreds

1. Combine coconut and sugar; sprinkle over alternate layers of fruits in compote or sauce dish.

Yield: Two servings

B. Cooked Fruits

Apples
___

✶ Applesauce

2 apples
2 Tbsp water
2 Tbsp sugar

1. Wash, peel, and core apples. Slice thin.
2. Combine apple slices and water in saucepan, cover and cook over moderate heat until tender (or cook in 1-1/2-q glass casserole in the microwave oven 3-5 minutes.
3. For smooth applesauce, purée the cooked fruit in a blender or put it through a food mill or sieve. For coarse applesauce, stir and break the apple slices into pieces with a fork.
4. Stir in sugar.

Yield: Two servings

✶ Cinnamon Applesauce: Prepare as above, adding 2 to 4 Tbsp of cinnamon candies ("red hots") in place of sugar. Stir and heat the sauce to dissolve candies.

Why candies instead of
    a) ground cinnamon
    b) cinnamon sticks ?

Apple Compote

    2 apples
    1/4 c water
    2 Tbsp sugar or 2-4 Tbsp cinnamon candies

1. Combine water, sugar, and apples in a saucepan.
2. Cover and cook over moderate heat until apples are tender and transparent.

Microwave Oven:

Combine all ingredients in a 1-1/2-q glass casserole; cover with plastic wrap and cook 4-6 minutes, stirring after 2-3 minutes.

Yield: Two servings

Baked Apple

    1 apple   1/16 tsp cinnamon
    1 Tbsp brown sugar   1 tsp table fat

1. Wash and core apple; cut a slit through the skin around the equator of the apple.
2. Place 1 Tbsp water in an 8-oz baking dish.
3. Place the cored apple in the dish and fill the hole with the mixed sugar, cinnamon, and table fat.
4. Bake about 45 minutes at 400°F (204.5°C). Baste occasionally with juices in the dish.

instead of fat: finely chopped nuts, raisins or candied ginger brown sugar or honey ← no cinnamon

Microwave Oven:

Follow steps 1 and 2; place in the microwave oven with a piece of paper towel placed over the top (to prevent spattering). Cook 2-2-1/2 minutes, basting after 1 minute.

Glazed Apples

For each apple

    1/4 c water
    2 Tbsp sugar

1. Prepare apples as for baking.
2. Place water, sugar, and prepared apples in a saucepan, cover, and cook over moderate heat for 10 minutes. Turn the apple over and cook 10 minutes longer. Baste the apples with juices in the pan every 5 minutes.
3. Test for doneness by piercing the interior center of the apple with a fork or sharp, pointed knife.
4. When apples are done, cook uncovered for 1 minute to harden glaze.

Microwave Oven:

Follow steps 1 and 2 except that apple(s) should be placed in a glass casserole of appropriate size. Cover with a plastic wrap, cook 1 minute, turn and baste, cook another minute; then cook uncovered 1/2 to 1 minute to glaze.

Apple Crisp

1-1/4 lb apples   cinnamon sugar

Topping:

3/4 c whole wheat pastry flour*   1/2 tsp apple pie spice
1 c rolled oats   1/3 c table fat
2/3 c sugar**   1/8 tsp salt

*or use all-purpose flour
**For reduced sugar, use 1/3 c sugar + 1 tsp Weight Watchers Sweetener

1. Wash, peel, core, and slice apples; place the sliced apples in the bottom of a lightly oiled 8" x 8" x 2" glass baking dish; sprinkle with cinnamon sugar.
2. Combine the flour, sugar, salt, and apple pie spice in a food processor (using the mixing blade) or in a mixer; blend briefly to mix.
3. Cut the table fat into chunks and add to the flour mixture.
4. Blend until the mixture resembles coarse cornmeal; stir in oats.
5. Spread the crumb mixture over the sliced apples and level.
6. Bake uncovered at 350°F (176.5°C) 30–35 minutes until the apples are tender and the top is lightly browned.
7. Serve hot or cold.

Microwave Oven:

Cook in the microwave oven 3 minutes, turn the dish 1/4 turn and cook 2–3 minutes longer. The top will not be browned; it can be browned by placing it under the broiler 1–2 minutes.

Yield: Six 4" x 2-2/3" portions

Hot Fruit Medley with Fresh Fruit

1 apple, peeled, cored, cut into chunks   2 Tbsp water
1 pear, peeled, cored, cut into chunks   1/4 c cinnamon candies
1 orange, peeled, sectioned

1. Combine the water, cinnamon candies, and apples in a 1-1/2 q saucepan and cook until the apples are almost tender.
2. Stir in the pears and oranges and simmer about 5 minutes more.
3. Serve hot or cold.

Microwave Oven:

Place the apple mixture in a 1-1/2-q glass casserole. Cook 1 minute. Stir in the oranges and pears and cook covered with a plastic wrap 1–2 minutes.

Yield: Three 1/2 c servings

Hot Fruit Medley with Canned Fruit

1 No. 2-1/2 can fruit salad   1 tsp curry powder
1 Tbsp table fat   1 Tbsp honey

1. Combine the juice from the canned fruit, honey, table fat, and curry powder in a 1-1/2-q saucepan and heat to boiling.
2. Place the drained fruit in a lightly oiled 8" x 8" x 2" glass baking dish.

3. Cover the fruit with the boiling syrup.
4. Bake at 350°F (176.5°C) 30 minutes. Serve hot.

Microwave Oven:

Cook the juice mixture in a glass casserole 1-2 minutes. Pour the boiling syrup over the fruit and cook in the microwave oven 2 to 3 minutes, uncovered.

C. Preparation of Dried Fruits

Because of the wide variety of dried fruits available with differing moisture content, it is not possible to give specific instructions as to their preparation. The label does not always indicate whether the fruit is tenderized or dried. Most manufacturers' recommendations suggest excessive amounts of water for rehydrating. Better retention of flavor and less need for additional sweetening result if no more water is used than can be reabsorbed by the fruit.

Basic Method for Rehydrating Fruit
_____

   1 c dried fruit
   1 c water

1. Combine dried fruit and water in a saucepan, and bring to a boil (or in a microwave oven 2 minutes).
2. Remove the fruit from the heat and allow to stand at room temperature for 1/2 to 3 hours.
3. Sweeten to taste. May be reheated for serving hot, if desired.

Bananas in Orange-Apricot Sauce
_____

2 oz dried apricots	2 large bananas
1/4 c water	1/4 c sugar
2 tsp arrowroot starch	3/4 c orange juice
	1 Tbsp grated orange rind

1. Combine chopped dried apricots and water in a 1-q saucepan and bring to a boil. Set aside.
2. Combine the orange juice and cornstarch in another 1-q saucepan; stir until smooth with a spring stirrer.
3. Heat over moderate heat, stirring constantly, until the mixture comes to a boil.
4. Remove from the heat and stir in the sugar and grated orange rind; combine with the apricots and chill.
5. Serve over sliced bananas (or pound cake, with yogurt, or cottage cheese).

Microwave Oven:

Heat apricots and water in a 1-q glass casserole 1 minute. Heat starch mixture in a 1-q glass casserole 1 minute. Stir well, and cook about 1/2 minute, uncovered.

Yield: Four 1/3 c servings of sauce over 1/2 banana

Spicy Fruit

4 oz dried prunes	2 tsp Minute tapioca
4 oz dried apricots	1/8 tsp salt
4 cloves, whole	1/4 c sugar
2 Tbsp finely chopped candied ginger	1/2 c orange juice
1 c water	1/2 c chopped walnuts (optional)

1. Tie the whole cloves in a small piece of cheesecloth for easy removal.
2. Place prunes and apricots in a food processor; use a blade chopper and chop fine.
3. Combine the water, chopped apricots, prunes, ginger, tapioca, salt, and cloves in a 1-1/2-q saucepan and bring to a boil. Simmer 1-2 minutes.
4. Add the remaining ingredients and heat to boiling. Stir in walnuts.
5. Serve hot or cold, removing cloves before serving.

Microwave Oven:

Place the dried fruit mixture in a 1-1/2-q glass casserole and cover with a plastic wrap. Process 3 minutes. Add the rest of the ingredients, stir, cover with a plastic wrap, and cook 2 minutes.

Yield: Three 2/3 c servings

D. Preparation and Use of Fruit Purées

Suitable fruits for puréeing include apricots, avocados, bananas, berries, cherries, mangoes, nectarines, papayas, peaches, pears, persimmons, pineapples, plums, and pomegranates.

1. Wash fruit, remove cores and pits, remove inedible peels such as pomegranate or fuzzy peach skins.
2. Blend 3 c chopped fruit in blender with 1/4 cup water and 1/2 tsp ascorbic acid. Sweeten to taste.
3. If fruit contains undesirable seeds, as in some berries and pomegranates, press purée through a sieve to remove the seeds before adding sugar.
4. The purée can be used as is or held in the refrigerator for 1 week.
5. To freeze, heat the purée until boiling to inactivate oxidative enzymes, fill freezer containers three-quarters full, seal, and freeze.
6. Use as a topping for cold or hot cereals, waffles, pancakes, quick breads, puddings, cakes, or ice cream; or dilute with water or juices and add gelatin to use for salads and desserts.

(Note: If a blender is not available, soft fruits can be puréed with a food mill; firm fruits will require cooking before they can be pressed through the mill.)

COMPARISON OF PROCESSED AND FRESH FRUITS

The costs of fruit products, of course, depends on whether the fruit is in season and the size of the crop for processing, as well as on the cost of processing and the demand for the various products. By filling in the columns in Table 3-1, fruits can be compared on a cost-per-serving basis.

Table 3-1   Comparison of Costs of Processed and Fresh Fruits

Fruit	Form	Market unit	Market unit Yield	Market unit Cost	Size of serving	Servings per market unit	Cost per serving
Example:				$			$
Applesauce	Canned	16 oz	2 c	0.42	1/2 c	4	0.105
Applesauce	Fresh apples sugar	pound pound	1-1/2 c 2 c	0.30 0.52	1/2 c 1 Tbsp	3 32 Total cost	0.10 0.016 0.116[a]

[a]Does not include cost of sugar and energy for cooking, but this would probably be less than 1¢.

Effect of Processing on Nutrient Retention

The caloric content of fruits is largely related to the amount of sugar and fat added to the fruit during processing and preparation. Compare the effects of different methods of processing on nutrient retention and the effect of sugar on caloric content by filling in Table 3-2 for apricots using USDA Handbook No. 8, Table 1 (Composition of Food, per 100 g). Other fruits can be expected to show similar results.

Table 3-2   Comparison of Nutrient Retention with Various Forms of Fruit, 100 g

Description of fruit	Water (%)	Food energy (cals)	Iron (mg)	Vitamin A value (I.U.)	Ascorbic acid[1] (mg)
Example:					
Apricots					
Raw					
Canned, solids and liquids: Water pack					
Juice pack					
Syrup pack, light					
Syrup pack, heavy					
Syrup pack, extra heavy					
Dried, sulfured: Cooked without sugar					
Cooked with sugar					
Frozen, sweetened					

[1]Other nutrients are not included because fruits are negligible sources of protein, calcium and B vitamins.

Questions

1. What nutrient appears to be most labile when processed?
2. What form of processing appears to be most destructive of nutrients?
3. What forms of fruits would be best to use in low-calorie diets?
4. What factors might be important to consider besides nutrient retention and cost in determining which form of fruit to use?

UNIT 4   VEGETABLE COOKERY

Suggested reading: <u>Basic Foods</u>, Chapter 7

Objectives

- To observe the effect of pH changes on the color of pigments in vegetables
- To practice cooking a variety of vegetables using a variety of methods
- To compare processed and fresh vegetables in terms of cost and nutrient retention

EFFECT OF pH CHANGES ON PIGMENTS IN VEGETABLES (<u>BF</u>, 122-126)

Three solutions are used to provide media of varying pH:

1. Neutral pH: 1/3 cup distilled water
2. Acidic pH: 1/3 cup distilled water mixed with 1/4 tsp cream of tartar
3. Alkaline pH: 1/3 cup distilled water mixed with 1/4 tsp baking soda

Four different vegetables are each cooked in the solutions to illustrate the effect of pH on the different pigments:

1. Carotene: carrots, peeled and sliced crosswise into 1/8"- thick slices
2. Chlorophyll: broccoli, broken into flowerets, yellow blooms discarded
3. Anthocyanin: red cabbage, thinly shredded
4. Anthoxanthin: cauliflower, separated into small flowerets

Procedure

1. Use about 1/2 cup of vegetable for each solution.
2. Cook the distilled-water sample first as a control. Record the boiling time required to achieve the desired degree of tenderness. Then cook the same vegetable in the acid and alkaline media for the same length of time.
3. Place each solution in a 1-qt stainless-steel saucepan, add 1/2 cup of vegetable, cover and place on high heat until boiling starts. When the vegetable starts to boil, reduce heat to simmer, stir the vegetable, cover, and continue cooking until tender (if the control) or the same length of time as the control if in the acidic or alkaline solution. Use the same heat settings for each sample.
4. Display cooked vegetables with a sample of the raw vegetable, and label with the variations used.
5. Record results in Table 4-1; compare with results given in <u>Basic Foods</u>, Table 7.2 (p. 124).

Table 4-1   Effect of pH on Pigments in Vegetables

Vegetable	Pigment	Color			
		Raw	Neutral	Acidic	Alkaline
Carrots	Carotene				
Broccoli	Chlorophyll				
Red cabbage	Anthocyanin				
Cauliflower	Anthoxanthin				

PREPARING AND COOKING VEGETABLES

A. Roots and Tubers

General Instructions

1. If the peel of the vegetable is to be eaten, then the root or tuber requires thorough scrubbing. If the root or tuber is to be peeled before cooking, then only loose soil need be rinsed off.
2. When peeling, be sure to remove eyes of potatoes, bruised or decayed spots, and the green discoloration (solanin) occasionally seen under the skin of white potatoes.
3. Even if the root or tuber is not to be peeled, remove decayed or bruised areas.
4. Many of the recipes below state that cooking liquid is to be drained off. It need not be discarded, however, unless the flavor is too strong and unacceptable for use in soups and sauces, as is the case with the cooking liquids from spinach and chard. (These liquids also have a high content of oxalic acid and thus should not be used.) Most recipes suggest using more water than is actually needed. Since cooking circumstances vary, these amounts are recommended to allow for evaporation from poorly fitting lids and to prevent burning (likely if pots with thin bottoms are used). With practice and good-quality utensils, it is possible to cook many of these vegetables with less liquid, so that there is often no excess to drain off. It is also possible to evaporate off the excess almost to dryness, being careful not to overcook the vegetable.
5. It is usually advisable to cover the saucepan while cooking vegetables for the following reasons: (a) it shortens the time required for boiling to start, and (b) it permits the use of less liquid by reducing evaporation. Both of these effects are important in improving nutrient retention during cooking.

Harvard Beets with Fresh Beets

1 bunch fresh beets
1 tsp salt

Sauce

1 Tbsp cornstarch
3 Tbsp sugar

2/3 c water
2 Tbsp vinegar or lemon juice

1. Cut tops off beets, leaving about 2" of stems on the beets.
2. Rinse surface dirt from the beets.
3. Place beets in a pressure cooker or large kettle. Cover with water, add salt.
4. Process at 15 lbs pressure for 15 minutes, or cook on surface unit for 45 minutes.
5. Pierce with sharp knife to determine if tender.
6. Drain off and discard cooking water. Cool beets in cold water.
7. Slice off stem and root ends of cooked beets, and remove skins.
8. Dice or slice beets, and set aside.
9. In a saucepan combine the water, vinegar, cornstarch, and sugar, mixing with a spring stirrer until smooth.
10. Heat sauce over moderate heat, stirring constantly, until the mixture starts to boil.
11. Add 2 cups of prepared beets and heat.

Yield: Four 1/2-cup servings

Harvard Beets with Canned Beets

1 1-lb can beets	1 Tbsp cornstarch
1/2 tsp salt	2 Tbsp vinegar or lemon juice
3 Tbsp sugar	

1. Drain the liquid from the canned beets into saucepan.
2. Add the salt, sugar, cornstarch, and vinegar, and mix with spring stirrer until smooth.
3. Follow steps 10 and 11 under Harvard Beets with Fresh Beets.

Microwave Oven:

Combine the beet juice, cornstarch, sugar, and salt in a 1-1/2-q casserole; mix well and heat uncovered in the microwave oven to the boiling point—about 3 minutes. Stir in the beets and the vinegar and cook 4 minutes in the microwave oven.

Yield: Four 1/2-cup servings

Parsnips Parmesan

1 lb parsnips	1/2 tsp salt
2 Tbsp grated Parmesan cheese	dash of pepper
1-3 tsp table fat	

1. Wash and peel parsnips; dice.
2. Place diced parsnips in a 1- or 2-quart saucepan with 1/3 cup water and salt.
3. Cover pan and simmer until parsnips are almost tender.
4. Remove cover and evaporate cooking liquid almost to dryness.
5. Stir in table fat, Parmesan cheese, and pepper as desired.

Microwave Oven:

Place pared and diced parsnips in a 1-1/2-q casserole with 1/4 c water and 1/2 tsp salt. Cook 6 minutes until tender. Drain off excess liquid and stir in the table fat and cheese. Heat 1 minute.

Yield: Four 1/2 c servings

Creamed Onions

1 lb small white boiling onions	2 c water
1/2 tsp salt	
Sauce:	

3/4 c milk	1/4 tsp salt
1 Tbsp table fat	pinch of pepper
1 Tbsp flour	pinch of nutmeg

1. Place unpeeled onions in saucepan, cover with water, and bring to a boil.
2. Remove from heat and drain; cool in cold water and peel.
3. Place peeled onions in saucepan with 2 c water and 1/2 tsp salt.
4. Simmer, uncovered, until tender when pierced with a sharp knife; add water if necessary.
5. In another saucepan combine milk, flour, and seasonings; mix with spring stirrer until smooth.
6. Heat over moderate heat, stirring constantly, until mixture starts to boil; remove from heat and add table fat.
7. Drain the liquid from the onions and add onions to the sauce; heat to serving temperature on surface unit or in oven.

Microwave Oven:

Heat unpeeled onions to boiling in a 1-1/2-q casserole—about 6 minutes. Cool and peel onions. Return peeled onions to the casserole with 1/2 c water and salt, cover with a plastic wrap, and cook until tender—about 5 minutes. Drain and set aside. Mix flour and milk together in another casserole until smooth and cook in the microwave oven 1 minute; stir well and cook to boiling point—about 2 minutes. Stir in table fat, nutmeg, and pepper. Add onions and heat 1 more minute in the microwave oven.

Yield: Three 1/2-cup servings

Steamed Carrots

1 lb fresh carrots	2 Tbsp minced parsley
1 Tbsp table fat	dash of pepper
1/4 tsp salt	

1. Wash and peel carrots, grate on coarse grater.
2. Melt table fat in saucepan and add carrots.
3. Cover and cook over moderate heat for about 6 minutes, stirring every 2 minutes. (Note: carrots should not be cooked until mushy; they need only be heated through.)
4. Stir in minced parsley, and season to taste with salt and pepper.

Microwave Oven:

Combine carrots, salt, and pepper in a 1-1/2-q casserole, cover with a plastic wrap, and cook 3 minutes. Stir, cover, and cook 3 more minutes. Stir in the table fat and parsley.

Yield: Four 1/2-cup servings

Turnips O'Brien

1 lb fresh turnips	2 Tbsp chopped red or green sweet pepper
1 Tbsp table fat	salt and pepper to taste

1. Wash turnips and place in saucepan, cover with water and simmer until tender when pierced with a sharp knife.
2. Drain, cool, peel and dice.
3. Melt table fat in pan, add chopped pepper and diced turnips.
4. Sauté lightly; season to taste.

Microwave Oven:

Place washed turnips in a 2-q casserole with 1 c of water. Cook 7 minutes, drain, cool, peel, and dice. Return the diced turnips to the casserole, add chopped peppers, table fat, and salt and pepper. Cook covered 2 minutes.

Yield: Three 1/2-cup servings

Mashed Rutabagas
_____

1 lb rutabagas	1 tsp lemon juice
1/3 c water	2 Tbsp brown sugar
1 Tbsp table fat	salt to taste

1. Wash and peel rutabagas; dice.
2. Combine diced rutabagas and water in a saucepan, cover and simmer over moderate heat until tender.
3. Evaporate cooking liquid almost to dryness; mash rutabagas with fork and add table fat, sugar, and lemon juice; salt to taste.

Microwave Oven:

Place peeled, diced rutabagas in a 1-1/2-q casserole with 2 Tbsp water and salt. Cover with plastic wrap and cook 7 minutes. Drain, stir in table fat, lemon juice, and brown sugar. Heat 1 minute.

Yield: Three 1/2 c servings

Candied Sweet Potatoes with Pineapple
_____

1 lb (2 medium) sweet potatoes	1 Tbsp table fat
1/2 c drained crushed pineapple	1/4 c brown sugar
2 Tbsp juice from pineapple	

Topping

1 Tbsp table fat	2 Tbsp brown sugar
1 Tbsp flour	

1. Wash potatoes, place in a saucepan and cover with water. Boil over moderate heat until tender; drain, cool, peel.
2. Cut potatoes into 2" chunks and place in a well-greased 1-qt casserole; cover with drained crushed pineapple.
3. Melt 1 Tbsp table fat in small saucepan or fry pan, add 1/4 cup brown sugar and 2 Tbsp pineapple juice; heat until bubbly. Pour the syrup over the sweet potatoes.
4. Bake uncovered in preheated over at 350°F (176.5°C) for 45 minutes, basting every 15 minutes.
5. Mix the flour and 2 Tbsp brown sugar in a small bowl and cut in 1 Tbsp table fat.
6. Remove sweet potatoes from the oven, turn the thermostat at 400°F (204.5°C).
7. Sprinkle the flour-sugar-fat mixture oven the top of the sweet potaotes. Return to the oven and bake until bubbling and brown.

Microwave Oven:

Place scrubbed yams or sweet potatoes in the microwave oven and cook 7 minutes per lb of potatoes. Potatoes should be pierced with a sharp pointed knife to allow steam to escape during baking. Peel the baked potatoes, cut into 2" chunks, and place in a lightly oiled glass baking dish. Cover with pineapple and topping and cook in the microwave oven 2-3 minutes.

Yield: Four 1/2-cup servings

Easy Glazed Sweet Potatoes (Yams)

1 1-lb can sweet potatoes (yams)
1-2 Tbsp table fat

1. Drain the juice from the can of yams into a saucepan and add the table fat.
2. Cook the juice over moderate heat to evaporate to one half.
3. Add the canned yams and heat and baste with juice for about 5 minutes.

Yield: Three 1/2-cup servings

Baked Potatoes

1. Choose potatoes of uniform size so that all will bake in the same length of time.
2. Scrub potatoes and cut off blemishes.
3. Potatoes may be handled in one of the following ways:
    a) Place scrubbed potatoes on a pan or on oven rack.
    b) Oil scrubbed potatoes and place on pan.
    c) Wrap potatoes in aluminum foil and place on pan or on oven rack.
4. Bake at 400°F (204.5°C) for about 1 hour for medium size potatoes.
5. To serve, cut two perpendicular slits in the top of the potato; hold the potato in a folded, clean towel and press gently to break up the inside.
6. Serve with table fat or sour cream, with or without chopped chives.

Microwave Oven:

Pierce scrubbed potato(es) with a sharp pointed knife and cook in the microwave oven 7 minutes per lb. Allow to stand a few minutes before serving.

Stuffed Baked Potatoes

1. Prepare potatoes as described for Baked Potatoes, steps 1 through 4.
2. Cut the potatoes in half lengthwise and scoop the inside out of the skin into the bowl of an electric mixer.
3. Mash the potatoes in the mixer or with potato masher, and add one of the filling combinations below. Amounts are for 3 medium-size potatoes (3 servings):

Au gratin filling

1/2 c grated sharp cheddar cheese   1/2 tsp salt
1/4 c yogurt or sour cream   dash of pepper
1 chopped green onion, including top

Caviar filling

1/3 c yogurt or sour cream   1/2 tsp salt
1 Tbsp caviar   dash of pepper
1/4 Tsp onion powder

⚞Mexican style filling

1/2 c Monterey Jack cheese	1/2 tsp salt
2 Tbsp chopped green chiles (canned, seeded)	dash of pepper

4. Fill the potato shells with the filling, heaping if necessary to use all of the filling.
5. Place the filled potatoes in a baking dish and bake at 400°F (204.5°C) for about 15 minutes, or until heated through and browned lightly on top.

Microwave Oven:

Stuffed potatoes can be heated in the microwave oven 2-3 minutes per lb.

Mashed Potatoes
_____

1 lb white potatoes	1/3-1/2 c NFDM
1 c water	2 Tbsp table fat (optional)
1/2 tsp salt	salt to taste

1. Wash and peel potatoes; remove eyes and bruised areas.
2. Cut the potatoes into pieces and place in saucepan with water and salt.
3. Cook covered over moderate heat until very tender.
4. Pour off and reserve the cooking liquid.
5. Mash the potatoes with a potato masher or place the cooked potatoes in the bowl of an electric mixer and whip until free of lumps.
6. Add NFDM, table fat (if desired), and potato cooking liquid as needed to produce fluffy mashed potatoes. If additional liquid is needed, add fluid milk.

Microwave Oven:

Place peeled, cut-up potatoes in a 2-q glass casserole with 1/4 c water and 1/2 tsp salt. Cover with a plastic wrap and cook 8 minutes per lb of potatoes.

Yield: Three 1/2-cup servings

Note: The table fat adds flavor but can sometimes be omitted if the potatoes will be served with gravy, as the table fat increases the calories.

German Potato Pancakes
_____

1 large egg	1/2 tsp salt
3 medium-size potatoes	1 Tbsp flour
1-1/2 tsp milk	dash of pepper
2 tsp oil	

1. Wash and peel the potatoes; grate coarsely.
2. Combine the grated potatoes with rest of the ingredients.
3. Drop batter by tablespoonful onto moderately hot, greased griddle.
4. Cook until golden brown on each side, turning once.

Yield: Three to four servings

B. Leafy Green Vegetables
General Instructions

1. Choose greens that have small, young leaves as these are usually less bitter, better flavored, and more tender than more mature large leaves.
2. Sort the greens and remove the yellow and decayed leaves or parts of leaves.
3. Cut off tough, stringy stems; tender stems may be left on.
4. Wash the greens in warm, not hot, water one or more times until water appears clean when leaves are removed. Hold large leaves under running water and spray-wash each side of the leaf.
5. Drain well. If greens are to be stored in the refrigerator, place the dry, washed leaves in plastic bags; expel as much air as possible from the bag before refrigerating.
6. Just before cooking, cut the large leaves crosswise into strips about 1" wide to reduce stringiness when cooked.
7. Bring vegetables to boil, or heat to steaming hot if waterless method is used, and uncover and stir the vegetables to release the organic acids; then re-cover and complete cooking.
8. After cooking, drain off excess cooking liquid before adding seasonings.

Bok Choy (Chinese Chard)

1 lb bok choy, chopped	dash of powdered ginger
2 Tbsp water	1 Tbsp water
1 tsp soy sauce	2 tsp cornstarch
1/2 tsp beef stock base	

1. Combine 2 Tbsp water, soy sauce, beef stock base, and ginger in saucepan.
2. Add bok choy, cover, and simmer over moderate heat until just barely tender—about 5 minutes, stirring occasionally.
3. Combine the 1 Tbsp water and 2 tsp cornstarch; stir mixture into the cooked bok choy, heat to boiling and serve hot.

Microwave Oven:

Combine the soy sauce, beef stock base, and 2 Tbsp water in a casserole and add the chopped bok choy. Cover with a plastic wrap and cook 2 minutes, stir, and cook 1-2 more minutes. Combine the cornstarch with 1 Tbsp water and stir it into the bok choy. Cook 1 more minute.

Yield: Three 1/2-cup servings

Chinese Cabbage

1 qt shredded Napa or Chinese cabbage	1/16 tsp pepper
1/2 c diagonally sliced celery	1/3 c thinly sliced green onions,
1/2 green pepper, thinly sliced	including tops
1/2 tsp salt	2-3 tsp table fat

1. Melt table fat in electric or stainless steel frying pan or wok.
2. Add the cabbage, celery, green pepper, salt, and pepper.
3. Cover and cook over moderate heat until just wilted, stirring occasionally, about 5 minutes. Do not overcook.
4. Just before serving, stir in the chopped green onions.
5. Season to taste and serve hot.

Microwave Oven:

Place in a 2-q casserole the cabbage, celery, green pepper, salt, pepper, and table fat. Cover with a plastic wrap and cook 2 minutes; stir and cook 2-3 minutes longer. Stir in green onions.

Yield: Three 1/2-cup servings

Mustard Greens

3 strips bacon	1/4 tsp salt
1 lb mustard greens, chopped	1/4 c water

1. Cut strips of bacon into small pieces and sauté in saucepan until crisp and brown. Remove the bacon and drain on absorbent paper, discarding the drippings.
2. Combine the chopped mustard greens, water, and salt in the same saucepan; cover, and simmer over moderate heat until tender, stirring occasionally.
3. Drain off the excess cooking liquid and stir in the crisp bacon pieces just before serving.
4. Correct seasoning; serve hot.

Microwave Oven:

Fold two paper towels in half. Place the slices of bacon on the towels and place one folded paper towel on top. Cook in the microwave oven 3 minutes. Place the chopped greens in a 2-q casserole with the water and salt. Cover with a plastic wrap and cook 3 minutes. Stir, cover, and cook 2-3 more minutes. Crumble the cooked bacon over the cooked greens, stir, and serve.

Yield: Three 1/2-cup servings.

Brussel Sprouts with Chestnuts

1/2 lb Brussel sprouts	1 Tbsp table fat
1/3 c water	dash each of nutmeg and pepper
1/2 tsp salt	1/4 c cooked, sliced chestnuts (optional)

1. Trim and wash Brussel sprouts; cut in half if large.
2. Place 1/2 c chestnuts in saucepan, cover with water and simmer 20 minutes. Drain, cool, shell, slice and set aside.
3. Combine prepared Brussel sprouts, 1/3 c water and salt in saucepan, cover, and simmer over moderate heat until tender; do not overcook.
4. Drain off excess cooking liquid; add table fat, sliced chestnuts, and nutmeg and pepper to taste; serve hot.

Microwave Oven:

Slash crosswise through the shell on the flat end of the chestnuts. Place the nuts in a glass pie plate and cook 2-3 minutes, stirring every minute until the nuts are soft when squeezed. Cool, shell, and chop the chestnuts. In a 1-1/2-q glass casserole combine the brussel sprouts, salt, and 1 Tbsp water. Cover with a plastic wrap and cook 2 minutes, stir, recover, and cook 2 more minutes. Stir in chopped chestnuts, table fat, nutmeg, and pepper.

Yield: Two 1/2-cup servings

Swiss Chard with Swiss Cheese

1 lb Swiss chard, chopped	1/2 c milk
1/4 c water	1 Tbsp flour
1/2 tsp salt	1/3 c grated Swiss cheese

1. Combine chopped chard, water, and salt in saucepan; cover; simmer over moderate heat, stirring occasionally, until tender. Drain off cooking liquid.
2. While chard is cooking, in another saucepan combine milk and flour with a spring stirrer, mixing until smooth.
3. Cook sauce over moderate heat, stirring constantly, until it starts to boil.
4. Remove sauce from heat and stir in grated Swiss cheese.
5. Combine the hot, cooked, drained chard with the cheese sauce and serve hot.

Microwave Oven:

Combine the chard, salt, and water in a 2-q glass casserole; cover with a plastic wrap, and cook 2 minutes. Stir, recover, and cook 2 more minutes. In a 1-q glass casserole mix together the milk and flour. Cover with a plastic wrap and cook 3/4 of a minute. Stir, recover, and cook 1 minute. Stir in grated cheese and pour over the hot chard. Reheat 1/2 to 1 minute if needed.

Yield: Three 1/2-cup servings

Kale with Egg Sauce

1 lb kale, chopped	2 hard-cooked eggs
1/2 c water	3 Tbsp prepared mustard
1/2 tsp salt	2 Tbsp vinegar

1. Combine chopped kale, water, and salt in saucepan; cover; simmer over moderate heat, stirring occasionally, until tender; drain.
2. Mash the yolks of 2 hard-cooked eggs in a small bowl and stir in the prepared mustard and vinegar.
3. Stir the yolk-mustard mixture into the drained, cooked kale.
4. Garnish with sliced hard-cooked egg whites. Serve hot, but do not heat after adding seasoning mixture.

Yield: Four 1/2-cup servings

Beet Greens Vinaigrette

3/4 lb beet greens, chopped	1 tsp olive or other oil
1/4 c water	1 tsp sugar
1/4 tsp salt	1 Tbsp chopped green onions,
1 Tbsp vinegar	including tops

1. Combine chopped beet greens, water, and salt in saucepan; cover; simmer over moderate heat, stirring occasionally, until tender.
2. Drain off excess cooking liquid.
3. Stir in the vinegar, oil, sugar, and chopped green onions.
4. Serve hot, but do not heat after adding seasonings.

Microwave Oven:

Combine the greens, 2 Tbsp water, and salt in a 2-q glass casserole; cover with a plastic wrap and cook 2 minutes. Stir, recover, and cook 1-2 minutes. Stir in remaining ingredients and serve.

Yield: Two 1/2-cup servings

Collard Greens with Green Chiles

1 lb collard greens, chopped
1/2 c water
1/2 tsp salt

1 canned green chile, seeded, chopped
1/4 c catsup

1. Combine chopped collards, water, and salt in saucepan; cover.
2. Simmer over moderate heat, stirring occasionally until tender.
3. Drain off excess cooking liquid and stir in the chopped green chiles and catsup. Serve hot, but do not heat after adding catsup.

Yield: Three 1/2-cup servings

Sesame Spinach

1 lb chopped spinach
1/4 c water

1/2 tsp salt
1 Tbsp table fat

2 Tbsp white sesame seeds

1. Combine chopped spinach, water, and salt in saucepan; cover.
2. Cook over moderate heat, stirring occasionally, until tender.
3. Drain off excess cooking liquid; season with table fat and sesame seeds; serve hot.

Microwave Oven:

Combine spinach, 1 Tbsp water, and salt in a 2-q casserole; cover with a plastic wrap and cook 2 minutes. Stir, recover and cook 1 minute. Drain off excess liquid and stir in the table fat and sesame seeds.

Yield: Three 1/2-cup servings

C. Other Vegetables

Trim and wash all vegetables. Prepare as directed.

Pennsylvania Dutch Red Cabbage

3 c shredded red cabbage
1 apple, unpeeled, cored, diced
2 Tbsp vinegar
1 Tbsp brown sugar

1/2 tsp salt
1/2 tsp onion powder
1-3 tsp olive oil or table fat

1. Heat oil or table fat in saucepan to coat bottom of pan.
2. Add all ingredients, cover; cook over moderate heat, stirring occasionally, until just barely tender. Do not overcook. Serve hot.

Microwave Oven:

Melt table fat in a 1-1/2-q casserole—about 1/2 minute. Place all ingredients in a casserole, cover with a plastic wrap, and cook 2 minutes. Stir and cook 2 minutes.

Yield: Three 1/2-cup servings

Sautéed Okra

2/3 lb okra, fresh or partially-
    thawed whole frozen
yellow cornmeal

1/2 tsp salt
1 Tbsp oil

1. Wash okra and cut off stem end; slice diagonally in 1/2" thick slices. Sprinkle with salt and roll slices in cornmeal.
2. Heat oil in electric frying pan or skillet over moderate heat; add okra slices coated with cornmeal.
3. Sauté until okra is lightly browned, stirring frequently.
4. Season to taste with salt and pepper. Serve hot.

Yield: Three 1/2-cup servings

Baked Acorn Squash

1 1-lb acorn squash
2 Tbsp table fat
1/4 c brown sugar

dash of nutmeg
1/4 c water

1. Wash outside of squash and cut in half; remove seeds.
2. Choose a Pyrex baking dish that will hold the two halves, cut side down. Grease the dish and place 1/4 c water in it.
3. Place the squash in the dish, cut side down.
4. Bake at 400°F (204.5°C) until tender when pierced with a sharp knife—about 45 minutes; or cook in electronic oven about 8 minutes.
5. Turn the cut side up and loosen the meat from the shell. Sprinkle with salt, and place half the table fat and brown sugar, mixed, in each half. Add a sprinkle of nutmeg if desired.
6. Reheat for serving.

Microwave Oven:

Follow steps 1 to 3; cook in the microwave oven 7 minutes. Follow steps 5 and 6 above, except reheat in the microwave oven about 1 minute.

Yield: Two servings

Zucchini Romano

1 lb zucchini
1/4 c chopped onion
1 Tbsp table fat

1/2 tsp salt
3 Tbsp grated Romano cheese

1. Trim ends from washed zucchini and slice diagonally in 1/2"-thick slices.
2. Melt table fat in saucepan, and add zucchini and chopped onions. Cook over moderate heat, stirring or shaking the pot at frequent intervals to prevent sticking. Cook only until tender.
3. Stir in the Romano cheese and transfer to ovenproof dish. Heat about 20 to 30 minutes to melt cheese and blend flavors. Serve hot.

Microwave Oven:

In a 1-1/2-q glass casserole combine the sliced zucchini, salt, chopped onion, and table fat. Cover with a plastic wrap and cook 3 minutes. Stir in the cheese and cook 2-3 minutes longer. Zucchini should be a little "undercooked."

Yield: Three 1/2-cup servings

Asparagus Oriental
_____

1 lb asparagus	1/4 c thinly sliced green onions,
1/2 c diagonally sliced celery	including tops
1/4 c sliced water chestnuts (canned)	1 Tbsp table fat
	1/2 tsp salt

1. Wash asparagus and discard lower stalks, unless they are tender.
2. Slice asparagus diagonally in 1/2"-thick slices.
3. Melt table fat in electric frying pan or wok; add asparagus, celery, and water chestnuts. Cook over moderate heat, stirring frequently, until just tender.
4. Season to taste with salt and pepper. Add the sliced green onions just before serving; serve hot.

Yield: Four 1/2-cup servings

Peas and Mushrooms
_____

1-1/2 lb fresh peas or 10-oz pkg	1/2 tsp salt
of frozen peas	1 Tbsp table fat
1/4 c water	1/4 lb fresh mushrooms

1. Shell and rinse peas, if fresh.
2. Combine peas, water, and salt in saucepan; cover, and simmer over moderate heat until tender—about 10 minutes.
3. Wash and slice mushrooms; sauté in table fat until just wilted.
4. Drain cooked peas and combine with mushrooms; serve hot.

Microwave Oven:

Combine the peas, 2 Tbsp water, and salt in a 1-q glass casserole, cover with a plastic wrap, and cook 3 minutes. Stir, recover, and cook 3-4 minutes. Drain and stir in the sautéed mushrooms.

Yield: Four 1/2-cup servings

Fiesta Yellow Squash
_____

1/4 lb crookneck or other summer squash	1/2 tsp salt
1/4 c sliced green onions, including tops	1/4 tsp crushed thyme
2 Tbsp chopped green sweet pepper	dash of pepper
1 Tbsp table fat	1 tsp lemon juice
2 Tbsp chopped sweet red pepper	

1. Melt table fat in large skillet or electric frying pan to coat bottom.
2. Trim ends off squash and wash; slice into 1/4"-thick slices.
3. Combine in pan the squash, chopped red and green peppers, salt, pepper, thyme, and lemon juice.
4. Cook over moderate heat until squash is tender-crisp.
5. Stir in the chopped green onions just before serving.

Microwave Oven:

Melt the table fat in a 1-1/2-q glass casserole—about 1/2 minute. Add the squash, green and red pepper, salt, thyme, pepper, and lemon juice and toss together. Cover with a plastic wrap and cook 3 minutes. Stir, recover, and cook 3-4 minutes. Stir in the green onions.

Yield: Four 1/2-cup servings

Green Beans with Almonds

2/3 lb fresh green beans, or	1/2 tsp salt
10-oz pkg frozen beans	1 Tbsp table fat
1/3 c water	1/3 c slivered almonds

1. Remove flower and stem end of fresh beans, wash, and cut into 2" lengths; or use frozen green beans.
2. Combine beans, water and salt in a saucepan; cover, and simmer over moderate heat until tender, stirring occasionally.
3. Sauté almonds lightly in table fat.
4. Drain excess cooking liquid from beans and stir in toasted almonds. Serve hot.

Microwave Oven:

Combine the green beans, salt, and 2 Tbsp water in a 1-1/2-q glass casserole, cover with a plastic wrap, and cook 3 minutes. Stir, recover, and cook 4 minutes. Drain and stir in the sautéed almonds.

Yield: Three 1/2-cup servings

Curried Black-Eyed Peas

3/4 lb fresh black-eyed peas, or	1/2 tsp salt
10-oz pkg frozen peas	1 tsp curry powder
1/3 c water	1 Tbsp table fat

1. Shell and wash peas.
2. Combine peas, water, and salt in saucepan and simmer covered over moderate heat until tender, about 10 minutes.
3. Add curry powder and table fat; serve hot.

Yield: Three 1/2-cup servings

COST COMPARISON OF FRESH AND PROCESSED VEGETABLES

Use Table 4-2 as a guide in comparing cost of assigned vegetables. Either consult Basic Foods, Appendix, Table 9 for yields of the various market forms of the vegetables, or prepare and measure the vegetables.

Table 4-2   Comparison of Costs of Fresh and Processed Vegetables

Vegetable	Form	Market unit		Size of serving	Servings per market unit	Cost per serving($)
		Yield	Cost ($)			

EFFECTS OF PROCESSING ON NUTRIENT RETENTION IN VEGETABLES

In Table 4-3 record the nutrients for fresh and processed green sweet peas. Since peas have a higher content of B vitamins than most other vegetables and fruits, these vitamins are included in the comparison. Use USDA Handbook No. 8, Table 1, Composition of food per 100 grams.

Questions

1. What form of processing is most destructive of nutrients?
2. What nutrients are most labile when processed?
3. Often the liquid in canned vegetables is discarded. Note the nutrient content of the liquid and comment on the advisability of this practice.
4. Note the difference in Vitamin A value of the solids and liquid for canned peas. Can you account for this?

Table 4-3   Comparison of Nutrient Content of Various Forms of Vegetable, 100 g

Description of vegetable	Water (%)	Food energy (cal)	Iron (mg)	Vit. A value (I.U.)	Thiamin (mg)	Ribo-flavin (mg)	Niacin (mg)	Ascorbic acid (mg)
Example: Peas, green, immature								
Raw								
Cooked, boiled, drained								
Canned, sweet: Solids and liquid								
Drained solids								
Drained liquid								
Frozen: Not thawed								
Cooked, drained								

UNIT 5   SALAD DRESSINGS

Suggested reading: Basic Foods, Chapter 5

Objectives

- To learn to prepare stable and temporary emulsions for use as salad dressings
- To explore ways of varying ingredients in these emulsions to obtain different flavor effects
- To compare costs and caloric contents of prepared and commercial salad dressings

PREPARATION OF SALAD DRESSINGS

A. Stable Emulsions (BF, 93)

Many of the dressings given below—especially the mixtures containing milk and flour—lack the long shelf-life possible with commercially prepared products. If refrigerated, they will keep about one month. They should not be frozen, however, as the emulsion breaks when they are thawed. Observe stringent hygienic procedures in preparing them: use clean utensils and keep fingers out of the mixtures; use clean rubber scrapers for transferring ingredients and mixtures.

Mayonnaise

1 large egg	1 tsp sugar
1 Tbsp vinegar	1/4 tsp dry mustard
1/2 tsp salt	1 c oil

Blender Method

1. Combine the egg, vinegar, salt, sugar, and dry mustard in the blender, cover, and blend at high speed for 5 seconds.
2. Without stopping the blender, remove the center section of the cover and add 1/4 cup of the oil, 1 tsp at a time. Then add the remaining oil, pouring it in a slow dribble into the vortex of the mixture in the blender.
3. Blend about 1 minute after all of the oil has been added.

Electric Mixer Method

1. Combine the egg, vinegar, salt, sugar, and dry mustard in the small bowl of the mixer, and mix at high speed, but not so high that the mixture splatters out of the bowl.
2. Without stopping the mixer, start adding the oil, 1/4 tsp at a time, until about 2 tsp have been added.
3. Then add the oil 1 tsp at a time until half the oil has been used; the remaining oil can be added about 1 Tbsp at a time.

Yield: 1-1/3 cups (97 K cal/Tbsp)

Note: Two egg yolks or two egg whites may be used in place of one whole egg. If the two egg whites are used, use only 3/4 cup of oil, as the emulsion sometimes breaks when a whole cup of oil is used.

Reconstituting Broken Emulsions (BF, 94-95)

1. Prepare a fresh emulsion, using blender or mixer method described above.
2. Add the broken emulsion, 1 tsp at a time, to either an egg yolk or a whole egg.
3. As soon as the emulsion starts to form, the broken emulsion may be added more rapidly, just as in preparing mayonnaise.

Hollandaise Sauce (BF, 95)

3 egg yolks	1/8 tsp salt
1-2 Tbsp lemon juice	1/4 c table fat

Blender Method

1. Place the egg yolks, lemon juice, and salt in the blender, cover, and blend for about 5 seconds at high speed.
2. Heat the table fat to the bubbly stage (but do not brown it).
3. Without stopping the blender, remove the center of the cover and slowly pour the hot table fat into the yolk mixture. Blend about 10 seconds after adding all of the fat.
4. To reheat, place the sauce in a Pyrex container placed in a pan of hot water.

Top-of-Range Method

1. Combine the yolks, lemon juice, and salt in a small saucepan, using a spring stirrer.
2. Add half of the table fat and cook over low heat, stirring constantly until the fat is melted.
3. Add the rest of the table fat while continuing to cook and stir rapidly until the sauce thickens.

Yield: 3/4 cup (50 K cal/Tbsp)

Note: Use the larger amount of lemon juice for a more tart sauce.

Note: A double boiler can also be used for cooking the Hollandaise Sauce. However, the sauce will curdle if cooked too long by either method.

Microwave Oven:

2 Tbsp table fat	1/8 tsp salt
1 egg yolk	2 tsp lemon juice
2 Tbsp cream	

1. Melt the table fat in a 1-c glass measure—about 15 seconds.
2. Add the remaining ingredients and mix well.
3. Cover with a plastic wrap and cook 15 seconds; stir and cook 15 seconds.
4. Remove and beat until light with a small French whip or fork.

Yield: 1/3 c (61 K cal/Tbsp)

B. Starch-Thickened Dressings

Cooked Salad Dressing

3/4 c water	1 Tbsp sugar
1/4 c NFDM	1 large egg
2 Tbsp flour	2 Tbsp table fat
1 tsp salt	2 Tbsp lemon juice
1/4 tsp dry mustard	

1. Combine the water, NFDM, flour, salt, dry mustard, sugar and egg in a 1-quart sauce-pan, and mix until smooth.
2. Cook over moderately high heat, stirring constantly with a spring stirrer, until the mixture comes to a boil.
3. Turn off the heat but leave the saucepan on the hot burner; stir in the table fat and lemon juice; stir until smooth and creamy.

   Microwave Oven:

   Combine the water, NFDM, flour, salt, mustard, sugar, and egg in a 2-c glass measure and mix well. Cover with a plastic wrap and cook 1 minute. Stir well and cook 1 minute. Stir in the table fat and lemon juice and cook 1 more minute. Stir again and refrigerate.

   Yield: 1-1/8 cups (25 K cal/Tbsp)

Imitation Mayonnaise

3/4 c water	1 large egg
1/4 c NFDM	1 Tbsp vinegar
2-1/2 Tbsp flour	1/2 tsp salt
1/2 tsp salt	1 tsp sugar
1 Tbsp sugar	1/2 tsp dry mustard
1 large egg	3/4 c oil
2 Tbsp lemon juice	

1. Follow steps 1 through 3 for Cooked Salad Dressing, (but omit the addition of table fat in step 3); set aside.
2. Follow steps 1 through 3 for Mayonnaise, Blender Method.
3. Transfer the mayonnaise from the blender to the saucepan of Cooked Salad Dressing and mix the two mixtures together until smooth.
4. Chill in the refrigerator to complete the thickening.

   Yield: 2-1/8 cups (53 K cal/Tbsp)

C. Temporary Emulsions (BF, 95)

French Dressing

1/2 c oil	1/4 tsp paprika
1/4 c vinegar	1 tsp sugar
1/4 c lemon juice	1/4 tsp tarragon
1/2 tsp salt	1/4 tsp marjoram
1/4 tsp dry mustard	1/4 tsp savory

1. Blend several minutes in a blender or shake together in a jar.

   Yield: 1 cup (63 K cal/Tbsp)

Italian Dressing

1/2 c olive or other oil	1/4 tsp crushed oregano
1/2 c wine vinegar	1/4 tsp crushed basil
1/2 tsp salt	1/4 tsp garlic powder
1/4 tsp dry mustard	2 Tbsp Romano grated cheese

1. Blend in blender for several minutes or shake together in a jar.

    Yield: 1 cup (65 K cal/Tbsp)

D. Variations in Seasonings and Ingredients

Russian Dressing

1/4 c mayonnaise	2 Tbsp low-fat yogurt
2 Tbsp chili sauce	1 Tbsp finely chopped green pepper

1. Combine ingredients and mix well.

    Yield: 1/2 cup (58 K cal/Tbsp)

Pineapple Cream Dressing

1/4 c mayonnaise	1 Tbsp sugar
2 Tbsp sour half-and-half	1/3 c well-drained crushed pineapple

1. Combine ingredients and mix well.

    Yield: 2/3 cup (55 K cal/Tbsp)

Avocado Dressing

1/3 c mayonnaise	2 Tbsp lemon juice
1 small green onion, including top	1/2 ripe avocado, peeled

1. Combine all ingredients in blender and blend until smooth.

    Yield: 2/3 cup (63 K cal/Tbsp)

Green Goddess Dressing

1/2 c mayonnaise	1 Tbsp finely chopped chives
1 finely chopped anchovy fillet	1/2 tsp crushed tarragon
1 Tbsp finely chopped green onion	1 Tbsp vinegar
1 Tbsp finely chopped parsley	

1. Combine all ingredients and mix well.

    Yield: 5/8 cup (83 K cal/Tbsp)

Caesar Dressing

1/4 c olive oil	1/4 tsp pepper
1 egg yolk	1 clove garlic, peeled
1 tsp Worcestershire sauce	1/4 tsp dry mustard
2 Tbsp lemon juice	1/4 tsp paprika
1 2-oz can anchovy fillets	1 tsp sugar
2 Tbsp Parmesan cheese	

1. Combine all ingredients in a blender and blend until smooth.

    Yield: 2/3 cup (67 K cal/Tbsp)

Roquefort Dressing

4 oz Roquefort cheese   1 Tbsp lemon juice
1-1/2 c sour half-and-half or yogurt

1. Combine ingredients in a blender and blend until smooth.

   Yield: 2 cups (35 cal/Tbsp with sour half-and-half; 25 cal/Tbsp with low-fat yogurt)

Sour Cream Dressing

1 c sour half-and-half   1/4 tsp lemon extract
2 Tbsp sugar

1. Combine ingredients and mix well. Serve chilled.

   Yield: 1 cup (25 K cal/Tbsp)

Tartar Sauce (Sweet)

1/4 c mayonnaise   1-1/2 tsp lemon juice
2 Tbsp sweet pickle relish   1/2 tsp onion salt

1. Combine ingredients.

   Yield: 3/8 cup (74 K cal/Tbsp)

Tartar Sauce (Tart)

1/4 c mayonnaise   1 Tbsp lemon juice
2 Tbsp finely chopped dill pickle   1/2 tsp onion powder

1. Combine ingredients.

   Yield: 3/8 cup (68 K cal/Tbsp)

Béarnaise Sauce

Add 1/2 tsp crushed tarragon and 1 Tbsp minced parsley to finished Hollandaise Sauce.

E. Low-Calorie Salad Dressings

Note: The caloric content of recipes in the preceding section can be reduced by using cooked salad dressing or imitation mayonnaise in place of regular mayonnaise, or by using low-fat yogurt in place of sour cream or sour half-and-half.

Low-Calorie French Dressing

1 c water   1 tsp arrowroot starch
2 tsp cornstarch   1 Tbsp oil
1/4 c wine vinegar   seasonings as listed under either French or Italian dressings

1. Combine water and cornstarch in a small saucepan and mix with a spring stirrer until smooth.
2. Cook over moderate heat, stirring constantly, until mixture boils.
3. Transfer cooked mixture to a jar; add oil, vinegar, and desired seasonings (as listed above under French or Italian dressing); shake well.
   Microwave Oven:
   Combine the water, cornstarch, and arrowroot starch in a 2-c glass measure and mix well. Cover with a plastic wrap and cook 1 minute. Stir well and cook 1 minute. Stir again and cook 30 seconds. Cool and add remaining ingredients.
   Yield: 1-1/4 c (9 K cal/Tbsp)

Low-Calorie Thousand Island Dressing

1 c low-fat yogurt   1 tsp prepared mustard
1/4 c catsup   1/2 tsp onion salt
1/4 c well-drained sweet pickle relish

1. Combine ingredients and mix well.

   Yield: 1-1/3 cups (13 K cal/Tbsp)

Tomato Juice Dressing (for tossed salads)

1/2 c tomato juice   1/2 tsp Weight Watcher's sweetener
1/4 c rice vinegar   1 tsp seasoning salt
1/4 c cream sherry   1/4 tsp salad herbs

1. Grind herbs to a powder in a mortar.
2. Combine all ingredients and mix well.

   Yield: 1 c (7 K cal/Tbsp)

COSTS OF PREPARED AND COMMERCIAL SALAD DRESSINGS

In Table 5-1 record the costs of ingredients for selected dressings, and calculate the cost per tablespoon. Compare the cost to a similar commercial product.

Question

What ingredients used in salad dressings are the major source of calories?

Table 5-1   Cost Comparison of Prepared and Commercial Salad Dressings

Salad Dressing	Ingredients	Market unit Cost ($)	Yield	Recipe Amount	Cost ($)	Total Cost ($)	Cost/ Tbsp ($)	Commercial dressing Yield	Cost ($)	Cost/ Tbsp ($)
Example: Blue cheese	Sour $\frac{1}{2}$&$\frac{1}{2}$	.87	16 fl oz	12 fl oz	.65					
	Blue cheese	1.15	4 oz	4 oz	1.15					
	Lemon juice	.87	7-1/2 fl oz	1 Tbsp	.06	1.86	0.058			

UNIT 6   SALADS

Suggested reading: <u>Basic Foods</u>, Chapter 8

Objectives

- To learn techniques of preparing basic salad ingredients
- To practice preparation of a variety of salads

PREPARATION OF BASIC SALAD INGREDIENTS

A. Cutting and Chopping Fruits and Vegetables

1. Fruits

The sectioning and preparation of citrus fruits and pineapple were discussed in Unit 3.

Apples and Pears

- Apples and pears may be served peeled or unpeeled.
- Cut fruit in quarters, and core.
- <u>Slice</u> by cutting each quarter into 2 pieces lengthwise, then cutting crosswise to form slices 1/8 to 1/4" thick (Fig. 6-1).
- <u>Dice</u> by slicing each quarter into 3 or 4 slices lengthwise, then cutting across the slices to make pieces 1/4 to 1/2" thick (Fig. 6-2).

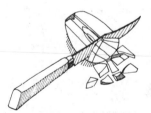

Fig. 6-1: Slice an apple by cutting each quarter into 2 pieces lengthwise, then cutting crosswise to form thin slices, 1/8 to 1/4" thick.

Fig. 6-2: Dice an apple by slicing each quarter into three or four pieces length-wise, then cutting crosswise into slices 1/2 to 1/4" thick.

2. Vegetables

Trim and wash vegetables before cutting or chopping (<u>BF</u>, 130-131, 166).

Greens

- Prepare for salads by tearing or cutting into bite-size pieces, 1 to 2" in each direction.
- Whole leaves are used to line salad bowls and plates.
- Lettuce can be shredded by slicing part or all of the head into slices 1/4 to 1/2" thick (Fig. 6-3). Cabbage can be shredded in the same way, but should be sliced to a thickness of about 1/8" or less.

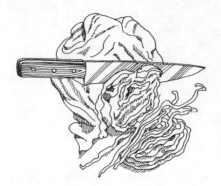

Fig. 6-3: Shred a whole head of lettuce or cabbage by slicing crosswise through the whole head.

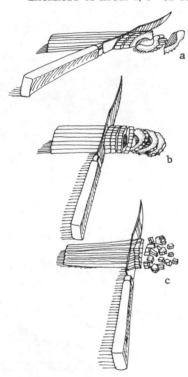

Fig. 6-4: Three ways to cut celery: (a) slice diagonally, (b) slice crosswise, (c) chop.

Celery, Asparagus, Carrots

- Diagonally sliced celery or asparagus is obtained by cutting diagonally or at an angle through the stalks (Fig. 6-4a).
- Celery and other vegetables are sliced crosswise by cutting straight across the vegetable (Fig. 6-4b).
- Chopped celery is prepared by slitting the piece of celery into lengthwise pieces and then cutting crosswise into 1/8 to 1/2"-thick pieces, depending on the size needed (Fig. 6-4c).

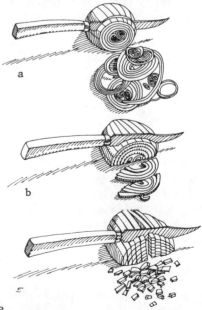

Onions

- Slice a whole onion by cutting across the onion to make slices of the desired thickness. These slices can then be separated into rings of varying size (Fig. 6-5a).

Fig. 6-5: Three ways to cut mature onions: (a) slice into whole rings, (b) slice into half rings, (c) chop.

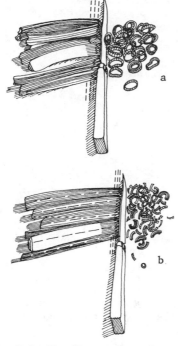

- Onions can be cut in half lengthwise, then placed cut side down against the chopping board, and sliced crosswise (Fig. 6-5b).

- To chop onions, cut in half lengthwise, place the cut side down, and slice it lengthwise into slices 1/4 to 1/2" thick. Hold these lengthwise slices together while cutting crosswise (Fig. 6-5c).

Green Onions

- When slicing only one or two green onions at a time, cut them into 3 to 4" lengths, and hold them together for slicing (Fig. 6-6a).
- To mince green onions finely, slit the white ends lengthwise and then cut into shorter lengths for slicing as thinly as needed (Fig. 6-6b).

Mushrooms

- Cut off discolored ends of stems and slice through the cap from the underside or stem end (Fig. 6-7).

Fig. 6-6: To slice green onions, cut the white ends and green tops into short lengths (a). To mince finely, slit the white ends lengthwise and slice crosswise (b).

Fig. 6-7: For even, unbroken mushroom slices, start at the stem end and slice down through the cap.

Fig. 6-8: Gather together several sprigs of parsley, slice with a knife or snip with kitchen shears.

Parsley

- Gather several sprigs together tightly, and slice with knife or snip with kitchen shears (Fig. 6-8).

B. Preparation of Croutons

Croutons are toasted cubes of bread frequently added to salads and soups for texture and flavor. There are two methods of preparing them.

Oven Method

      sliced bread
      soft table fat

1.   Trim crusts from bread.
2.   Spread both sides of each slice lightly with soft table fat.
3.   Cut each slice into 1/2" cubes, and place in a single layer on a baking sheet.
4.   Bake at 300°F (149°C) until dry and lightly browned.

Frying-Pan Method

      sliced bread
      olive oil
      garlic

1.   Trim crust from bread.
2.   Heat 1/4 cup olive oil with a clove of garlic, using low heat, for 5 to 10 minutes.
3.   Brush both sides of each slice lightly with seasoned oil.
4.   Cut the slices into 1/2" cubes, and brown in a hot frying pan, stirring frequently to prevent burning. Remove cubes as they become properly browned.

Seasoning

To season croutons, place freshly prepared croutons in a paper bag with seasonings, and shake vigorously. Seasonings often used include salt, grated Parmesan or Romano cheese, crushed, dried, or minced fresh herbs, and paprika (for color).

PREPARATION OF SALADS

A. Tossed Green Salads (BF, 155-167, 170)

Trim, wash, and chill a variety of salad greens suitable for use in tossed salads: head lettuce, romaine, red leaf, butterhead lettuce, escarole, endive, spinach, cabbage, and watercress. Also prepare accent ingredients such as radishes, cucumbers, green onions, tomatoes, celery, broccoli and cauliflower flowerets, bean sprouts, mushrooms, sweet peppers, avocadoes, and carrots. In addition, prepare and have available a variety of dressings (Unit 5). Finally, plan and prepare a tossed green salad using the available greens, accent ingredients, and garnishes, and serve with an appropriate dressing.

B. Fruit Salads (BF, 171-172)

Waldorf Salad

      1 apple   2 Tbsp Pineapple Cream or Sour Cream
      1/4 c finely chopped celery   Dressing, or Mayonnaise
      2 Tbsp chopped walnuts

1.   Dice unpeeled apple.
2.   Combine apple, celery, walnuts, and dressing.

      Yield: Two 1/2-cup servings

Mexicali Salad

1 red apple
1/8 head iceberg lettuce
1/3 cucumber

1/2 c canned mandarin orange slices
1/2 c pineapple wedges
1/3 c Pineapple Cream Dressing

1. Slice unpeeled apple.
2. Chop lettuce coarsely and slice cucumber into half slices.
3. Drain mandarin-orange slices and pineapple wedges.
4. Combine all ingredients with dressing.

Yield: Four 1/2-cup servings

Seven-Fruit Salad

1/2 c chopped red apple
1/2 c seeded Tokay grape halves
1/2 c pineapple wedges, drained
1/2 c mandarin orange slices, drained
1/2 c banana slices

1/2 c Thompson seedless grapes
1/2 c miniature marshmallows
1/2 c angel flake coconut
1/2 c Sour Cream Dressing

1. Combine all ingredients and mix with dressing.

Yield: Six 1/2-cup servings

Cabbage-Apple Salad

2 c thinly shredded cabbage
3/4 c diced red apple, unpeeled

1/2 c pineapple wedges
1/4 c Pineapple Cream Dressing

1. Combine all ingredients.

Yield: Six 1/2-cup servings

Fruit Jumble

1/2 c grapefruit sections
1/2 c Thompson seedless grapes
1 pear, diced and peeled

1/2 c mandarin oranges or
         fresh orange sections
1/3 c Sour Cream Dressing

1. Combine all ingredients.

Yield: Four 1/2-cup servings

Pineapple Boat

1 ripe pineapple
1 c cantaloupe balls
1 c watermelon balls

1 c Thompson seedless grapes
1 c cubed peach, apricot, or nectarine
1/2 c Sour Cream Dressing

1. Dip fresh peaches, apricots, or nectarines in orange or pineapple juice to prevent enzymatic browning.
2. Prepare pineapple boat as described in Unit 3.
3. Combine chopped pineapple with other fruits, and mix in the dressing.
4. Place the fruit mixture into the pineapple boats.

Yield: Six 1/2-cup servings

Note: Boats can also be prepared from watermelons or cantaloupes; canned pineapple wedges can be used for the fruit.

Orange Salad Cups

2 large oranges	1/4 c diced, peeled avocado
1/2 c diced Red Delicious apple, unpeeled	2 Tbsp Pineapple Cream Dressing
1/2 c diced, peeled pear	

1. Prepare orange cups by making a slit around the orange to one side of center. Remove and discard the smaller half of the peel. Use the curved, flat handle of a spoon to separate the rest of the peel from the fruit, thus forming a cup from the larger half of the peel. Scallop the upper edge of the cup with kitchen shears (BF, Figs. 6.4-5, pp. 120-121).
2. Prepare orange sections as described in Unit 3.
3. Combine the fruits and dressing, and fill the cups.

Yield: Two servings

C. Gelatin Salads   (BF, Chap. 17)
Microwave Oven Method for Gelatins:

1. In a 1-c glass measure, combine 1/4 c liquid and 1 envelope gelatin.
2. Cook in the microwave oven 1 minute. Stir well and add to the remaining ingredients.

Golden Salad

3/4 c pineapple juice (or juice from canned pineapple)	1 Tbsp (1 envelope) unflavored gelatin
	1/2 c orange juice
1/4 c sugar (more if pineapple juice is unsweetened)	1/2 c pineapple tidbits
	1/2 c mandarin oranges, well drained
1/8 tsp salt	1 c chopped cantaloupe

1. In a saucepan combine the pineapple juice, sugar, salt, and gelatin.
2. Cook over moderate heat, stirring constantly, until the mixture is steaming hot and the sugar and gelatin are completely dissolved.
3. Remove from heat, and stir in the orange juice. Chill until the mixture is the consistency of thick, raw egg white.
4. Stir in the pineapple tidbits, mandarin oranges, cantaloupe.
5. Pour the mixture into a lightly oiled mold, and chill until it sets.

Yield: Five 1/2-cup servings

Cranberry-Orange Relish Mold

1 c whole cranberry sauce	1 small orange
1 c orange juice	1-1/2 Tbsp (1-1/2 envelopes) unflavored gelatin
1/4 c chopped celery	
1/4 c chopped walnuts	1/4 c sugar

1. Combine 1/2 cup orange juice, sugar, and gelatin in a saucepan.
2. Heat with constant stirring until steaming hot and sugar and gelatin are completely dissolved.
3. Remove from heat, and stir in the rest of the orange juice and the cranberry sauce; chill while preparing orange.

4. Trim off stem end of orange and chop into 1" chunks.
5. Either put orange chunks through a food grinder, or place half at a time in the blender and blend coarsely.
6. Stir the ground orange into the gelatin mixture, and chill until it reaches the consistency of thick, raw egg white.
7. Stir in the celery and walnuts, and pour the mixture into a lightly oiled mold.

   Yield: Four 1/2-cup servings

Pineapple-Cheese Salad
_____

1-1/4 c pineapple juice (or juice from   6 ounces Neufchatel or cream cheese
    canned pineapple)   1 Tbsp (1 envelope) unflavored gelatin
1/2 c sugar
1/2 c crushed pineapple, well drained

1. Combine the sugar and gelatin with 3/4 cup pineapple juice in a saucepan, and heat, stirring constantly, over moderate heat until mixture is steaming hot and the sugar and gelatin are completely dissolved.
2. Remove from heat and add 1/2 cup pineapple juice and the crushed pineapple.
3. Chill until mixture reaches the consistency of thick, raw egg white.
4. Place the softened cheese in the large bowl of the electric mixer and beat until creamy and smooth.
5. Add the slightly thickened gelatin to the cheese, and beat until smooth.
6. Pour the mixture into a lightly oiled mold, and chill until the mixture sets.

   Yield: Four 1/2-cup servings

Chicken Mousse
_____

1-1/2 c chicken stock   1/4 c chopped celery
1 Tbsp (1 envelope) unflavored gelatin   2 Tbsp sliced, stuffed green olives
1/2 tsp onion powder   2 Tbsp Imitation Mayonnaise
1 c cooked chopped chicken meat

1. Combine the gelatin and 1/2 cup stock in a saucepan, and, stirring constantly, cook over moderate heat until the gelatin is dissolved.
2. Remove from the heat and stir in 1 cup chicken stock and the onion powder.
3. Chill until mixture reaches the consistency of thick, raw egg white.
4. Stir in the chicken meat, celery, mayonnaise, and stuffed green olives. Pour into a lightly oiled mold, and chill until the mixture sets.

   Yield: Five 1/2-cup servings

Note: Because of the handling required to bone cooked chicken, it is desirable to heat the chicken meat in the stock before combining ingredients. Simmer about 5 minutes to destroy any bacteria that may be present, especially since the chicken is being used in a dish that will not require further cooking.

Jellied Tuna Salad
_____

1-1/4 c milk   1 Tbsp (1 envelope) unflavored gelatin
1 egg   1 c canned tuna, drained, flaked
1/2 tsp salt   1 tsp prepared mustard
dash of pepper   1/2 c chopped celery
2 Tbsp lemon juice   1/4 c pickle relish
1/2 tsp onion powder

1. Combine the egg, salt, pepper, gelatin, and 1 cup milk in a saucepan.
2. Cook over moderate heat, stirring constantly, until the mixture is steaming hot and the gelatin is dissolved.
3. Remove from heat and add 1/4 cup milk. Chill until mixture reaches the consistency of thick, raw egg white.
4. Stir in the lemon juice, onion powder, tuna, mustard, celery, and pickle relish.
5. Pour the mixture into a lightly oiled mold, and chill until the mixture sets.

Yield: Five 1/2-cup servings

Tomato Aspic

3/4 c tomato juice	1 tsp Worcestershire sauce
1 Tbsp (1 envelope) unflavored gelatin	2 Tbsp lemon juice
3/4 c tomato-vegetable juice, such as V-8	1/2 c chopped celery
1/2 tsp onion powder	1/2 c chopped green pepper
1/2 tsp sugar	1/2 c chopped cucumber

1. Combine the tomato juice and gelatin in a saucepan and, stirring constantly, cook over moderate heat until gelatin is dissolved.
2. Remove from heat, and add the tomato-vegetable juice, lemon juice, onion powder, sugar, salt, and Worcestershire sauce.
3. Chill until mixture reaches the consistency of thick, raw egg white.
4. Add the chopped celery, green pepper, and cucumber.
5. Pour the mixture into a lightly oiled mold, and chill until it sets.

Yield: Five 1/2-cup servings

Jellied Fruit Nectar

1-1/2 c apricot nectar	1 c thinly shredded cabbage
1 Tbsp (1 envelope) unflavored gelatin	1 c grated carrot
2 Tbsp sugar	

1. Combine 3/4 cup apricot nectar and the gelatin and sugar in a saucepan, and, stirring constantly, cook over moderate heat until the sugar and gelatin are completely dissolved.
2. Remove from heat, and add the rest of the apricot nectar.
3. Chill until mixture reaches the consistency of thick, raw egg white.
4. Stir in the grated carrot and shredded cabbage.
5. Pour into a lightly oiled mold, and chill until mixture sets.

Yield: Five 1/2-cup servings

D. Vegetable Salads (BF, 170)

Zucchini Salad

3 small zucchini	1/2 tsp chopped chives
1/4 basket cherry tomatoes	2 Tbsp Italian Dressing
12 black olives, halved	

1. Slice zucchini diagonally into 1/2"-thick slices.
2. Place the Italian Dressing in a saucepan, and add the sliced zucchini; cover and cook

over moderate heat, stirring occasionally, until steaming hot—about 3 minutes.

3. Remove from heat, and add the cherry tomatoes cut in half, halved olives, and the chopped chives.
4. Allow to marinate for several hours or overnight in the refrigerator.

Microwave Oven:

Place the Italian Dressing in a 1-1/2-q glass casserole, add the sliced zucchini, cover with a plastic wrap, and cook 1 minute; stir and cook 1 more minute. Follow steps 3 and 4 above.

Yield: Three servings

Spinach Salad
------

1 bunch fresh spinach	1 green onion, including top, sliced
1/4 of a cauliflower	1 Tbsp chopped parsley
1/2 avocado	2 Tbsp French Dressing
1/4 c sliced radishes	

1. Trim and wash spinach, drain dry, and chop into bite-size pieces.
2. Wash cauliflower and break into flowerets.
3. Peel avocado, cut into quarters, and slice into 1/2"-thick slices.
4. Combine all ingredients.

Yield: Three to four servings.

Fresh Mushroom Salad

1-1/2 c washed, sliced mushrooms	1/4 c sliced ripe pitted olives
1 green onion, sliced thin	1 Tbsp minced parsley
1/2 c diagonally sliced celery	1/2 c slivered carrots
1/4 c Italian Dressing	

1. Wash mushrooms and slice from stem through caps, as illustrated in Fig. 6-7.
2. Peel carrots and shave crosswise into thin slices, using floating-blade peeler or slit on grater.
3. Slice green pepper into thin strips, and slice celery and green onions as illustrated in Figs. 6-4a and 6-6a.
4. Combine vegetables with Italian Dressing, toss lightly to coat, and marinate several hours or overnight in the refrigerator.

Yield: Five 1/2-cup servings

Cole Slaw

1-1/2 c thinly shredded red or green cabbage	1/4 c sweet pickle relish
1/4 c thinly sliced green pepper	1/2 tsp celery seed
1/4 c thinly sliced green onions, including tops	2 Tbsp Imitation Mayonnaise

1. Combine ingredients and mix well.

Yield: Three 1/2-cup servings

Dilled Vegetables

2 c assorted cooked, drained vegetables   1/2 tsp dill weed
(such as green or wax beans, peas, carrots,   2 Tbsp lemon juice
asparagus, broccoli, cauliflower, or beets)   1 Tbsp oil
1/4 c thinly sliced green onions, including tops   1 Tbsp sugar
1/4 c sliced celery

2.21

1. Combine all ingredients and mix well. Allow to marinate for several hours or overnight in the refrigerator.

Yield: Four 1/2-cup servings

Three-Bean Salad

1/2 c each green, wax, and kidney beans,   2 Tbsp tarragon vinegar
cooked and drained   1 Tbsp oil
1/2 c thinly sliced green or red sweet pepper   3 Tbsp sugar
1/4 c thinly sliced green onions, including tops

1. Combine all ingredients and allow to marinate overnight in the refrigerator.

Yield: Four 1/2-cup servings

Potato Salad

3 medium potatoes   2 Tbsp pickle relish
1/2 c chopped celery   1 tsp prepared mustard
1 hard-cooked egg   1/2 tsp salt
3 Tbsp Imitation Mayonnaise   1/4 tsp caraway seeds

1. Wash potatoes and place in saucepan, cover with water, and cook covered until tender when pierced with a sharp knife.
2. Cool potatoes in cold or ice water, peel, and remove blemishes.
3. Cut cooked, peeled potatoes into 1/2" cubes.
4. Combine diced potatoes and all other ingredients. Mix well.

Yield: Four 1/2-cup servings

Macaroni Salad

1 c elbow macaroni   2 Tbsp pitted ripe olives, sliced
2 c water   2 Tbsp chopped pimiento
1/2 tsp salt   2 Tbsp sweet pickle relish
1 hard-cooked egg   1/4 tsp onion powder
1/4 c chopped celery   1 Tbsp sesame seed
3 Tbsp Imitation Mayonnaise

1. Place water and salt in saucepan and bring to a boil; stir in macaroni, reduce heat, cover, and simmer until macaroni is tender and all of the water is absorbed.
2. Combine the cooked macaroni with the other ingredients and mix well.
3. Chill several hours in the refrigerator before serving.

Yield: Five 1/2-cup servings

E. Main Dish Salads (BF, 172-173)

Special care is required in the preparation of cooked meats for use in salads, because the meat is not cooked after boning and chopping. It can thus become contaminated with pathogenic bacteria from chopping boards, knives, and other utensils, as well as by human hands. It is important that all utensils be cleaned properly and that the meat be kept chilled and not allowed to remain at room temperature except for very brief periods.

Chicken Salad

1/2 c cooked chicken meat, coarsely chopped
1/4 c chopped celery
2 tsp lemon juice
1 Tbsp Imitation Mayonnaise
1 Tbsp slivered almonds

1 c shredded iceberg lettuce
1 hard-cooked egg
2 slices pickle
2 large lettuce leaves

1. Combine chicken, celery, lemon juice, mayonnaise, and almonds.
2. Arrange several large lettuce leaves on a plate or in a bowl.
3. Layer the shredded lettuce on the large lettuce leaves.
4. Mound the chicken salad mixture on top of the shredded lettuce.
5. Garnish with halves of hard-cooked eggs, tomato slices or quarters, and slices of pickle.

Yield: One serving

Crab or Shrimp Salad

2 large lettuce leaves
1 c shredded iceberg lettuce
3 oz cooked crabmeat (canned) or shrimp
1 small tomato
1 hard-cooked egg

2 cooked asparagus spears
3 pitted ripe olives
3 lemon wedges, seeded
1/4 c Low-Calorie Thousand Island
3 slices pickle   Dressing

1. Arrange large lettuce leaves on place or in a bowl and top with shredded lettuce.
2. Distribute the crabmeat over the shredded lettuce and garnish with tomato slices or quarters, hard-cooked egg halves, asparagus, olives, pickles, and lemon wedges.
3. Serve the Low-Calorie Thousand Island Dressing as a side dish.

Yield: One serving

Stuffed Tomato Salad

1 large ripe tomato
1/2 c canned tuna, drained, flaked
1/4 c chopped celery
1/4 tsp onion powder
1 large lettuce leaf

1 Tbsp Imitation Mayonnaise
3 sprigs parsley
1 pitted ripe olive
3 slices pickle

1. Peel the tomato after immersing it in boiling water for a few seconds or holding it over a gas flame. For either method, hold the tomato by piercing it at the stem with the tines of a fork.
2. Remove and discard the stem-end core of the tomato.
3. Prepare the tomato for stuffing by one of the three ways (BF, p. 183): (a) Slice off a thin layer at the top or stem end, and scoop out the inside; (b) cut the tomato into six

wedges, but only part way through, so that the wedges can be spread apart to resemble the petals of a flower; (c) slice the tomato crosswise into three thick slices.

5. For the scooped-out tomato (a), combine tuna, celery, onion powder, mayonnaise, and chopped pulp of the tomato, and fill the tomato shell with stuffing, topped by an olive. For the second method (b), spread the wedges of the tomato apart, place the filling in the center, and top with an olive. For the sliced tomato (c), chop up the top slice and mix it in with the filling; place half the filling on the bottom slice, then add the center slice, the rest of the filling, and an olive.

6. Place the stuffed tomato on a large lettuce leaf on a plate, and garnish with sprigs of parsley and pickle slices.

Yield: One serving

Chef's Salad

2 large lettuce leaves	2 slices ham
1 c shredded lettuce	2 slices turkey
2 slices Swiss cheese	2 asparagus spears
2 slices American processed cheese	2 slices pickled beets
1 hard-cooked egg	2 slices pickle
2 ripe, pitted olives	3 sprigs parsley
1/3 c Roquefort, Blue Cheese, or Thousand Island Dressing	

1. Place the large lettuce leaves on plate or in bowl and top with the shredded lettuce.
2. The cheese and meat slices should be of the type that is sliced very thin. Cut these into julienne strips by slicing into strips 1/8 to 1/4" thick.
3. Arrange the strips of meat and cheese, asparagus spears, beet slices, hard-cooked egg, pickle slices, olives, and parsley on the shredded lettuce.
4. Serve with preferred dressing as a side dish.

Yield: One serving

Pineapple-Ham Salad

2/3 c chopped cooked ham	1 large lettuce leaf
1/2 c pineapple chunks or tidbits	1/3 c shredded lettuce
2 Tbsp thinly sliced green pepper	2 Tbsp Russian Dressing
1 Tbsp thinly sliced green onion, including tops	2 or 3 green pepper rings

1. Place large lettuce leaf on plate or in bowl, and top with shredded lettuce.
2. Combine the ham, pineapple, green pepper, green onion, and dressing.
3. Place ham mixture on shredded lettuce, and garnish with rings of green pepper.

Yield: One serving

Cottage Cheese and Fruit

2 large lettuce leaves	1 peach half
2/3 c low-fat cottage cheese	2 slices pineapple
1 pear half	1 plum or prune
2 apricots	1 maraschino cherry
1/4 c Avocado Dressing	

Fruits may be either fresh or canned. If fresh, dip in pineapple or orange juice to prevent enzymatic browning.

1. Place lettuce leaves on plate or in bowl.
2. Place the slices of pineapple on lettuce, overlapping slightly.
3. Mound the cottage cheese on top of the pineapple, exposing some of the pineapple around the edges.
4. Arrange the peeled pear half, pitted apricot halves, peeled peach half, and plum or prune around the sides.
5. Top cheese mound with maraschino cherry.

   Yield: One serving

Stuffed Avocado Salad
_____

1 large avocado half	2 Tbsp Sour Cream Dressing
2/3 c low-fat cottage cheese	1 orange
2 Tbsp chopped walnuts	1 grapefruit
1 maraschino cherry	2 lettuce leaves

1. Cut avocado in half, remove pit and peel; dip each half in pineapple juice to prevent enzymatic browning.
2. Place lettuce leaves on plate.
3. Combine cottage cheese, walnuts, and Sour Cream Dressing; mix well.
4. Fill the avocado half with the cottage cheese mixture, piling it high in the center.
5. Place filled avocado half on lettuce leaf, and top with cherry.
6. Prepare about 1/4 cup each of orange and grapefruit sections, and arrange them around the base of the stuffed avocado.

   Yield: One serving

UNIT 7   CEREAL PRODUCTS

Suggested reading: Basic Foods, Chapter 9

Objectives

- To prepare a variety of cereal grains and compare their texture, flavor, appearance, nutritional values and costs
- To prepare and use cereal products in a variety of dishes

PREPARATION AND COMPARISON
OF CEREAL GRAINS AND PRODUCTS

A. Cooked Cereals

Table 7-1 lists a variety of brands of cereals and shows the proportions of water and cereal recommended for two servings, as listed on the package. People vary in their preference for cereal consistency; some like it gruel or souplike, while others favor the consistency of pudding. Prepare the cereals as directed and indicate their consistencies.

1. Place the water and 1/2 tsp salt in a saucepan, and bring to a boil.
2. Stir in the cereal; reduce heat, and simmer 2 to 3 minutes. An electric surface unit may be turned off when the cereal is added, allowing residual heat in the unit to complete the cooking.
3. Observe and record the consistency while hot in Table 7-1.

Microwave Oven:

In a 1-q glass bowl, combine the water, cereal, and salt. Cook 3 minutes, stir, cover with a plastic wrap, and cook 2-4 minutes longer.

Question

If the consistency is too thin or too thick, what changes are required to obtain the desired consistency?

B. Grains

Consult Table 7-2 for the proportion of grain and water and for the cooking time. Use 1/2 tsp salt with each variation.

Boiling-Water Method

Use for each grain listed in Table 7-2.

1. Place the water and salt in a 1-1/2-qt saucepan and bring to a boil.
2. Stir in the grain, cover, reduce heat, and simmer the specified time, or until tender and all of the water is absorbed. Test for tenderness by pressing grain between fingers.
3. Transfer the cooked grain to a small bowl and cover with aluminum foil; place in 150°F (65.5°C) oven to keep warm for class observation. Enter observations in Table 7-2.

Table 7-1 Proportions of Water and Cereal for Cooking Breakfast Cereals

| Cereal | For Two Servings | | Consistency |
	Water (c)	Cereal (c)	
Cream of Rice	1-1/2	1/4 + 2 Tbsp	
Cream of Wheat (Farina)	2	1/3	
Grits	2	1/2	
Malt-O-Meal	1-2/3	1/3	
Quick Oats	1-1/2	2/3	
Regular Oats	1-1/2	2/3	
Wheatena	2	1/2	
Wheat Hearts	2	1/2	
Zoom	1	1/2	

Cold-Water Method

Use for short-grain white rice only.

1. Place cold tap water, short-grain rice, and salt in a 1-1/2-qt saucepan. Cover and bring to a boil.
2. Stir, cover, and reduce heat; simmer until tender—about 15 to 20 minutes.
3. Follow step 3 under Boiling-Water Method above.

Instant- or Minute-Rice Method

Bring water and salt to a boil; stir in rice; turn off heat. Allow to set 5 to 10 minutes, then follow step 3 under Boiling-Water Method.

Microwave Oven:

White rice: Place 1-1/4 c water in a 2-q casserole, cover, and heat 4 minutes. Add 1/2 c rice, 1/4 tsp salt, and 1 tsp oil; cover and heat 10 minutes. Rest 5-10 minutes before serving.

Brown rice: Place 1-1/2 c water in a 2-q casserole, cover, and heat 4 minutes. Add 1/2 c brown rice, 1/4 tsp salt, and 1 tsp oil; cover and heat 20 minutes. Rest 5-10 minutes before serving.

Table 7-2 Proportions of Water and Grain, Cooking Time, and Evaluation
of Grains and Pasta

Product	Cereal (c)	Water (c)	Time[a] (mins)	Observations
Short-grain white rice	1/2	1	15-20	
Long-grain white rice	1/2	1	15-20	
Converted rice	1/2	1-1/4	25	
Short-grain brown rice	1/2	1-1/4	40-45	
Long-grain brown rice	1/2	1-1/4	40-45	
Wild rice	1/2	1-1/4	25	
Minute rice	3/4	3/4	—[b]	
Bulgur wheat (cracked)	1/2	1	15	
Pearl barley	1/4	1	30	
Short-grain white rice	1/2	1	15-20[c]	
Pasta	1/2	1	10-15	
Pasta	1/2	3	10-15	

[a]Time is counted from time boiling starts.
[b]Minute rice is not boiled.
[c]Started in cold water.

Evaluation

1. Compare the flavor and appearance of the different varieties of grains.
2. Compare the short-grain white rice cooked by the two methods, and account for differences observed.

C. Pastas

Observe the different types of pastas and identify the various shapes by name (BF, 206, Fig. 9.5). Prepare a variety of different types, such as macaroni, noodles, and spaghetti, and observe their size, appearance, and texture when cooked. Enter observations in Table 7-2.

Water-Absorption Method

| 1 c water | 1/2 c or 2 oz (Avoir.) pasta |
| 1/2 tsp salt | |

1. Place water and salt in 2-qt saucepan, and bring to a boil.
2. Stir in the pasta or gradually ease it into the boiling water if pieces are large.
3. Cover pan and simmer 10 to 15 minutes until water is absorbed and pasta is tender.

Excess-Water Method

| 3 c water | 1/2 c or 2 oz (Avoir.) pasta |
| 1/2 tsp salt | |

1. Place water and salt in 4-qt pot, and bring water to a boil.
2. Add pasta and cook until tender.
3. Drain off excess water.

Microwave Oven:

Place 1 c water in 2-q container (for spaghetti and lasagna use Pyrex meat loaf dish). Cover and heat 3 minutes. Add pasta, 1/8 tsp salt, and 1 tsp oil. Heat 10 minutes. Let rest 5-10 minutes.

Questions

1. Account for differences in appearance and flavor of pastas cooked in only the amount of water absorbed during cooking compared to pastas cooked in excess water.
2. Discuss the effect on nutrient retention of the two methods of cooking pastas.

D. Comparison of Nutrient Values and Costs
of Ready-to-Eat and Cooked Cereals

With the advent of nutritional labeling, comparison of nutrients in cereals is much easier than it was formerly. There are still some problems, however, with cooked cereals. The packages of some cereals to be cooked give 1 oz of dry cereal as the serving size, but they fail to say what volume 1 oz of dry cereal is or how it relates to the recipes on the package. (Some manufacturers do indicate that 1 oz is 1/4 or 1/3 cup of dry cereal.) Another problem is that serving sizes are not uniform on all products; one brand indicates 1/2 cup, another 2 cups of cooked cereal per serving, and, of course, these are not comparable.

One of the most important nutrients supplied by cereals is protein—important especially for those who eat cereals instead of eggs and meat for breakfast. In Table 7-3 a variety of cooked and ready-to-eat cereals are compared on the basis of the amount of cereal required to supply 5 grams of protein, a reasonable amount for breakfast. The cereals are ranked according to the cost of the amount of cereal required to supply the protein. The number of calories and the percentages of recommended iron and thiamin are also shown, since these factors can also be considered in choosing cereals. All figures refer to the cereal without added milk.

The method used for calculating the data in Table 7-3 is shown at the end of the table; thus current prices can be substituted, or calculations on other cereals not included in the table can be made.

Table 7-3   Nutrient and Cost Comparisons of Cereals Based on Quantities Supplying 5 grams of Protein (listed in order of increasing cost per 5 grams of protein)

Cereals	Per Package			Per Serving[c]					Per 5 g of Protein[f]				
	Servings[a]		Cost $[b]	Cost $	Kcal-ories	Pro-tein g	Iron %[d]	Thia-min %[d]	Serv-ings (e)	Kcal-ories	Iron %[d]	Thia-min %[d]	Cost $
	Size oz	Num-ber											
Roman Meal	1	28	1.05	.038	130	5	10	10	1.0	130	10	10	.038
Rolled oats	1	42	1.65	.039	110	5	4	10	1.0	110	4	10	.039
Wheat Hearts	1	28	1.23	.044	110	4	4	15	1.25	138	5	19	.055
Malt-O-Meal	1	24	0.91	.038	100	3	45	25	1.67	167	75	42	.064
Grits	1-1/2	26	1.37	.053	150	4	6	10	1.25	188	8	12	.066
Wheatena	1	22	1.19	.054	110	4	4	—	1.25	138	5	—	.068
Cream of Wheat	1	28	1.35	.048	100	3	45	10	1.67	167	75	42	.080
Zoom	1	15	0.73	.049	80	3	4	6	1.67	100	7	10	.082
Life	1	15	1.43	.095	110	5	25	25	1.0	110	25	25	.095
Special K	1	11	1.41	.128	110	6	25	25	0.83	92	21	21	.106
Wheaties	1	12	1.05	.088	110	3	—	25	1.67	184	—	42	.147
Shredded Wheat	5/6	18	1.13	.063	90	2	4	2	2.5	225	10	5	.158
Puffed Wheat	1	12	0.78	.065	50	2	—	—	2.5	125	—	—	.162
Granola	1	16	1.55	.097	140	3	6	6	1.67	234	10	10	.162
Corn Flakes	1	18	1.21	.067	110	2	10	25	2.5	275	25	62	.168
Wheat Chex	1	22	1.49	.068	110	2	25	25	2.5	275	62	62	.170
Instant Oats	1-1/4	8	1.29	.161	140	4	25	25	1.25	175	31	31	.201
Total	1	8	1.09	.136	110	3	100	100	1.67	184	167	167	.227
Rice Krispies	1	13	1.39	.107	110	2	10	25	2.5	275	25	62	.268
Sugar Frosted Flakes	1	20	1.76	.088	110	1	10	25	5.0	550	50	125	.440
Column numbers:	1	2	3	4	5	6	7	8	9	10	11	12

[a]The number of servings per package is listed on the nutrient label panel.
[b]Costs listed are prices per package for the San Francisco area in 1981.
[c]Information is from nutrient label on package, except for cost per serving.
[d]Percentage of U.S. Recommended Daily Allowance (BF, 614, Table 12). Amounts fulfilling less than 2% of the recommended allowance are not listed on the nutrient label and are thus omitted from this table.
[e]Number of servings (as listed on the package) required to supply 5 grams of protein.
[f]Calculated from information supplied on nutrient labels, as follows (with table columns numbered left to right from 1 to 12):

Calculations

Column 2 ÷ Column 1 = Column 3
5 g protein ÷ Column 5 = Column 8
Column 4 x Column 8 = Column 9
Column 6 x Column 8 = Column 10
Column 7 x Column 8 = Column 11
Column 3 x Column 8 = Column 12

Example: Zoom

$ .40 ÷ 20 = $ .020
5 g ÷ 3 g = 1.67 servings/5 g protein
80 cals x 1.67 = 100 cals
4 x 1.67 = 7% RDA iron   } per
6 x 1.67 = 10% RDA thiamine } 1.67
$ .020 x 1.67 = $ .033   } servings

Questions

1. Table 7-3 shows that regular oats contain more protein but less thiamin per serving than instant oats. Check ingredient listings on the packages and account for these differences.
2. What nutrients do cereals supply in fair amounts?
3. Indicate which cereals have been fortified with vitamins and minerals. Is the fortification the same for all cereals?
4. Which of the nutrients listed in the answer to Question 2 are destroyed by heat? (See also Basic Foods, Table 1-5, pp. 14, 15.)
5. Why is it advisable to limit cooking time of cereals to just the time that produces palatability of the product and no more?

USE OF GRAINS AND CEREALS IN FOOD PREPARATION

A. Rice and Barley Dishes

Rice Pilaf
_____

1/2 c long-grain brown rice	1/2 tsp curry powder
1 c chicken stock	2 tsp table fat
1 tsp chicken stock base	1/4 c sliced or slivered almonds
1 thinly sliced green onion, including tops	1/8 tsp salt

1. Place chicken stock, chicken stock base, and salt in a 1-qt saucepan and bring to a boil.
2. Stir in the rice, cover, reduce heat, and simmer about 40 minutes or until tender and the stock is absorbed.
3. Place table fat in small frying pan, and sauté almonds until lightly toasted.
4. Stir sliced green onions, toasted almonds, and curry powder into the cooked rice; serve hot.

Yield: Three 1/2-cup servings

Bulgur Pilaf
_____

1/2 c bulgur wheat	1 oz canned mushrooms
1 c beef stock	1 piece celery, sliced
1 tsp beef stock base	2 tsp table fat
3 sprigs parsley	1/4 c salted peanuts

1. Place beef stock and beef stock base in 1-qt saucepan, and bring to a boil.
2. Stir in the bulgur wheat, cover, reduce heat, and simmer 15 minutes.
3. Place table fat in small frying pan and sauté celery until it is slightly translucent.
4. Add the drained mushrooms, sautéed celery, and peanuts to the cooked bulgur; correct seasoning.
5. Serve hot, garnished with minced parsley over the top.

Yield: Two 1/2-cup servings

Barley Pilaf

1/4 c barley	1/3 c chopped onion
1 c lamb stock	1/4 c chopped green peppers
1/2 tsp salt	1/4 c sliced mushrooms
1/8 tsp each of savory and basil	2 tsp table fat

1. Place lamb stock and salt in 2-qt saucepan and bring to a boil.
2. Stir in the barley; cover, reduce heat, and simmer 30 to 40 minutes or until tender.
3. Sauté onions, green peppers, and mushrooms in table fat until slightly translucent.
4. Stir the onion, pepper, mushrooms, basil, and savory into the cooked barley; serve hot.

   Yield: Three 1/2-cup servings

Green Rice

1/3 c enriched short-grain rice	1/4 c thinly sliced green onions,
3/4 c chicken stock	including tops
1/4 tsp salt	2 Tbsp minced green pepper
dash of pepper	2 Tbsp minced parsley

1. Place chicken stock and salt in 2-qt saucepan and bring to a boil.
2. Stir in rice, cover, reduce heat, and simmer 10 minutes.
3. Stir finely chopped or minced vegetables into rice and cook until all the liquid is absorbed and the rice is tender.
4. Season to taste; serve hot.

   Yield: Two 1/2-cup servings

Chiles Rellenos con Queso

1 c water	1 c grated Monterey Jack cheese
1/4 tsp salt	1 c sour half-and-half
1/2 c converted rice	1 whole canned green chile

1. Place the water and salt in a 2-qt saucepan and bring to a boil.
2. Stir in the rice; cover, reduce heat, and simmer 20 minutes or until the rice is tender and the water is absorbed.
3. Remove the seeds from the green chile and chop it finely.
4. Combine the cooked rice, grated cheese, sour half-and-half, and chopped green chile, and pour into a greased 1-qt casserole.
5. Bake at 350°F (176.5°C) for 25 minutes, or heat in the microwave oven 10 minutes.

   Yield: Four 1/2-cup servings

Rice Pudding

1/4 c enriched short-grain white rice	2 eggs
1/2 c water	1 tsp vanilla
1/4 tsp salt	3/4 tsp grated lemon peel
1-1/2 c milk	3 Tbsp seedless raisins
3 Tbsp sugar	

1. Place water and salt in a 1-qt saucepan and bring to a boil.
2. Stir in the rice; cover, reduce heat, and simmer 15 minutes.

3. Beat eggs together in a 1-qt casserole, mix in sugar, vanilla, lemon peel, and milk. Stir in cooked rice and raisins.

4. Place casserole in a pan of hot water and bake in 350°F (175.6°C) oven until custard-rice mixture is thickened—about 1 hour.

Yield: Four 1/2-cup servings

B. Noodle Dishes

Noodles Romanoff
────────────────

3 oz egg noodles	1/8 tsp garlic powder
1-1/3 c water	1/2 tsp onion powder
1/4 tsp salt	1/2 tsp Worcestershire sauce
1/3 c large-curd cottage cheese	2 drops hot red-pepper sauce
1/2 c sour half-and-half	1/4 c grated Parmesan cheese

1. Place water and salt in a 2-qt saucepan and bring to a boil.
2. Stir in noodles; cover, reduce heat, and simmer 5 minutes.
3. Remove cover and evaporate over a low heat almost to dryness.
4. In a mixing bowl combine the cottage cheese, sour half-and-half, garlic and onion powders, Worcestershire sauce, and hot sauce.
5. Add the cooked noodles and mix; pour into a greased casserole and sprinkle the top with the Parmesan cheese.
6. Bake in a 350°F (176.5°C) oven for 25 minutes. Serve hot.

Yield: Four 1/2-cup servings

Homemade Noodles
────────────────

1 egg	1/8 tsp salt
1 tsp oil	cornstarch
3/4 c bread flour (high gluten potential)	

1. Mix together the oil and egg until mixture is homogeneous.
2. Stir in the flour and salt with a fork, then work with the fingers to form a dough.
3. Place the dough, and any crumbs of flour left in the bowl, on a bread board that has been covered with a pastry cloth and lightly floured.
4. Knead the dough, using a minimum of additional flour, for about 10 minutes.
5. Allow the dough to rest for 10 minutes; then roll it out as thin as possible.
6. Sprinkle cornstarch over the rolled-out dough, spreading it evenly over the surface with the fingers.
7. Roll the dough up like a jelly roll.
8. Slice the roll of dough crosswise into slices 1/8 to 1/2" thick, depending on the width of noodle desired, to form noodles.
9. Unroll the slices and spread the noodles on the bread board to dry.
10. Cook either freshly prepared noodles or dried noodles in the same ways purchased noodles are cooked.

UNIT 8   SAUCES AND PUDDINGS

Suggested reading: <u>Basic Foods</u>, Chapter 10

Objectives

- To learn methods of preparing starch-thickened mixtures
- To apply starch cookery principles to preparation of a variety of sauces and puddings
- To compare costs of prepared and purchased sauces and puddings

PREPARATION OF STARCH-THICKENED MIXTURES

General Instructions

1. Starch pastes can be cooked rapidly over direct heat if a saucepan with a thick bottom is used to reduce the mixture's tendency to stick or burn.
2. Aluminum pans should not be used for sauces and puddings containing milk, as oxides in the pan can cause a gray discoloration of the mixture.
3. Rapid stirring is required to keep the starch suspended and to remove milk proteins that tend to precipitate on the bottom of the pan. The spring stirrer (Fig. 8-1), held vertically, slightly compressed, and rotated around the pan, effectively prevents sticking of these mixtures and permits rapid stirring without splashing.
4. Stocks that are full flavored, not watered down, yield the best flavor in the finished sauce. Juices from frying, broiling, and roasting pans may be reclaimed by adding water to the drippings and scraping and stirring to separate them from the pan. Stock for sauces should be fat-free. It is easiest to chill the stock and lift off the solidified fat from the top. If this is not possible, the stock can be poured into a narrow container, such as a jar, and the fat skimmed off the top with a spoon or baster. If there is only a small amount of fat, it can be removed from the stock by floating a single layer of paper towel on the surface. Repeat the procedure until all the fat has been removed.

Fig. 8-1: Spring stirrer.

5. The stock should be smooth and free of lumps. Lumps of coagulated meat juices can often be broken up by blending in an electric blender or by pressing through a sieve, or both.
6. For sauces and gravy that require browned flour (BF, 201), there are two methods that may be used, one using fat and the other fat-free. Flour cannot be browned satisfactorily in meat drippings that are a mixture of meat juice and fat drippings. If fat is used, it must be free of meat juices or water.
    a) With Fat: Place oil or melted fat in a clean, dry pan and stir in the flour. Cook over moderate heat, stirring constantly, until the desired degree of brownness has been obtained. Avoid overbrowning, as it has a deleterious effect on the flavor.

b) <u>Without Fat</u>: Place flour in a clean dry pan and cook over moderate heat, stirring constantly, until it is as brown as desired.

7. Ingredients for sauces can be prepared ahead and kept in the refrigerator for a few days or in the freezer for several months. Flour can be browned and stored in this way, as can strained and fat-free stock. Sauces themselves can be frozen, but will curdle when thawed. They can, however, be made smooth by stirring while reheating.

8. Obtaining the proper consistency in sauces is sometimes a problem, especially if one does not stop to measure the liquid or if heating is too slow or evaporation too great. To thicken a sauce, combine a small amount of starch with a cool liquid in a bowl or jar, and stir the mixture into the hot sauce; cook to boiling. To thin a sauce, add liquid as necessary.

9. Specification of salt and other seasonings for sauces is impossible, because the salt content of stock is extremely variable, and because a sauce will also be affected by the salt content of the fat used and of seasonings such as meat stock base or bouillon. Seasoning should be corrected to taste after all other ingredients have been added. The use of pepper, herbs, and other seasoning depends on personal preferences. It is advisable to experiment with the addition of just one herb at a time and become familiar with the flavor. Then two or more can be combined and tried.

Methods of Preparing Starch Pastes

Roux Method

1. Place oil or melted fat in a clean, dry pan; add flour and mix into a smooth paste. Flour may be browned or not, as desired.
2. Stir in the liquid gradually to form a lump-free mixture.
3. Cook over moderate to high heat, stirring constantly, until paste starts to boil.
4. Reduce or turn off the heat, and simmer for about 1 minute with residual heat in the surface unit, stirring occasionally.

Liquid Dispersion Method I

1. Mix the starch and part of the liquid together in the saucepan until smooth and free of lumps.
2. Add the remaining liquid, either hot or cold, and cook over moderate to high heat, stirring constantly, until paste starts to boil. Add table fat, if desired.
3. Reduce or turn off heat, and simmer for about 1 minute on residual heat in the surface unit, stirring occasionally.

Liquid Dispersion Method II

1. Combine the starch and part of the liquid in a bowl, or shake them together in a jar.
2. Stir mixture into boiling stock or scalding hot milk; heat to boiling.
3. Reduce or turn off heat, and simmer for about 1 minute on residual heat in the surface unit, stirring occasionally.

<u>Microwave Oven</u>:

1. Combine the liquid and starch in a 1- to 2-q Pyrex bowl or casserole; mix until smooth. Heat covered until the mixture boils, stirring well at the end of each minute.

PREPARATION OF SAUCES AND PUDDINGS

A. White Sauce

Table 8-1 shows the proportions of ingredients required for white sauces of differing consistencies. The uses of these sauces are listed in Basic Foods, p. 201, Table 10.1.

Prepare white sauces with differing consistencies and by the two methods, salting to taste (usually 1/4 to 1/2 tsp). Compare them to each other; then compare the flavor of the sauces with and without table fat.

Table 8-1   Ingredients and Proportions
for White Sauce

Consistency	Milk (c)	Flour (Tbsp)	Fat[1] (Tbsp)
Thick	1	1	1
Medium	1	2	2
Thick	1	3	2
Very thick	1	4	3

[1]White sauce can be prepared without fat, or with oil, table fat, or meat drippings. Use 1/4 tsp salt with table fat, otherwise use 1/2 tsp salt.

B. Meat and Vegetable Sauces

The ingredients and proportions for all meat and vegetable sauces are listed in Table 8-2. The following recipes refer to the amounts given in the table.

Gravy or Brown Sauce

1. Prepare sauce by roux or liquid-dispersion method.
2. If the meat juices used have become nicely browned, it may not be necessary to brown the flour (BF, 201). If they lack color, brown the flour by either of the methods (with or without fat) described above under General Instructions (6).

Use the brown sauce as a gravy for stews, roast meats, meatballs, steaks, chops.

Béchamel Sauce

1. Prepare the sauce, using either the roux or liquid-dispersion method, depending on whether fat is used.
2. Season to taste with herbs, spice, or onions.

Use as a cream gravy for pork or veal or as a cream sauce for vegetables.

Mornay Sauce

1. Prepare the sauce using the liquid-dispersion method.
2. Just before serving, heat to boiling and add cheese; do not heat after adding cheese.

Use with fish, eggs, and vegetables.

Table 8-2 Ingredients and Proportions for Meat and Vegetable Sauces

Sauce	Liquid		Starch		Fat[2]		Other Ingredients[3]	Yield (c)
	Kind[1]	Amt. (c)	Kind	Amt. (Tbsp)	Kind	Amt. (Tbsp)		
Brown sauce (gravy)	brown stock	1	flour	3	oil or table fat	2		1
Béchamel *only*	milk *milk* stock	1/2 1/2	flour	2	table fat	2	*1 Tbsp. cooked onion*	1
Mornay *milk*	white stock	1	flour	2			2 Tbsp grated Swiss cheese / 2 Tbsp grated Parmesan cheese	1
Curry	white stock	1	corn-starch	1-1/2	table fat	2	1 tsp curry powder / 1 Tbsp dehydrated onion	1
Cheese	milk	1	flour	2			1 c grated cheese	1-1/4
Sweet-and-sour	pineapple juice	3/4	corn-starch	1			1/4 c catsup / 2 Tbsp vinegar / 1 Tbsp soy sauce / 1/4 c brown sugar / ginger[4]	1

[1]Stock should be fat-free and well flavored. Milk can be nonfat, low-fat, whole, or half-and-half; higher fat content of milk increases caloric content but also provides a richer, creamier flavor and consistency.

[2]Most sauces can be prepared satisfactorily without fat. Oil, table fat, or meat drippings can be used interchangeably, depending on the flavor desired. Fat increases the caloric content of sauces.

[3]The amount of salt required depends on the saltiness of the stock used and whether the fat contains salt. The amount added will usually be about 1/4 tsp. Always correct seasoning to taste in sauces, and add pepper if desired.

[4]Ginger can be fresh grated (1 tsp), dried ground (1/2 tsp), or crushed ginger (2 tsp) (see Appendix II). Do not add salt to this sauce.

Curry Sauce

1. Prepare the sauce, using either method.
2. Add the curry powder and dehydrated onions as soon as the starch and liquid are combined.

Use for curried meats, or serve with fish, poultry, or vegetables.

Cheese Sauce

1. Prepare the sauce, using the liquid-dispersion method.
2. Just before serving, heat to boiling and stir in the cheese. Do not heat after adding cheese.

Use with vegetables, in casseroles, or serve over toast or noodles.

Sweet-and-Sour Sauce

1. Combine the starch and pineapple juice, mixing until smooth.
2. Add the other ingredients, heat to boiling, and discontinue cooking.

Use as a dip for Fried Won Ton and Tempura, or as a sauce for pork, chicken, shrimp, or meatballs.

Piquant Sauce

1/2 peeled carrot	1/4 c tomato sauce
1/4 seeded green pepper	1/4 c dry red wine
1/4 small onion	1/4 c beef stock
1 sprig parsley	Pinch each of basil and thyme
1/2 clove garlic	1 Tbsp arrowroot starch
1/4 c mushrooms	Salt and pepper to taste
1/2 tsp wine vinegar	

1. Use the chopping blade in the food processor to finely chop the carrot, green pepper, onion, parsley, garlic, and mushrooms.
2. Transfer the finely chopped vegetables to a 1-qt casserole and cook 5 minutes in the microwave oven.
3. Mix the starch with the beef stock until smooth and stir into the cooked vegetables.
4. Add the remaining ingredients and cook 5 minutes in the microwave oven.
5. Adjust the seasoning.
6. Use with omelet, fish, meat loaf, and other meat dishes.

   Yield: 1-1/2 c

Marinara Sauce

1 onion, peeled	1 tsp arrowroot starch
1 clove garlic, peeled	1/2 c dry white wine
1 can (15 oz) tomatoes	1/8 tsp oregano
1 anchovy fillets	1/8 tsp basil
1 Tbsp olive oil	1/4 tsp salt
	1/8 tsp sugar

1. Use the chopper blade in the food processor to finely chop the onion, garlic, and anchovy.
2. Transfer the chopped ingredients to a 1-qt casserole and add the remaining ingredients; cover, cook in the microwave oven 10 minutes.
3. Serve over spaghetti and top with Parmesan cheese.

   Yield: Two c

C. Dessert or Sweet Sauces

Because sugar and acids interfere with maximum thickening of starch, it is preferable to add them to the sauce after the starch has been gelatinized. Heating of the paste after the addition of the acid ingredients should be avoided.

Ingredients and their proportions for dessert sauces are shown in Table 8-3. Sauces may be thickened with starch or egg or both; these will be compared. Starch-thickened sauces must reach the boiling point for complete gelatinization; egg-thickened custard sauces must not be boiled or they will curdle. Cook custard sauces only until steaming hot; the mixture will coat a silver spoon (BF, 347, Fig. 19.7).

Vanilla Sauce

1. Put the milk and egg yolks in a saucepan, and mix with a spring stirrer until blended smooth and homogeneous.
2. Cook over low heat, stirring constantly until mixture is steaming hot and will coat a silver spoon.
3. Remove from heat, and stir in the table fat, salt, sugar, and vanilla.

Lemon Sauce I

1. In a saucepan, mix together the water and cornstarch until smooth.
2. Cook over moderate to high heat, stirring constantly, until paste starts to boil.
3. Reduce heat and simmer one minute; then stir in the sugar, salt, table fat, lemon juice, and lemon rind.
4. Yellow food coloring may be added if desired.

Lemon Sauce II

1. In a saucepan, mix together the water and egg yolks until smooth and homogeneous.
2. Cook over low heat, stirring constantly, until the mixture is steaming hot and will coat a silver spoon.
3. Stir in the table fat, sugar, salt, lemon juice, and lemon rind.
4. Yellow food coloring may be added if desired.

Orange Sauce

1. In a saucepan, mix together the water and cornstarch until smooth.
2. Cook over moderate to high heat, stirring constantly, until mixture boils.
3. Stir in the sugar, orange juice concentrate, table fat, salt, and grated orange rind.
4. Orange food coloring may be added if desired.

Table 8-3 Ingredients and Proportions for Dessert Sauces

Sauce	Liquid Kind	Liquid Amt. (c)	Corn-starch (Tbsp)	Egg Yolks	Table fat (Tbsp)	Sugar (c)	Salt (tsp)	Other Ingredients	Yield (c)
Vanilla sauce	milk	1/2	—	3	3	1/2	1/16	1 tsp vanilla	2/3
Lemon sauce I	water	3/4	1	—	2	1/2	1/16	2 Tbsp lemon juice 1 tsp grated lemon rind	3/4
Lemon sauce II	water	1/2	—	3	3	1/2	1/16	3 Tbsp lemon juice 1 tsp grated lemon rind	2/3
Orange sauce	water	1/2	1	—	1	1/2	1/16	1/4 c frozen orange–juice concentrate 1 tsp grated orange rind	3/4
Almond sauce	milk	1/2	—	3	3	1/2	1/16	1/4 c almond paste 1/2 tsp vanilla 1/2 tsp almond extract	3/4
Caramel sauce	milk	1/2	—	3	3	1/2	1/16	1 tsp vanilla	2/3
Butterscotch sauce	milk	1/2	—	3	4	1/2[a]	1/16	1 tsp vanilla 1/4 c toasted sesame seed	2/3
Chocolate sauce	milk	1/2	—	3	2	3/4	1/16	1/4 c cocoa powder 1 tsp vanilla	2/3
Hawaiian sauce	water	2/3	1	—	1	1/4	1/16	1/3 c fruit-punch concentrate	1
Strawberry sauce	water	1/3	2	—	1	1/3[b]	1/16	1 12-oz pkg frozen straw-berries thawed	1-1/2
Hard sauce	—	—	—	—	8	1[c]	—	1 tsp vanilla	1

[a]Brown sugar, packed into cup.
[b]More sugar may be needed if strawberries are unsweetened.
[c]Confectioners' sugar, sifted before measuring.

Almond Sauce

1. In a saucepan, mix together the milk and egg yolks until blended.
2. Cook over low heat, stirring constantly, until mixture is steaming hot and will coat spoon.
3. Remove from heat and stir in the table fat, almond paste, sugar, salt, almond extract, and vanilla extract.

Caramel Sauce

1. In a saucepan, mix together the milk and egg yolks until blended.
2. Cook over low heat, stirring constantly, until mixture is steaming hot and will coat spoon.
3. Remove from heat, and stir in table fat, salt, and vanilla.
4. Place the sugar in a heavy iron frying pan and heat until sugar is lightly browned.
5. Stir the carmelized sugar into the sauce.

Butterscotch Sauce

1. In a saucepan, mix together the milk and egg yolk until blended.
2. Cook over low heat, stirring constantly, until mixture is steaming hot and will coat spoon.
3. Remove from the heat and stir in the brown sugar, butter, salt, vanilla and sesame seeds.

Chocolate Sauce

1. In a saucepan, mix together the milk, cocoa powder, and egg yolks until blended.
2. Cook over low heat, stirring constantly, until the mixture is steaming hot and will coat spoon.
3. Remove from heat and stir in the butter, sugar, salt, and vanilla.

Hawaiian Sauce

1. In a saucepan, mix together the water and starch until smooth.
2. Cook over moderately high heat, stirring constantly, until mixture starts to boil.
3. Remove from heat and stir in the sugar, salt, table fat, and fruit-punch concentrate.

Strawberry Sauce

1. Place the thawed strawberries in a blender and blend until smooth.
2. Mix together the water and starch in a saucepan and stir in the strawberry purée. Sliced strawberries, fresh or frozen, may be added if desired.
3. Cook over moderate to high heat, stirring constantly, until mixture starts to boil.
4. Remove from heat and stir in sugar, salt, and table fat.

Hard Sauce

1. Place butter in the bowl of the electric mixer, and add sifted confectioners' sugar and vanilla.
2. Beat at high speed until light and fluffy.
3. Spread in an 8 x 8'' baking dish and chill; then cut into squares for use on puddings. The squares may be frozen.

D. Puddings

Puddings are simply thick sauces containing a higher concentration of starch than the dessert sauces. Bread crumbs and egg are alternative thickening agents in puddings. Starch-thickened puddings are cooked on the surface unit of the range, while bread- and egg-thickened puddings are usually baked. Soufflé-type puddings, with a high proportion of eggs, must be baked surrounded by hot water to prevent excessive heat. Table 8-4 shows the ingredients and proportions for a variety of puddings. Pudding mixtures become thicker as they cool.

Table 8-4   Ingredients and Proportions for Puddings

Pudding	Liquid Type	Amt. (c)	Corn-starch (Tbsp)	Eggs (large)	Sugar (Tbsp)	Table fat (Tbsp)	Salt (tsp)	Other Ingredients	Yield (c)
Blancmange	milk	1	1-1/2		3	2	1/16	1 tsp vanilla	1
Caramel	milk	1	1-1/2		4	2	1/16	1/2 tsp vanilla	1
Butterscotch	milk	1	1-1/2		4[a]	4		1/2 tsp vanilla	1
Chocolate	milk	1	1		4	1	1/8	1/2 tsp vanilla 1/4 c cocoa powder	1
Bread	milk	1		1	4	2	1/16	1/8 tsp nutmeg 1/8 tsp cinnamon 1/2 tsp vanilla 1/4 c raisins 2 slices fresh bread	1-2/3
Tapioca cream	milk	1		1	2 1		1/16	2 Tbsp minute tapioca 1 tsp vanilla	1
Tapioca fruit	pine-apple juice	1			4[b]		1/16	2 Tbsp minute tapioca 1/4 c water 1/4 c drained crushed pineapple	1-1/3

[a]Brown sugar, packed into cup.
[b]Additional sugar may be required if unsweetened pineapple juice is used.

Blancmange (Vanilla Pudding)

1. In a saucepan, mix together the milk and cornstarch until smooth.
2. Cook over moderately high heat, stirring constantly, until mixture starts to boil.
3. Turn off heat and stir in sugar, salt, table fat, and vanilla.
4. Transfer the pudding to a bowl, cover with plastic wrap, and chill.

Caramel Pudding

1. In a saucepan, mix together the milk and cornstarch until smooth.
2. Cook over moderately high heat, stirring constantly, until the mixture starts to boil.
3. Turn off the heat and add the table fat, salt, and vanilla.
4. In a heavy frying pan heat the sugar until it turns light brown; then add it to the pudding, mixing well.
5. Transfer the pudding to a bowl, cover with plastic wrap, and chill.

Butterscotch Pudding

1. Follow the directions for <u>Blancmange</u>, stirring in brown sugar instead of granulated sugar in step 3.

Chocolate Pudding

1. In a saucepan, mix together the milk, cornstarch, and cocoa powder until smooth.
2. Follow procedure for <u>Blancmange</u>.

Bread Pudding

1. Cut the 2 slices of fresh bread into 1/2" cubes.
2. Place the bread cubes in the bottom of a greased 1-qt casserole.
3. Sprinkle the raisins over the bread cubes, and dot with table fat.
4. Using a French whip, mix together the milk, sugar, egg, salt, nutmeg, cinnamon, and vanilla until blended.
5. Pour the milk-egg mixture over the bread in the casserole.
6. Set the casserole in a pan of hot water and bake at 375^OF (190.5^OC) until it sets—about 35 minutes. The hotter the water surrounding it, the faster the pudding bakes; boiling water may be used providing casserole and contents are room temperature.
7. Serve hot or cold, topped with Hard Sauce, if desired.

Tapioca Cream Pudding

1. In a saucepan, mix together the milk, tapioca, and yolk of an egg.
2. Cook over moderate heat, stirring constantly, until the mixture starts to boil.
3. Turn off the heat but leave the pan on the hot surface unit; stir in 2 Tbsp sugar, salt, and vanilla.
4. Beat the egg white to the soft-peak stage, add 1 Tbsp sugar, and beat just until the peaks stand up when the beater is removed.
5. Fold the egg-white foam into the warm tapioca, using a French whip.
6. Transfer the pudding to a bowl, cover with plastic wrap, and chill.

Tapioca Fruit Pudding

1. In a saucepan, mix the tapioca and water together, and heat until steaming hot, stirring constantly.
2. Add the pineapple juice, and continue heating until mixture starts to boil, stirring continuously.
3. Turn off heat and stir in the drained pineapple, sugar, and salt.
4. Transfer the pudding to a bowl, cover with plastic wrap, and chill.

Apple Brown Betty

1 c crushed graham crackers	1/2 c brown sugar
2 Tbsp melted table fat	1/8 tsp nutmeg
1/2 tsp vanilla	1/8 tsp cinnamon
3 c peeled, diced apples	1/16 tsp salt

1. Crush the graham crackers in a plastic bag with a rolling pin.
2. Add the vanilla to the melted table fat and mix into the graham cracker crumbs.
3. Place one-third of the crumb mixture in the bottom of a greased 1-qt casserole, and top with half the diced apples.
4. Combine the brown sugar, cinnamon, nutmeg, and salt until blended, and spread half of this mixture over the apples.
5. Repeat the layers and finish with a layer of crumbs.
6. Cover the casserole and bake at 375°F (190.5°C) until apples are tender—about 30 minutes.
7. Remove the cover and increase oven temperature to 400°F (204.5°C) to permit the pudding to brown.
8. Serve hot with Hard Sauce, if desired.

Yield: About 2-1/2 cups

Lemon Soufflé

1 c milk	1 tsp grated lemon rind
3 Tbsp flour	2 Tbsp table fat
1/2 c sugar	2 egg yolks
1/8 tsp salt	2 egg whites
1/4 c lemon juice	

1. In a saucepan, mix together the milk and flour until smooth.
2. Cook over moderately high heat, stirring constantly, until mixture starts to boil.
3. Turn off heat and stir in half the sugar (1/4 c), salt, table fat, lemon juice, lemon rind, and egg yolks. Leave on surface unit to keep warm.
4. Place egg whites in a small bowl and beat to soft peaks; add remaining sugar and beat just to the stiff peak stage.
5. Fold the egg-white foam into the lemon mixture, using a French whip.
6. Pour the mixture into a 2-qt casserole.
7. Set the casserole in a pan and surround with hot or boiling water.
8. Bake at 375°F (190.5°C) until set—about 30 minutes.
9. Serve hot or cold.

Yield: Four 1-cup servings

E. Evaluation of Sauces and Puddings

Puddings and sauces can be evaluated somewhat subjectively in three areas:

- Flavor: Note whether flavor is weak, strong, adequate, too sweet or not sweet enough, too salty or not salty enough, too spicy, and the like.
- Consistency: Note whether the consistency is watery, dry, too thin, too thick or mucilaginous (tapioca).
- Texture: Note whether the product is smooth, lumpy, curdled, or grainy.

Evaluate a selection of sauces and puddings in each of the areas, and enter observations in Table 8-5.

Besides noting the above characteristics, try to pinpoint the reasons for problems. Are lumps the result of inadequate initial mixing or insufficient mixing while cooking? Was the fruit too sweet or too sour for the amount of sugar? Did curdling result because the temperature was too hot or because the product was cooked too long? This type of analysis aids in improving skills and techniques so that such problems can be avoided in the future.

Table 8-5   Evaluation of Sauces and Puddings

Sauce or Pudding	Flavor	Consistency	Texture	Comments

COMPARISON OF PREPARED AND PURCHASED SAUCES AND PUDDINGS

1. Compare costs of prepared sauces and puddings with canned or dried mixes for equivalent products, following the example shown in Table 8-6.
2. If possible, compare quality and flavors of prepared and purchased products.
3. In Table 8-6 the cost of ingredients are used as a basis for comparison of prepared products with purchased ones. What are some of the hidden costs in preparation of products other than the cost of the ingredients used?
4. Comment on how the following factors also affect the choice between using a purchased product or preparing it from scratch:

- Nutrient and caloric content
- Time required for preparation
- Availability of ingredients
- Flavor and quality of product
- Variety of products available for purchase compared to variety that can be prepared

Table 8-6   Cost Comparisons of Prepared and Purchased Sauces and Puddings

Product	Ingredients	Market Unit		Recipe		Total Cost ($)	Cost per 8 oz ($)
		Measure	Cost ($)	Amount	Cost ($)		
Example:							
White sauce (prepared)	Milk (NFDM)	1 lb.	1.50	1/3 c[a] .05 lb	.075		
	Flour	1 lb (60 Tbsp)	.19	2 Tbsp	.006		
	Margarine	1 lb (32 Tbsp)	.80	2 Tbsp	.050	.131	.131
White sauce (canned)	—	10-1/2 oz	.69	—	—	.69	.526[b]

[a] 1 c instant NFDM = 68 g; 1/3 c = 22.67 g; converting to pounds, 22.67 ÷ 454 g/lb = .05 lb of NFDM used to make 1 c white sauce.

[b] $.69 ÷ 10.5 x 8 = $.526/8 oz canned white sauce. Unless consistency of the canned sauce is compared with that of the prepared sauce, it is difficult to determine if they are comparable in cost. It may be that the canned sauce is so thick that when diluted to the same consistency with water it would yield 12 oz instead of 10.5, which would change the price relationship.

Questions

1. How does the use of arrowroot starch in sauces affect the consistency and appearance of the sauce compared to sauces using cornstarch?
2. Why should sauces containing starch be brought to a boil?
3. Why should sauces containing egg and no starch not be boiled?
4. What technique is used to make a sauce without fat?

UNIT 9   FLOUR AND LEAVENING

Suggested reading: <u>Basic Foods</u>, Chapters 11 and 12

Objectives

- To determine the gluten potential of flours and relate the gluten content of flour to its use in baked products
- To determine sources of carbon dioxide gas and conditions required for production of the gas from various leavening agents

GLUTEN POTENTIAL AND COMPARISON OF FLOURS

The various brands of all-purpose flour vary in their gluten potential because some are made entirely of soft wheat while others are mixtures of hard and soft wheats. Good-quality yeast breads require a flour with a high gluten potential. Gluten potential is not indicated on flour labels, however; it can only be determined by isolating the gluten from the flour.

Separation of Gluten from Flour

1. To develop the gluten, place 1/2 cup water in a small bowl, stir in 1 cup flour, and mix with a circular motion for about 5 minutes.
2. Stir in 2 level Tbsp flour, and mix well.
3. Place 1 level Tbsp flour on a bread board, and spread it out to a circle of about 4" diameter.
4. Scrape all the dough from the bowl onto the bread board, and roll it over to coat with flour.
5. Knead 5 minutes by pressing with the palm and folding over the dough.
6. Additional flour may be used if needed, but add only the minimum amount necessary to prevent stickiness.
7. The dough should be soft and pliable to obtain full gluten development; it should not tear when folded during kneading.
8. When kneading is completed, wash the starch from the dough and isolate the gluten by holding the dough under a gentle stream of cool water while folding and working the dough. Avoid manipulations that cause the dough to separate into strings and pieces; try to keep the dough together in one mass and allow the stream of water to wash out the starch. This will take 10 to 15 minutes.
9. When the water squeezed from the dough is clear, all the starch has been washed out, if the water looks milky, the dough still contains starch.
10. After all the starch has been washed out, squeeze as much water as possible from the dough and weigh it.

Comparison of Flours

Prepare gluten balls from a variety of all-purpose flours. Enter the weight of the wet gluten in Table 9-1. Also compare prices per pound of the flours.

Table 9-1   Comparison of Gluten Content and Cost of Flours

Flour: Type and Brand	Wet Gluten (g)	Cost/lb ($)	Observations
High protein	1.8 oz		

Results will show a considerable variety in gluten content. Starting from the amount of flour prescribed above, a flour containing 45-75 g of wet gluten is suitable for yeast breads; one with 30-45 g gluten is suitable for pastry and biscuits; one with 20-30 g is suitable for muffins; and a flour yielding less than 20 g of gluten is suitable for fine cakes.

LEAVENING

Measurement of Carbon Dioxide Production

A qualitative comparison of the carbon dioxide production from leavening agents is possible with the use of the apparatus shown in Fig. 9-1. It is used as follows:

1.   Fill a 250 ml graduated cylinder with water and cover the top with a small piece of aluminum foil. Quickly invert the cylinder in the pan of water and remove the foil. The pan should be large enough to hold the water in the flask when it runs out during the collection of the carbon dioxide gas.
2.   A piece of rubber or plastic tubing is fitted with glass tubing on each end. At one end the glass tubing is bent so that it will extend into the cylinder for several inches. The glass tubing at the other end is inserted into the stopper for the Erlenmeyer flask.
3.   The Erlenmeyer flask holds the leavening agent, which, under proper conditions, reacts and produces carbon dioxide gas. Therefore, the cylinder should be filled with water and

the tubing set in place at the time the leavenings are placed in the flask. The flask should be stoppered immediately so that all the CO_2 produced can be collected. The CO_2 gas is not visible, but when placed in this closed system, it will replace the water in the cylinder. Thus it is possible to measure the amount of CO_2 produced from different leavenings and under differing circumstances.

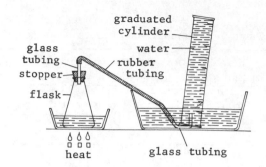

Fig. 9-1: A diagram of the apparatus for measuring the carbon dioxide production of various leavening agents.

4. The apparatus must be placed near the surface unit on the range so that heat can be used as specified for the production of CO_2. It is safer to heat the flask in a pan of water, rather than place it on direct heat.

5. After collecting the CO_2 for each variation given below, record in Table 9-2 the amount collected at room temperature and after heating. Immediately remove the glass tubing from the cylinder and the stopper from the flask to prevent a vacuum implosion of the flask.

6. If the same apparatus is used for more than one determination, wash and dry the flask between uses. Leavenings should not be placed in a wet flask, as this will start the reaction. The flask can be dried quickly by holding it at the neck with tongs while rotating it over a flame or hot surface unit. Do not place a hot flask on a cold surface or in water, for it will break; it can be air cooled. Refill the graduated cylinder with water for each determination.

Table 9-2   Carbon Dioxide Production from Various Leavening Agents

Variations	Carbon Dioxide		
	Room Temperature (ml)	Heated (ml)	Total (ml)
1. Baking soda and water			
2. Baking soda and buttermilk			
3. Tartrate baking powder and water			
4. Sodium aluminum sulfate-phosphate baking powder and water			
5. Yeast and water			
6. Yeast, sugar, and water			

Variations for Comparison of Leavening Agents

Follow the procedure outlined above for each of the following variations, and record the results in Table 9-2.

1. Place 1/4 tsp baking soda (NaHCO$_3$) in the <u>dry</u> flask; add 1/4 cup tap water and stopper immediately. Mix contents and speed the reaction by rotating the flask in a circular motion, swirling the contents. Collect the CO_2 at room temperature for 5 minutes, then place the flask in a pan of boiling water and collect CO_2 for 10 minutes or until the cylinder is filled with CO_2. Record millilitres of CO_2 collected.
2. Place 1/4 tsp baking soda in the dry flask. Add 1/4 cup buttermilk and stopper immediately. Proceed as specified for variation 1.
3. Place 1/2 tsp tartrate baking powder in the dry flask and add 1/4 cup tap water; stopper immediately. Proceed as specified for variation 1.
4. Place 1/2 tsp sodium aluminum sulfate-phosphate baking powder in the dry flask, add 1/4 cup tap water, and stopper immediately. Proceed as specified for variation 1.
5. Place 1/2 tsp active dry yeast in the flask, and add 1/2 cup hot tap water (115°F or 46°C); stopper immediately, and swirl to mix and dissolve the yeast. Collect the CO_2 at room temperature for 10 minutes. Then place the flask in a pan of warm water (95°F or 35°C) and collect the CO_2 for 30 minutes. (It is not necessary to swirl flask while collecting; it may be left unattended.) Record data.
6. Place 1/2 tsp active dry yeast and 1/2 tsp sugar in the flask, and add 1/2 cup hot tap water (115°F or 46°C). Stopper the flask immediately and proceed as specified for variation 5.

Questions

1. Explain the results observed with variations 1 and 2.
2. Explain the results observed with variations 3 and 4.
3. Explain the results observed in variation 1 compared to those observed in 3 and 4.
4. Explain the results observed in variations 5 and 6.

UNIT 10   QUICK BREADS

Suggested reading: <u>Basic Foods</u>, Chapter 13

Objectives

- To learn the techniques, procedures, and ingredients required for preparation of quick breads
- To apply correct standards to the evaluation of quick breads
- To compare costs of prepared and convenience products
- To compare nutrient content of selected quick breads

PREPARATION OF QUICK BREADS

A. General Instructions

1. Unless specified otherwise, all flour measurements are to be made by stirring the flour, spooning it into the cup, and leveling.
2. All recipes use double-acting, or SAS (sodium aluminum sulfate-phosphate), baking powder. The baking powder should be fresh and free of lumps. Keep the container tightly closed when not in use.
3. Sifting is not necessary for mixing dry ingredients. Mix the dry ingredients with a French whip (Fig. 10-1), a flat wire whip, a fork, or in the electric mixer. For most recipes the flour, leavening, and seasonings should be well blended.
4. If whole-wheat flour is used, be sure that it is fresh; rancid flour causes bitterness in products prepared from it. Buy whole-wheat flour from markets that keep it refrigerated, at least in warmer climates. Whole-wheat pastry flour is required for muffins, cookies, cakes, waffles, and pancakes; it is finely ground flour from soft wheat and may be available only from specialty food stores.
5. When milk is specified in a recipe, whole, low-fat, nonfat, or diluted evaporated or concentrated milk may be used. Nonfat dry milk (NFDM) may be reconstituted, using 1/3 cup NFDM to make 1 cup liquid milk; or the equivalent of water and NFDM powder may be used

Fig. 10-1: A French whip is useful for mixing dry ingredients together, for mixing batters, and for folding egg-white foams into other ingredients.

directly without reconstituting, mixing the NFDM with the dry ingredients before adding the equivalent amount of water. The term NFDM refers to the dry powder without water added.

6. Large eggs are used in recipes unless otherwise stated. Small, medium, or extra-large eggs may produce incorrect results.
7. When greased pans are specified, a light coating of pan spray may be used, or solid shortening may be applied with a small square of paper. The shortening can also be melted and applied with a brush. Oil may form a gummy residue on baking sheets in areas between the cookies or breads.
8. Approximate baking times and yields are indicated. Baking time may vary depending on actual oven temperature, the size of the product being baked, the pan material, and the placement of the pan in the oven. Watch product closely during baking to prevent over-cooking.
9. Quick breads may be kept warm until serving time in a 150-175°F (65.5-79.5°C) oven. Cover lightly to prevent excessive drying if time is to be more than 15 minutes.

B. Unleavened Breads

Chapaties

1 c whole-wheat flour
1/2 tsp salt
1/3 c water

1. In a bowl, mix together the flour and salt, using a fork; stir in the water gradually, working into a smooth, pliable dough.
2. Shape the dough into 8 balls of equal size.
3. Place the balls, one at a time, on a bread board covered with a pastry cloth and lightly floured; coat the rolling pin with flour by rolling it over the floured cloth to prevent the dough from sticking to it.
4. Roll the rolling pin over the dough in one direction to form an oval about 3" long.
5. Roll the dough in the crosswise direction until circles of about 5 to 6" diameter are formed.
6. Cook the circles of thin dough on an ungreased, moderately hot griddle about 2 minutes on each side.

Puris

1. Prepare Chapati dough, following steps 1 through 5.
2. In a frying pan, heat about 1/2" of fat to 375°F (190.5°). Fry the puris about 1-1/2 minutes on each side or until lightly browned.
3. Drain on absorbent paper.

Tortillas

1 c Masa (flour prepared from alkaline-treated corn)
1/4 tsp salt
2/3 c water

1. Mix all the ingredients together in a bowl to form a dough; divide into about 6 parts.
2. Take each part and shape it into a ball in the hands; pat it rhythmically between the palms of the hands to form a flat circle of dough about 7" in diameter.
3. Cook the circles of dough on a lightly greased, moderately hot griddle for about 2 minutes on each side; they do not need to be browned.

C. Steam-Leavened Breads

Popovers

1/2 c all-purpose flour	1 large egg
1/4 tsp salt	1 tsp oil
1/2 c milk	

1. Preheat oven to 425°F (218.5°C).
2. Grease four 5-oz Pyrex custard cups.
3. In a bowl beat together the eggs and oil until blended, using a French whip, rotary hand beater, or electric mixer.
4. Add half the milk and mix well.
5. Add the flour and salt, and beat until smooth. Add the remaining milk and mix well.
6. Pour 1/4 cup of batter into each of the prepared cups; place the cups on a baking pan with a space of at least 3" on each side.
7. Bake at 425°F (218.5°C) for 20 minutes; reduce oven temperature to 325°F (163°C), and bake 15 minutes.
8. Using a sharp, pointed knife, cut a short slit in each popover to allow steam to escape. Turn off the oven and leave the popover in the hot oven 10 minutes longer to complete cooking.

Serve hot as a breadstuff with fruit preserves for breakfast, brunch, or other meals.

Yorkshire Pudding

1. Follow the directions for Popovers, but bake in greased 5 x 9 Pyrex baking dish or 8"-diameter casserole or baking pan.
2. Cut into 3 to 6 portions; serve as the breadstuff with roast beef or as the starchy food in the meal.

Cream Puffs

1/2 c water	1/2 c all-purpose flour
1/4 c table fat	2 large eggs

1. Preheat oven to 400°F (204.5°C).
2. Place the water and table fat in a 1-qt saucepan and heat to boiling; do not allow water to boil excessively, as too much may evaporate.
3. Turn off the heat, but leave the pan on the heat while stirring in the flour with a table fork or flat whip, mixing rapidly. The dough should form a ball and clear the sides of the pan (BF, 232, Fig. 13.4).
4. Beat in the eggs one at a time, using a sturdy flat wire whip, table fork, or electric mixer.
5. The dough should be stiff enough to hold its shape at this point. It can be placed in a pastry bag or cookie press for shaping as desired or dropped by spoonfuls onto an ungreased baking sheet. Parchment paper may be used to line the baking pan.
6. Use teasponful amounts to make miniature puffs, several tablespoonfuls for large cream-puffs or to shape into elongated ovals for eclairs (BF, 232, Fig. 13-5). Leave about 3" spaces between large puffs and about 1" between small ones.
7. Bake 25 to 50 minutes, depending on size. Observe the puffs for a few minutes after they are removed from the oven, and return them to the oven if they appear to be collapsing. If in doubt, turn off the oven and leave the puffs in the oven for about 10 minutes.

8. Cool puffs before filling. Slice a thin layer off the top and remove the moist filament from the inside. Replace the top after filling.
9. Suggested fillings include:

- Sweetened whipped cream, with confectioners' sugar sprinkled on top.
- A mixture or layers of sweetened whipped cream and drained fresh or frozen berries.
- Chilled custards and puddings or Spanish cream; topped with whipped cream.
- Chicken, ham, tuna, crab, or shrimp salad mixtures.
- For eclairs, sweetened whipped cream or custard, topped with Chocolate Glaze.

Note: See Index for recipes of above items.

D. Thin-Batter Breads: Crepes, Pancakes, and Waffles

Crepes (French Pancakes)

1/3 c milk	1/3 c all-purpose flour
1/4 c water	1/8 tsp salt
2 large eggs	1/2 tsp vanilla
2 tsp oil	1 Tbsp sugar

1. Place milk, water, eggs, and oil in blender, and blend until smooth.
2. Add vanilla, sugar, salt, and flour; blend 10 seconds; scrape down with a rubber scraper, and blend 40 seconds. Refrigerate at least 2 hours before cooking, or overnight. Batter keeps in the refrigerator for several days or can be frozen. Mix well before cooking.
3. Brush the bottom of a 6" (bottom diameter) frying pan lightly with melted table fat.
4. Heat the pan over moderate heat.
5. Place 2 Tbsp batter in the pan and immediately rotate the pan to spread the batter evenly over the bottom surface.
6. Cook over moderate to high heat for 30 to 45 seconds, until lightly browned on the bottom and the crepe becomes opaque, losing its translucent appearance.
7. Use a rubber scraper to loosen the crepe around the edges and to assist in turning it over. Cook 15 seconds on the second side (BF, 235, Fig. 13.7).
8. Stack the crepes on a plate as they are cooked. The cooked crepes may be stored in the refrigerator for several days, or they may be wrapped and frozen for later use.
9. Crepes are used to make Blintzes and Gateau Florentine (See Index).

Yield: Eight or nine 6"-crepes

Crepes Suzette

1. Prepare 2 cups of one of the fruit-flavored dessert sauces from Unit 8.
2. Transfer the sauce to a pan that is wide and not too deep, such as an electric frying pan.
3. Heat the sauce until bubbly; place a crepe in the sauce, turn gently to coat both sides with sauce, fold in half and then into quarters; place two or three crepes on a serving plate for each serving.
4. Spoon some of the sauce over the top.

Basic Recipe for Pancakes (Griddle Cakes)

The proportions of ingredients for plain pancakes and variations are shown in Table 10-1.

1. Combine the flour, salt, leavening agent(s), and sugar in a bowl, mix well with a French whip, flat wire whip, or in the electric mixer.

Table 10-1   Ingredients and Proportions for Pancakes[1]

Variations	Liquid Kind	Liquid Amt. (c)	Oil (Tbsp)	All-purpose flour (c)	Salt (tsp)	Baking powder (tsp)	Baking soda (tsp)	Sugar (Tbsp)	Other Ingredients
Basic recipe	milk	1	2	1	1/2	1-1/2	0	1	
Buttermilk	butter-milk	1	2	1	1/2	1/2	1/2	1	
Cheese	milk	1	2	1	1/2	1-1/2	0	1	3/4 c grated cheese
Bacon	butter-milk	1	2	1	1/2	1/2	1/2	1	3 slices bacon
Chocolate	milk	1	2	1	1/2	1-1/2	0	3	2 Tbsp cocoa
Whole-wheat	butter-milk	1	2	0	1/2	1/2	1/2	1	1 c whole-wheat pastry flour
Soya	milk	1	2	3/4	1/2	1-1/2	0	1	1/4 c soy flour

[1]Yield of recipes, using 1 c flour: 6 to 7 pancakes, about 5" diameter, each baked from 1/4 c batter.

2. In another bowl combine the egg and oil, mixing until homogeneous with a French whip, flat wire whip, or in the electric mixer.
3. Add the milk to the egg and oil and mix well.
4. Add the liquid ingredients to the dry ingredients and mix just until batter is smooth; do not overmix.
5. Cook the batter on a moderately hot, lightly greased griddle; use 1/4 cup batter for a pancake about 5" in diameter.
6. Cook the pancake on one side until bubbles form on top surface; turn it over before the bubbles break.
7. Cook on the second side until lightly browned; turn the pancake only once.
8. If pancakes are too brown when cooked this way, reduce heat; if too light, increase the heat.
9. Pancakes are best eaten freshly cooked. If necessary, keep them in a warm oven, 150-175ºF, separated by double layers of paper towels.

Buttermilk Pancakes

Follow steps outlined for the basic recipe (above), but substitute the ingredients indicated in Table 10-1.

Cheese Pancakes

Add the grated cheese to the flour mixture; complete as directed in basic recipe.

Bacon Pancakes

1. Cut slices of bacon into small pieces and sauté until crisp and brown. Drain the bacon chips on absorbent paper and discard fat drippings.
2. After pouring the batter onto the griddle, sprinkle with a few pieces of crisp bacon. Cook as directed.

Chocolate Pancakes

Add the cocoa powder and extra sugar to the dry ingredients, and mix as directed.

Whole-wheat Pancakes

Substitute whole-wheat pastry flour for the all-purpose flour and mix as directed.

Soya Pancakes

Add the soy flour to the all-purpose flour and mix as directed.

Potato Pancakes

The recipe for Potato Pancakes appears in Unit 4.

Basic Recipe for Waffles

The proportion of ingredients for plain waffles and for variations is shown in Table 10-2.

Table 10-2   Ingredients and Proportions for Waffles[1]

Variations	Liquid Kind	Amt. (c)	Oil (c)	Eggs	All-purpose flour (c)	Salt (tsp)	Baking powder (tsp)	Baking soda (tsp)	Other Ingredients
Basic recipe	milk	1	1/3	2	1-1/4	1/2	2	0	
Buttermilk	buttermilk	1	1/3	2	1-1/4	1/2	1/2	1/2	
Bacon	buttermilk	1	1/3	2	1-1/4	1/2	1/2	1/2	4 slices bacon
Cheese	milk	1	1/3	2	1-1/4	1/2	2	0	1 c grated cheese
Chocolate	milk	1	1/3	2	1-1/4	1/2	2	0	2 Tbsp cocoa 3 Tbsp sugar
Whole-wheat	buttermilk	1	1/3	2	0	1/2	1/2	1/2	1-1/4 c whole-wheat pastry flour

[1]Yield of recipes, using 1-1/4 c flour: about 4 waffles.

1. Preheat waffle iron while mixing waffles.
2. Combine the flour, salt, and leavening agent(s) in a bowl; mix well with a French whip, or in the electric mixer.
3. Separate the yolks and whites of the eggs.

4. Combine the egg yolks and oil, beating until blended; stir in the milk.
5. Add the liquid ingredients to the dry ingredients and mix until smooth.
6. In another bowl, beat the egg whites to soft peaks.
7. Fold the egg-white foam into the batter, using a French whip.
8. Pour 1—1-1/4 c batter onto the hot waffle iron; if the iron is square or rectangular, pour the batter so that it will spread to the corners. Immediately close the iron and cook the waffle. Follow the manufacturer's instructions for the amount of batter to use and for timing the cooking.
9. To keep the waffles warm, store in single layers on double paper towels in a warm oven.

Buttermilk Waffles

Follow the steps outlined for the basic recipe (above), substituting the ingredients indicated in Table 10-2.

Bacon Waffles

1. Cut slices of bacon into small pieces and saute until crisp and brown. Drain the bacon chips on absorbent paper and discard the fat drippings.
2. Sprinkle 1 to 2 Tbsp crisp bacon pieces over the batter in the waffle iron; then close the iron and bake.

Cheese Waffles

Add the grated cheese to the flour mixture and mix as directed.

Chocolate Waffles

Add cocoa powder and sugar to dry ingredients and mix as directed.

Whole-Wheat Waffles

Substitute whole-wheat pastry flour for the all-purpose flour and mix as directed.

Homemade Pancake and Waffle Mix

8 c whole-wheat pastry flour	4 Tbsp baking powder
3 c instant NFDM	4 tsp salt
1 c nutritional yeast (optional)	

Place ingredients in a jar or mixer, and mix until blended.

Yield: 10-1/2 cups mix

This mix supplies extra protein from NFDM and from the nutritional (not baker's) yeast. The yeast and NFDM also supply extra B vitamins and minerals. Since pancakes and waffles are often eaten with syrups and other highly concentrated sweets, it is wise to add nutrients to an otherwise not very nutritious food.

Pancakes from Homemade Mix

1 egg	3/4 c milk (or water)
2 tsp oil	1 c mix

1. Combine the egg and oil in a small mixing bowl and beat until blended; stir in the milk.
2. Stir in the mix.
3. Bake on a moderately hot, lightly greased griddle. One-fourth cup batter makes 5"-diameter cake.

Yield: Six 5" griddle cakes.

Waffles from Homemade Mix

2 eggs	1 c milk
1/3 c oil	1-1/2 c mix

1. Separate the yolks and whites of the eggs.
2. In a small bowl combine the egg yolks and oil until blended; stir in the milk.
3. Stir in the mix.
4. Beat the egg whites to soft peaks and fold the foam into the batter.
5. Pour 1 cup of batter onto the heated waffle iron and bake.

Yield: Four waffles

Serving Pancakes and Waffles

Pancakes and waffles are commonly served with syrup, honey, or jam. Here are some alternatives.

- Top waffles with creamed meats: chicken, tuna, crab, dried beef, ham.
- Use Dessert Sauces (Unit 8) instead of syrups.
- Use fresh, canned, or frozen fruit purées, unsweetened or lightly sweetened (Unit 3).
- Top with fresh fruits in season, sweetened if needed, and sour half-and-half or yogurt.

E. Thick-Batter Breads: Muffins and Coffee Cakes

Basic Recipe for Muffins

Ingredients for a variety of muffins are listed in Table 10-3.

1. Preheat the oven to 425°F (218°C).
2. Prepare muffin pans for 12 muffins; use paper liners or grease cups.
3. Combine the flour, leavening, salt, sugar, and other dry ingredients in a bowl, mixing with a French whip or flat wire whip until blended.
4. Combine the egg and oil in another bowl, mixing with a French or flat wire whip until oil is well emulsified in the egg; stir in the milk and other liquid ingredients.
5. Make a well in the dry ingredients and add all of the liquid ingredients. Mix with a rubber scraper or flat wooden spoon using folding and cutting motions with a minimum of manipulation until the ingredients are just barely mixed. The mixture should be lumpy, but there should not be any "pockets" of dry ingredients (BF, 238, Fig. 13.10). Avoid stirring around the bowl as this develops the gluten excessively.
6. Fill muffin cups about 1/2 full; clean up drips of batter on the pan around the cups.
7. Bake 15 minutes and test for doneness by pressing lightly with the finger near the center of the muffin. If the muffin is done, it will spring back where pressed. If necessary, continue baking and test at 3 to 5 minute intervals, depending on how close to done they appear to be.
8. Remove the muffins from pan immediately to prevent soggy bottom crusts.

Microwave Oven:

Place about 1/4 c batter into greased microwave muffin pans (plastic) or 5 oz Pyrex custard cups, or use paper liners. Baking time depends on the number of muffins being baked: 1 muffin = 1 minute; 5 muffins = 4 minutes. Overbaking reduces tenderness. Remove from the pan and invert as soon as baked to prevent a soggy bottom on the muffins.

Table 10-3 Ingredients for Muffin Variations[1]

Variations	Milk (c)	Oil (c)	Egg	All-purpose flour (c)	Salt (tsp)	Baking powder (Tbsp)	Sugar (c)	Other Ingredients
Basic recipe	1	1/4	1	2	1/2	1	1/4	
Bran	1	1/3	1	1-1/2	1/2	1	1/2	1-1/2 c bran
Corn	1	1/3	1	1	1/2	1	1/4	1 c yellow corn meal
Oatmeal	1	1/4	1	1	1/2	1	1/4	1 c uncooked rolled oats; 1/2 c raisins
Whole-wheat	1	1/4	1	0	1/2	1	1/4	1-3/4 c whole-wheat pastry flour
Apple	3/4	1/4	1	2	1/2	1	1/3	1 c grated raw apple; 1 Tbsp pineapple juice
Blueberry	1	1/4	1	2	1/2	1	1/4	3/4 c well-drained canned blueberries or 1 c drained fresh
Orange	3/4	1/4	1	2	1/2	1	1/4	1/4 c thawed frozen orange-juice concentrate; 1 Tbsp grated orange rind
Pineapple	2/3	1/4	1	2	1/2	1	1/3	2/3 c drained canned crushed pineapple
Pumpkin-nut	2/3	1/4	1	2	1/2	1	1/2	2/3 c canned pumpkin; 1/2 c chopped walnuts; 1 tsp pumpkin pie spice[2]

[1]Yield: about 12 muffins. Other variations are possible by using whole-wheat flour in such variations as the bran, oatmeal, carrot, or pumpkin. Or spice and/or nuts can be added to the bran, oatmeal, or whole-wheat variations.

[2]Or 1/2 tsp cinnamon, 1/4 tsp nutmeg, and 1/4 tsp allspice.

Bran Muffins

Add the bran to the liquid ingredients indicated in Table 10-3 and mix as directed.

Corn Muffins

Stir the corn meal into the dry ingredients and mix as directed. This batter may be baked in muffin pans, corn stick pans, or a flat baking dish or pan.

Oatmeal Muffins

Stir the uncooked rolled oats and raisins into the dry ingredients and mix as directed.

Whole-Wheat Muffins

Use 1-3/4 cup whole-wheat pastry flour instead of all-purpose flour and mix as directed.

Apple Muffins

Peel and coarsely grate enough apple to make 1 cup; immediately stir the pineapple juice into the apple to prevent excessive browning; then stir the grated apple into the liquid ingredients and mix as directed.

Blueberry Muffins

Well-drained canned, frozen, or fresh blueberries can be stirred into the completed batter, or the blueberries can be distributed into the muffin cups and the finished batter spooned on top. Cook as directed.

Orange Muffins

Add the undiluted, thawed, frozen orange juice and grated orange rind to the liquid ingredients and mix as directed.

Pineapple Muffins

Add the drained, crushed pineapple to the liquid ingredients and mix as directed.

Pumpkin-Nut Muffins

Stir the nuts and spice into the dry ingredients.

Quick Coffee Cake

1 egg	2 c all-purpose flour
1/3 c oil	1 Tbsp baking powder
1 c milk	1 tsp salt
1/2 tsp vanilla	3/4 c sugar

Topping

1/2 c brown sugar
1/2 tsp cinnamon
2 Tbsp table fat, melted
1/4 c chopped walnuts

1. Preheat the oven to 350°F (176.5°C).
2. Grease a 9 x 9'' baking pan.
3. In a small bowl, mix together the egg and oil until the oil is well emulsified; stir in the milk and vanilla.

4. Combine the flour, baking powder, salt, and sugar, mixing until blended.
5. Make a well in the dry ingredients and add the liquid ingredients.
6. Combine the two mixtures, folding and cutting to mix, with a minimum of strokes; the batter should be lumpy, not smooth.
7. Pour the batter into the prepared pan.
8. Mix together the brown sugar and cinnamon; stir in the melted table fat and the nuts.
9. Distribute the topping mixture over the batter in the baking pan.
10. Bake for 35 to 40 minutes or until done.
11. Serve from the pan; do not invert.

Applesauce Coffee Cake

1-1/4 c all-purpose or whole-wheat pastry flour	7/8 c canned applesauce
1/2 tsp baking soda	1/4 c oil
3/4 tsp apple-pie spice or 1/2 tsp cinnamon and 1/8 tsp each nutmeg and allspice	1/2 c raisins
	1/4 c chopped walnuts (optional)
	1/2 tsp salt
	1/2 c sugar

1. Preheat oven to 350°F (176.5°C).
2. Grease a 6 x 9 x 2" or 8"-square baking pan.
3. Combine the flour, soda, salt, sugar, and spice; stir in the nuts and raisins.
4. Stir in the applesauce and oil, mixing only until the ingredients are combined; do not overmix.
5. Pour the batter into the baking pan and spread evenly.
6. Bake immediately for 25 minutes or until done.
7. The cake may be served plain or with Broiled Frosting (see Index), hot or cold, directly from the pan.

Questions

1. If buttermilk is used instead of sweet milk in the Basic Recipe for muffins, how much baking soda and baking powder should be used? Why can't baking soda alone be used?
2. Table fat may be used in muffin recipes instead of oil; explain how the directions should be changed for table fat.
3. What effect on the leavening of the Applesauce Coffee Cake would be expected if the batter is mixed too long or if it is allowed to stand at room temperature before baking?

F. Biscuits

Ingredients for a variety of biscuits are listed in Table 10-4.

Basic Biscuit Recipe

1. Preheat oven to 425°F (218°C).
2. Combine the flour, salt, leavening, sugar, and other dry ingredients in a mixing bowl.
3. Add half the fat and cut in with a pastry blender or two tables knives until the mixture resembles coarse corn meal.
4. Add the remaining fat and cut in until the fat is the size of large peas (BF, 239, Fig. 13.13).
5. Stir in the milk to form a soft dough, adding milk if necessary.
6. Cover the bread board with a pastry cloth and flour lightly.
7. Turn the dough out onto the bread board and roll it over in flour.

Table 10-4 Ingredients for Biscuit Variations[1]

Variations	All-purpose flour (c)	Salt (tsp)	Baking powder (tsp)	Baking soda (tsp)	Sugar (Tbsp)	Fat[2] (Tbsp)	Milk (c)	Other Ingredients
Basic recipe	2	1/2	3	0	1	6	2/3	
Buttermilk	2	1/2	2	1/4	1	6	0	2/3 c buttermilk
Whole-Wheat	0	1/2	3	0	1	6	2/3	1-3/4 c whole-wheat pastry flour
Cheese	2	1/2	3	0	1	6	2/3	1 c grated Cheddar cheese
Orange	2	1/2	3	0	2	6	1/2	1/4 c frozen orange-juice concentrate; 12-15 sugar cubes; 1 Tbsp grated orange rind
Drop	2	1/2	3	0	1	6	1	
Scones	2	1/2	3	0	3	6	0	2 eggs; 1/2 c sour half-and-half
Shortbread	2	1/2	3	0	2	6	0	2/3 c half-and-half
Dumplings	1	1/4	1-1/2	0	0	3	1/4	1 egg
Cinnamon rolls	2	1/2	3	0	0	6	2/3	1/4 c brown sugar; 1/2 c raisins; cinnamon sugar[3]
Pecan rolls	2	1/2	3	0	0	6	2/3	1/4 c brown sugar; 1/2 c chopped pecans; cinnamon sugar

[1]Yield: 12-15 biscuits, 2" in diameter, 1" high. Use cheese with whole-wheat, buttermilk in some of the other variations, or add nuts to the orange to obtain other variations.

[2]Fat should be solid fat; either shortening or table fat; use 1/4 tsp less salt if using table fat.

[3]Cinnamon sugar: Combine 1/3 c granulated sugar and 1 tsp cinnamon.

8. Knead the dough about 20 times by folding it in half and pressing it together, turning a quarter turn with each fold.

9. Roll the dough to a thickness of at least 1/2" with a rolling pin.

10. Cut with a floured biscuit cutter or pastry wheel into desired shapes (BF, 241, Fig. 13. 16).

11. Place the biscuits on an ungreased baking sheet with 1/2" spaces between biscuits; brush the tops with melted table fat.

12. Bake 10 to 12 minutes or until done, testing for doneness by pressing lightly with the finger near the center of the biscuit. If the biscuit is done it will spring back where pressed.

Buttermilk Biscuits

Follow the basic recipe substituting buttermilk for sweet milk and using baking soda with the baking powder. All baking powder may be used, but the biscuits will not brown as well.

Whole-Wheat Biscuits

Substitute whole-wheat pastry flour for the all-purpose flour. Knead the dough 30 times instead of 20.

Cheese Biscuits

Stir the grated cheese into the flour-fat mixture.

Orange Biscuits

1. Stir the grated orange rind into the flour-fat mixture.
2. Combine the milk and the thawed, undiluted orange-juice concentrate before adding to dough.
3. Dip the sugar cubes, one at a time, into some undiluted, thawed orange-juice concentrate and then press one cube into the center of each biscuit. Bake as directed.

Drop Biscuits

1. Add all the fat at once to flour mixture, then stir in the milk.
2. When dough is ready, drop by spoonfuls onto a greased baking sheet and bake for about 12 minutes or until done.

Scones

1. Beat the eggs together until blended and reserve 2 tablespoons.
2. Mix together the beaten eggs and the half-and-half and stir into the flour-fat mixture to form a soft dough; add milk if needed.
3. Prepare as directed, cutting the rolled-out dough into triangles with a pastry wheel or pizza cutter.
4. Place the triangles on an ungreased baking sheet and brush the tops with the reserved egg. Bake 12 to 15 minutes or until done.

Shortbread (Shortcake)

1. Use half-and-half in place of milk and prepare as directed.
2. Roll the dough to a thickness of about 1" and cut with a 3"-diameter round cutter.
3. Bake as directed for biscuits.

Dumplings

1. Add all the fat at once to the flour mixture and prepare dough as directed, but do not knead it.
2. The dough may be dropped by the spoonful into boiling sauce or stock or it may be rolled out and cut into strips for use in cobblers.

Cinnamon Rolls

1. Preheat the oven to 400°F (204.5°C); grease an 8 x 8 x 2" baking pan.
2. Substitute brown sugar for granulated, and prepare dough as directed, kneading 20 times.
3. Roll the dough into a rectangle about 1/4" thick and brush the surface with melted table fat.
4. Sprinkle the dough with cinnamon sugar and raisins.
5. Roll up the dough tightly, beginning at the wide side. Seal well by pinching the edges of the roll together (BF, 320, Fig. 16.19).
6. Slice the roll of dough crosswise into slices about 3/4" thick.
7. Lay the slices side by side in the greased baking pan, with the cut side up, in a single layer and brush the top surface with melted table fat.
8. Bake about 15 minutes or until done.
9. Rolls can be iced with Flat Icing (see Index).

Pecan Rolls

Follow procedure for Cinnamon Rolls, omitting raisins and using chopped pecans. These are also good when made with whole-wheat pastry flour.

Homemade Biscuit Mix

8 c all-purpose or whole-wheat
        pastry flour
1-1/2 c shortening

4 tsp salt
4 Tbsp baking powder

1. Combine the flour, salt, and leavening in the bowl of an electric mixer.
2. Add half the fat and mix at low speed until the fat is finely divided and the mixture resembles coarse corn meal.
3. Cut in the rest of the fat using a pastry blender or 2 knives so that the pieces of fat are about the size of peas.
4. Store in an airtight container in a cool place.

Biscuits from Homemade Biscuit Mix

2-1/4 c mix
2/3 c milk (about)

1. Measure the mix by spooning it lightly into the cup; level.
2. Stir in sufficient milk to form a soft dough.
3. Follow basic recipe for Biscuits.

Muffins from Homemade Biscuit Mix

2-1/4 c mix
1/4 c sugar

1 egg
1 c milk

1. Measure the mix by spooning it lightly into the cup; level.
2. Add the sugar and cut it into the mix with a pastry blender to further subdivide the fat.
3. Mix the egg and milk together until blended; then add mixture to dry ingredients.
4. Follow basic recipe for Muffins.

EVALUATION AND COMPARISON OF QUICK BREADS

Evaluation standards vary for each type of quick bread. The standards include interior and exterior characteristics as well as the flavor of the product. Each type of product has a score sheet with the characteristics for judging the product and the scoring system (see Tables 10-5—10-7). For characteristics scored less than the maximum (3 points), indicate the reason the lower score was given. The purpose of evaluations is to determine causes of poor quality so that they can be corrected in the future. It is important to be able to identify causes of problems: insufficient liquid in the dough, not enough or too much manipulation, overcooking or undercooking, loss of leavening because of mishandling, or incorrect proportion of ingredients.[1]

A. Causes of Poor Quality in Pancakes and Waffles

1. Irregular shape
   a. Pancakes: batter too thin
   b. Waffles: too much or too little batter in the waffle baker
2. Crust color too light: skillet or baker not hot enough
3. Crust color too dark: skillet or baker too hot
4. Pancakes too thick: batter too thick
5. Toughness: overmixing, cooked too slowly, incorrect proportion of ingredients
6. Not sufficiently cooked on interior of pancakes: batter too stiff, skillet too hot
7. Waffles stick to baker: batter incorrect consistency, baker not properly seasoned, baker too hot or cold when batter added, insufficient fat in the batter
8. Poor flavor: ingredients with off-flavor, such as rancid fat or rancid whole-wheat flour or wheat germ; incorrect proportion or kinds of leavening.

B. Causes of Poor Quality in Muffins

1. Irregular shape or peaked top: incorrect proportion of ingredients, overmixing, too much batter in cups, oven temperature too high
2. Crust color too light: overmixing, oven not hot enough, underbaking
3. Crust color too dark: too much sugar, oven too hot, overbaking
4. Crust color uneven: overmixing, too much batter in cups, uneven or too high heat in oven
5. Top crust too smooth: overmixing, too much liquid
6. Tough: too much flour or egg, not enough shortening, overmixing, overbaking
7. Interior streaks: egg and milk not well blended
8. Coarse or uneven cells: liquid ingredients not well blended; overmixing
9. Tunnels: incorrect proportion of ingredients, overmixing, too much batter in cups, oven temperature too high
10. Dry texture: batter too stiff, overbaking
11. Gummy, moist, waxy interior texture: liquid ingredients not well blended, underbaked
12. Heavy: overmixing, underbaking
13. Poor flavor: poor-quality ingredients, wrong proportion of ingredients

---

[1]Information on desirable characteristics and causes of poor quality in baked products is adapted from Baking Basics, published by the Self-Rising Flour and Corn Meal Program, Inc., 14 East Jackson Boulevard, Room 1010, Chicago, Illinois 60604.

C. Causes of Poor Quality in Biscuits

1. Irregular shape: too much liquid, dough not rolled out uniformly, biscuits cut out unevenly, oven heat uneven
2. Color too light: dough too stiff, oven temperature too low
3. Color too dark: oven temperature too high, baked too long
4. Color uneven: uneven oven heat, shape uneven, incorrect placement in oven
5. Bottom crust too dark: not baked on shiny pan
6. Yellow or brown spots: dry ingredients not well mixed before adding liquid: lumps in baking powder or baking soda
7. Tough: too much flour or not enough fat, overmixing, oven temperature too low
8. Rough top crust: too much liquid, insufficient kneading
9. Not flaky on interior: not enough fat; too much or too little mixing of fat with flour, insufficient kneading
10. Coarse, uneven cells: overmixing or kneading
11. Too dry: dough too stiff, overbaking
12. Heavy: too much shortening, too much liquid, overmixing, underbaking
13. Poor flavor: poor quality of ingredients, wrong proportion of ingredients

COST COMPARISON OF PREPARED AND PURCHASED PRODUCTS

Since biscuits, muffins, and other baked products are not standardized in size, it is impossible to compare these products on the number of pieces. The most equitable comparison, therefore, is on the basis of weight. Thus, to compare refrigerated biscuits, biscuit mix, and homemade biscuits, it is necessary to prepare each type of product according to directions and relate the weight of the baked breadstuff to the amount of the mix used or to the ingredients used to make it. Cost can then be calculated on 100-g amounts of the baked product.

Table 10-8 can be used for making these calculations. An example is shown with biscuits. Only one brand of mix (the most expensive) was compared and two of the least expensive brands of refrigerated biscuits.

Quality characteristics of the purchased products should be compared with the prepared products, as there are differences in eating quality.

NUTRIENT COMPARISON OF BAKED PRODUCTS

Any given baked product, biscuits, for example, has certain ingredients that do not change, like flour, fat, and milk. Biscuits can be varied by adding ingredients, such as cheese or nuts, or by using a variety of different flours. Tables of food composition show the nutrient composition only of baked products prepared according to the basic recipe. These tables can be used to compare the nutrient composition of biscuits with muffins or with pancakes. To compare the effect of using whole-wheat flour, oats, bran, or nutritional yeast in baked products, one can calculate nutrient comparisons of these ingredients themselves. Basic Foods, Table 11.3, p. 216, provides nutrient comparisons of a variety of flours and meals used in baked products.

Table 10-9 is provided for nutrient comparisons of baked products or of the ingredients used in baked products.

Table 10-5   Score Sheet for Pancakes and Waffles

<u>Desirable characteristics</u>

- Color: evenly browned, neither too dark nor too light
- Shape and Size: uniform for product
- Grain: fine, thin-walled cells, evenly distributed
- Texture: tender and moist, but not sticky; crisp crust on waffles
- Flavor: pleasing, well-blended, with no bitterness

Score: Good — 3   Fair — 2   Poor — 1

Pancake-Waffle Variations	Color	Shape; Size	Interior Grain	Texture	Flavor	Comments

Table 10-6   Score Sheet for Muffins

Desirable characteristics

- Color: uniform golden brown
- Crust: top pebbled, slightly rough but shiny, tender
- Shape: slightly rounded top without peak
- Grain: round, even cells, without tunnels
- Texture: tender, moist, light
- Flavor: pleasing, with no bitterness

Score: Good — 3   Fair — 2   Poor — 1

Muffin Variations	Color	Crust	Shape	Grain	Texture	Flavor	Comments

Table 10-7   Score Sheet for Biscuits

Desirable characteristics

- Color: top and bottom evenly golden brown, sides lighter; no yellow or brown spots
- Shape: level top, straight sides
- Crust: relatively smooth, tender, free of excess flour
- Grain: flaky—pulls off in thin sheets when top and bottom are separated while warm; even cells, medium fine
- Texture: tender, light, slightly moist
- Flavor: pleasing, with no bitterness

Score: Good — 3   Fair — 2   Poor — 1

Biscuit Variations	Color	Shape	Crust	Grain	Texture	Flavor	Comments

Table 10-8   Cost Comparisons of Purchased and Prepared Baked Products[1]

Baked Product Ingredients		Market Unit		In recipe		Yield[1] (g)	Cost per 100 g[2] ($)
		Size	Cost ($)	Amount	Cost ($)		
Biscuits, refrigerated	—	7.5 oz	0.22	—	—	200	0.11
Biscuits, refrigerated	—	7.5 oz	0.28	—	—	200	0.14
Biscuit mix	—	40.0 oz	1.19	—	—	1600	0.074
Biscuits, prepared	flour	1 lb (4 c)	0.19	2 c	0.095		
	margarine	1 lb (32 Tbsp)	0.80	6 Tbsp	0.150		
	baking powder	7 oz (21 Tbsp)	0.75	1 Tbsp	0.036	480	0.077
	milk(NFDM)	1 qt	0.30	2/3 c	0.050[3]		
	sugar	1 lb (32 Tbsp)	0.45	1 Tbsp	0.0		

[1]After baking the product, cool and weigh.
[2]Cost per 100 g of baked product.
[3]Using NFDM, a 4-lb pkg makes 20 qt ($6.00 or $0.30 per qt; the recipe called for 2/3 c liquid milk or 1/6 qt ($.30 ÷ = $.05).

Table 10-9   Nutrient Comparisons of Baked Products and Ingredients Used in Baked Products

Baked Product or Ingredient	Measure	Food Energy (cal)	Protein (g)	Calcium (mg)	Iron (mg)	Vitamin A (IU)	Thiamin (mg)	Riboflavin (mg)	Niacin (mg)

UNIT 11   PASTRY AND PIES

Suggested reading: <u>Basic Foods</u>, Chapter 14

Objectives

- To prepare and evaluate pastry made with varying ingredients and by different methods
- To prepare pastry and fillings for a variety of pies
- To prepare puff pastry

PREPARATION AND EVALUATION OF PASTRY

A. Methods of Preparing Pastry

Table 11-1 lists the proportions of ingredients for pastry prepared with different types of fat and shows the method most suitable for each fat. The pastry method of mixing is described for use with solid fats and the emulsion method for liquid fat or oil.

Table 11-1   Ingredients and Proportions for Pastry

Type of Pastry	All-purpose flour (c)	Salt (tsp)	Fat Type	Amount (c)	Amount (Tbsp)	Water (Tbsp)
Pastry Method						
Double crust	2	3/4	shortening[1]	2/3	+ 2	4
Single crust	1-1/2	1/2	shortening[1]	1/2	+ 1	3
Double crust	2	3/4	lard	2/3		4
Single crust	1-1/2	1/2	lard	1/3	+ 2	3
Double crust	2	1/4	table fat	3/4	+ 1	3
Single crust	1-1/2	1/4	table fat	1/2	+ 1	2
Emulsion Method						
Double crust	2	3/4	oil	1/2		4
Single crust	1-1/2	1/2	oil	1/4	+ 2	3

[1]Preferably a shortening without such added emulsifiers as mono- and diglycerides

Pastry Method

1. To measure the flour, stir and spoon it lightly into a cup; then level.
2. Combine the flour and salt in a bowl; add half the solid fat.
3. Cut the fat into the flour with a pastry blender or two table knives until it is finely divided and resembles coarse corn meal.
4. Add and cut in the remaining solid fat until the pieces are about the size of large peas.
5. Sprinkle the water over the flour-fat mixture and stir with a table fork; then work with the fingers to form a ball of dough.
6. Place the ball of dough in a plastic bag and refrigerate 10 to 15 minutes to allow the water to equalize throughout the dough.
7. See directions for rolling out pastry under Pie Shells, steps 2 through 6.

Emulsion Method

1. Measure the stirred flour into a cup; then level.
2. Combine the flour and salt in a bowl.
3. Measure the oil in a graduated liquid measuring cup and add the water to the oil.
4. Mix the oil and water together with a fork and then stir in 1 or 2 Tbsp flour-salt mixture to form a paste.
5. Use a rubber scraper to transfer all the oil-water-flour paste to the rest of the flour-salt mixture; mix to form a dough.
6. Place the ball of dough in a plastic bag and refrigerate for at least 10 minutes.
7. Roll the dough out between sheets of waxed paper.

B. Evaluation of Pastry

Samples of pastry can be baked in flat pieces on baking sheets for comparison of different types of fats or flours (whole-wheat or white pastry flour).

1. Use half the ingredients shown for a single-crust pastry.
2. Roll the crust to a thickness of 1/8", preferably using a pastry guide to control thickness of the pastry.
3. With a blunt-tipped fork, prick the pastry uniformly over its entire surface.
4. Bake at 475°F (246°C) for 5 to 8 minutes until lightly browned.

Use Table 11-2 as the score sheet for the pastry determining which of the following reasons has caused poor quality in the pastry.
1. Tough crust: too little fat; excessive water; overmixing after addition of water or excessive handling while rolling out the dough
2. Solid crust: too little fat; overmixing of fat and flour; overmixing after addition of water; oven temperature too low
3. Crust color too pale: overmixing; oven temperature too low; underbaked
4. Crust color too dark: oven temperature too high; overbaked
5. Thick, soft crust: too little fat; excessive water; pastry rolled too thick; oven temperature too low
6. Crumbly crust: excessive fat; fat and flour overmixed; lack of water; lack of gluten potential in the flour
7. Poor flavor: poor-quality ingredients; incorrect proportion of ingredients; over- or under-baked

Table 11-2   Score Sheet for Pastry

Desirable characteristics

- Shape: even thinness all over
- Color: light golden brown, darker brown edges
- Crust appearance: rough, slightly blistered
- Texture: flaky and crisp; not soggy or compact
- Tenderness: easily cut or broken; not crumbly
- Flavor: pleasing; no scorched, salty, or rancid flavors

Score: Good — 3   Fair — 2   Poor — 1

Pastry	Shape	Color	Crust	Texture	Tenderness	Flavor	Comments

PREPARATION OF PIES

A. Preparing the Pastry for Pies

Single-Crust Unbaked Pie Shell

1. Prepare the recipe for a single-crust pie.
2. Cover a bread board with a pastry cloth and flour lightly, rubbing the flour into the cloth over an area about 14" in diameter.
3. The dough should be a smooth round ball; flatten it with the hands on the bread board until it is about 1" thick.
4. Coat the rolling pin with flour by rolling it over a section of the floured cloth.
5. Roll the rolling pin over the dough in one direction to form an elongated shape; lift the pin off the dough slightly as it approaches the edge of the dough to prevent excessive thinness at the outer edges.
6. Then roll over the dough in a direction perpendicular to the first, still lifting the rolling pin near the edges.
7. Roll the dough into a circle about 13" in diameter for a 9"-diameter pie.
8. Fold the dough in half and lay the folded edge across the middle of the pie pan (BF, 251, Figs. 14.1-2).
9. Unfold the dough and ease it down into the pie pan; do not stretch or pull it; be sure that it fits into the pie pan where the side and bottom of the pan meet.
10. Trim the extra crust from the edges, leaving an overhang of about 1" of crust around the rim of the pan.
11. Fold the overhang under the crust between the pastry and the pan so that the folded edge is even with the outer rim of the pan.
12. Pinch the pastry around the rim between the thumbs and forefingers to form a scalloped rim on the pastry shell.
13. The pastry shell is now ready to be filled and baked.

Single-Crust Baked Pie Shell

1. Follow steps 1 through 12 for the Unbaked Pie Shell.
2. Using a table fork, prick the pastry uniformly and repeatedly around the sides of the pan and all over the bottom of the crust.
3. Bake at 450°F (232°C) 5 to 8 minutes or until lightly browned; do not overbake.
4. Cook before filling.

Microwave Oven:

1. Follow steps 1 through 12 for Unbaked Pie Shell and step 2 of Single-Crust Baked Pie Shell. Use a glass pie plate.
2. Take a paper towel and fold it into quarters, then fold it to form a triangle. Cut from the folded point of the triangle to within 1" of the top of the triangle. Trim the corners of the triangle so that when unfolded it is a circle with slits from the center almost to the outer edge.
3. Place the circle of paper towel on top of the pricked pie crust. Invert a 7" or 8" plate on top of the towel.
4. Bake in the microwave oven 4 minutes.
5. Remove the plate and paper towel and bake 2 minutes.
6. Turn one-quarter turn and bake 1 more minute.

Two-Crust Pies

1. Prepare recipe for double-crust pie.
2. Divide the dough in half; using half the dough, follow steps 2 through 9 for the Unbaked Pie Shell.
3. Be sure the crust fits the pan well; then trim the pastry even with the outer edge of the pan.
4. Place the filling in the pastry-lined pie pan, filling about two-thirds full, unless raw fruit is used, in which case it can be filled all the way.
5. Roll out the other half of the dough, following steps 3 through 7 for the Unbaked Pie Shell.
6. Fold the dough in half and cut slits in the pastry to allow steam to escape while the pie is baking.
7. Moisten the pastry on the rim of the pastry-lined pan lightly with water so that a better seal can be formed when the two crusts are put together.
8. Place the fold of the top crust across the middle of the pie and unfold. Trim, leaving an overhang of about 1".
9. Press the two crusts lightly together around the rim of the pan.
10. Fold the top crust over and under the bottom crust all around the rim of the pan.
11. Pinch the pastry around the rim between the thumbs and forefingers to form a scalloped rim.
12. Bake in preheated oven according to time and temperature required for the filling.

B. Pie Fillings

CUSTARD PIES

Ingredients for custard pies and some variations are listed in Table 11-3. Amounts are sufficient for 9" pies.

Table 11-3   Ingredients for Custard Pies

Variations	Milk (c)	Eggs	Sugar (c)	Salt (tsp)	Vanilla (tsp)	Gelatin (Tbsp)	Other Ingredients	Type of Pie Shell
Vanilla I	2-1/3	4	1/2	1/4	1	0	1/4 tsp nutmeg	unbaked
Vanilla II	2-1/3	3	1/2	1/4	1	1[1]	1/4 tsp nutmeg	baked
Chocolate	2-1/3	3	1/2	1/4	1	1	3 Tbsp cocoa powder	"
Coconut	2-1/3	3	1/2	1/4	1	1	1 c angel-flake coconut	"
Pumpkin	1	3	1/2	1/4	1	0	1-1/3 c canned pumpkin 1 tsp pumpkin pie spice[2]	unbaked

[1] 1 Tbsp unflavored gelatin = 1 envelope
[2] Or use 1/2 tsp cinnamon, 1/4 tsp nutmeg, and 1/4 tsp allspice

Vanilla Custard Pie I

1. Beat the eggs together until blended; then add the sugar, milk, salt, and vanilla, and blend well.
2. Pour the custard mixture into an unbaked pastry shell. The custard mixture is quite thin and is easily spilled. Avoid spillage by placing the pastry-lined pie pan on the oven shelf

while the shelf is partly pulled out. Then pour the custard mixture into the pie shell, gently push the shelf in, and close the oven door. Work quickly to avoid losing the oven heat.

3. Bake the custard pie in a preheated 450°F (232°C) oven for 15 minutes; then reduce the oven temperature to 350°F (176.5°C) for about 10 minutes more or until the custard is set. Test by inserting the tip of a table knife about 1" from the center of the pie; the pie is done if the blade comes out clean. The center of the pie may still be soft, but the residual heat in the pie will finish the cooking.

Microwave Oven:

Pour the custard mixture into a prebaked crust in a glass pie plate. Cook 5 minutes. Gently, using a rubber scraper move the "set" edges toward the center. Cook 5-6 minutes until center "jiggles like gelatin." Rest 10-15 minutes. A knife inserted in the center should come out clean.

Vanilla Custard Pie II

1. Beat the eggs in a 2-qt saucepan until blended. Beat in the sugar, salt, milk, and gelatin until smooth.
2. Cook over moderate heat, stirring constantly with a spring stirrer that scrapes the bottom of the pan, until the mixture is steaming hot and coats a silver spoon. Do not overcook or it will curdle.
3. Remove from heat and stir in the vanilla.
4. Chill until mixture starts to thicken; stir vigorously and then pour into a cooled, baked 9" pastry shell.
5. Chill several hours until set.
6. May be garnished with sliced almonds or other nuts, or shaved milk or bitter chocolate.
   Microwave Oven Method:
   Follow steps 1 and 2, but combine ingredients instead in a glass bowl. Cook 4 minutes, stir well, cook 2 minutes, stir, cook 2 minutes, stir, and cook 1/2 to 1 minute longer until it coats the spoon. Follow steps 3 to 6.
   Note: The mixture can be chilled more rapidly in the freezer, but do not put hot glass containers directly on the freezer shelf. Place folded towel under them.

Chocolate Custard Pie

1. Combine sugar, salt, and cocoa in a small bowl, mixing with a French whip until smooth and free of lumps.
2. Beat the eggs in a 2-qt saucepan until blended; then stir in the sugar-cocoa mixture, milk, and gelatin.
3. Follow steps 2 through 6 for Vanilla Custard Pie II.

Coconut Custard Pie

1. Follow steps 1 through 3 for Vanilla Custard Pie II.
2. Chill until the mixture starts to thicken, then stir in the coconut and pour into a cooled, baked 9" pastry shell.
3. Chill several hours until set.

Pumpkin Custard Pie

1. Combine the sugar and spice in a small bowl, mixing with a fork so that there are no lumps of spice.
2. Beat the eggs together in a large bowl until blended; then stir in the pumpkin, sugar-spice mixture, milk, salt, and vanilla until well blended.
3. Follow steps 2 and 3 under Vanilla Custard Pie I.

Mince Pie

1/2 a 9-oz pkg condensed mincemeat	1 c half-and-half
1/4 c brown sugar	1 Tbsp unflavored gelatin
1 c peeled, chopped apples	1/3 c chopped walnuts
1/4 c chopped dried apricots	1 Tbsp grated orange rind
1/2 c water	baked 9" pastry shell
1 egg	

1. Combine the water, sugar, mincemeat, apples and apricots in a 1-qt saucepan and heat to boiling.
2. Beat together the egg, half-and-half, and unflavored gelatin until blended and stir into the mincemeat mixture.
3. Cook over moderate heat, stirring constantly, until the mixture is steaming hot.
4. Remove from the heat and stir in walnuts and orange rind.
5. Chill until the mixture starts to thicken; then stir it to distribute the fruit and pour it into a cooled, baked 9" pastry shell.
6. Chill until set.

Pecan Pie

4 eggs	1 tsp vanilla
1/2 c brown sugar	1/4 tsp salt
1/2 c corn syrup	1-1/3 c pecan halves
1/4 c table fat, melted	unbaked 9" pastry shell

1. Beat the eggs together in a bowl until blended; stir in the sugar, syrup, table fat, salt, and vanilla; blend well.
2. Mix in the pecan halves and pour into an unbaked 9" pastry shell.
3. Bake in a preheated oven at $375^{o}F$ $(190.5^{o}C)$ 35 to 40 minutes or until table knife inserted 1" from the center comes out clean.
4. Cool. Serve cold or slightly warm.

MERINGUE, CHIFFON, AND CREAM PIES

Ingredients for some meringue, chiffon, and cream pies are listed in Table 11-4. Amounts are sufficient for filling a baked 9" pastry shell.

Lemon Meringue Pie

1. Separate eggs; place whites in large, clean bowl and yolks in a 2-qt saucepan.
2. Beat yolks and add water gradually while mixing until mixture is blended.
3. Stir in the cornstarch and salt and mix until smooth and free of lumps.
4. Cook over moderately high heat, stirring constantly with spring stirrer, until the paste starts to boil.
5. Turn off heat but leave pan on surface unit while stirring in 2/3 c sugar, table fat, and lemon juice and rind. Leave pan on surface unit while preparing meringue.
6. Beat the egg whites to the soft-peak stage; add 5 Tbsp sugar and beat to stiff peaks.
7. Pour the lemon filling into the cooled, baked 9" pastry shell and top with meringue; be sure that meringue adheres to the crust all around the edge of the pie. Swirl designs in the meringue with a spoon or table knife (BF, 280, Fig. 14.7).
8. Bake in preheated oven at $425^{o}F$ $(218^{o}C)$ for 5 to 8 minutes or until lightly browned.

Table 11-4 Ingredients for Meringue, Chiffon, and Cream Pies

Variations	Milk (c)	Water (c)	Eggs	Sugar (c) (Tbsp)	Salt (tsp)	Corn-starch (Tbsp)	Gelatin (Tbsp)	Vanilla (tsp)	Table fat (Tbsp)	Other Ingredients
Lemon-meringue	0	1-1/2	3	2/3 + 6	1/4	5	0	0	1	1/3 c lemon juice 1 tsp grated lemon rind
Lemon chiffon	0	1-1/2	2	3/4	1/4	0	1-1/2	0	0	1/3 c lemon juice 1 tsp grated lemon rind
Pumpkin chiffon	3/4	0	3	3/4	1/2	0	1-1/2	1	0	1-1/3 c canned pumpkin 1 tsp pumpkin–pie spice[1]
Vanilla cream	2	0	3	1/2 + 6	1/4	2	0	1	1	
Chocolate cream	2	0	3	2/3 + 6	1/4	2	0	1	1	3 Tbsp cocoa powder
Coconut cream	2	0	3	1/2 + 6	1/4	2	0	1	1	1 c angel-flake coconut
Butterscotch cream	2	0	3	0 6	1/4	2	0	1	2	1/2 c dark brown sugar
Banana cream	2	0	3	1/2 + 6	1/4	2	0	1	1	1-2 ripe sliced bananas 2 Tbsp pineapple juice
Orange cream	1-1/2	0	3	1/2 + 6	1/4	2	0	0	1	1/4 c undiluted frozen orange juice

[1] Or use 1/2 tsp cinnamon, 1/4 tsp nutmeg, and 1/4 tsp allspice

Lemon Chiffon Pie

1. Separate eggs; place whites in a large, clean bowl and yolks in a 2-qt saucepan.
2. Beat yolks and add water gradually while mixing until mixture is blended.
3. Stir in the salt, sugar, and gelatin and cook over moderately high heat, stirring constantly with spring stirrer, until the mixture is steaming hot.
4. Remove from the heat and stir in the lemon juice and rind.
5. Chill until the gelatin mixture starts to thicken and is the consistency of uncooked egg white.
6. Beat the egg whites to the soft-peak stage; add 1/4 c sugar and beat to stiff peaks.
7. Add the partially thickened gelatin mixture to the egg whites and mix until blended.
8. Pour the mixture into a cooled, baked 9" pastry shell.
9. Chill until set.

Pumpkin Chiffon Pie

1. Separate the eggs; place whites in a large bowl and yolks in a 2-qt saucepan.
2. Stir the milk into the yolks, mixing until blended.
3. Combine 1/2 c sugar and the spice.
4. Stir the vanilla, gelatin, salt, pumpkin, and sugar-spice mixture into the yolk-milk mixture and cook over moderate heat, stirring constantly with a spring stirrer, until the mixture starts to boil.
5. Chill until the pumpkin mixture starts to thicken.
6. Beat the egg whites to the soft-peak stage; add 1/4 c sugar and beat to stiff peaks.
7. Fold the pumpkin mixture into the egg whites, mixing until blended.
8. Pour the mixture into a cooled, baked 9" pastry shell.
9. Chill until set.

Vanilla Cream Pie

1. Separate the eggs; place the whites in a large bowl and the yolks in a 2-qt saucepan.
2. Add the milk to the yolks, mixing until blended; stir in the salt and cornstarch until smooth and free of lumps.
3. Cook over moderate heat, stirring constantly with a spring stirrer, until the mixture starts to boil.
4. Turn off the heat and leave the pan on the hot surface unit while stirring in 1/2 c sugar, table fat, and vanilla. Leave the pan on the surface unit, with heat turned off, while preparing meringue.
5. Beat the egg whites to the soft-peak stage; add 6 Tbsp sugar and beat to stiff peaks.
6. Pour the cream filling into a cooled, baked 9" pastry shell.
7. Spread the meringue over the top; be sure that the meringue adheres to the crust all the way around. Swirl designs in the meringue with a spoon or table knife.
8. Bake in preheated oven at 425°F (218°C) 5 to 8 minutes or until lightly browned.
9. Chill until set.

Chocolate Cream Pie

1. Combine the cocoa with 1/4 c sugar, mixing until free of lumps.
2. Follow steps 1 through 9 for Vanilla Cream Pie, adding the cocoa-sugar mixture at step 2 and the other 1/4 c sugar at step 5.

Coconut Cream Pie
_____

1. Follow procedure for Vanilla Cream Pie, stirring in coconut at step 4.

Butterscotch Cream Pie
_____

1. Follow directions for Vanilla Cream Pie adding 1/2 c dark brown sugar, packed, instead of granulated sugar, at step 4.

Banana Cream Pie
_____

1. Follow steps 1 through 5 for Vanilla Cream Pie.
2. Slice one or two peeled bananas and toss in pineapple juice to prevent enzymatic browning. Drain and place slices in bottom of cooled, baked 9" pastry shell. Cover with prepared filling.
3. Follow steps 7 through 9 for Vanilla Cream Pie.

Orange Cream Pie
_____

1. Follow steps 1 through 4 for Vanilla Cream Pie.
2. Add the undiluted, thawed, frozen orange-juice concentrate with the sugar and table fat at step 4.
3. Follow steps 5 through 9 for Vanilla Cream Pie.

Strawberry Parfait Pie
_____

 1 3-oz pkg lemon-flavored gelatin   1 pt strawberry ice cream
 1 c boiling water   1 c fresh or frozen strawberries
 1/2 c juice from strawberries   baked 9" pastry shell
      or cold water

1. Stir gelatin into the boiling water until completely dissolved; mix in the cold water or juice drained from frozen strawberries.
2. Divide the ice cream into fourths and stir it into the warm gelatin until it is melted and the mixture starts to thicken.
3. Fold the drained fresh or frozen strawberries into the gelatin mixture and pour into the pastry shell.
4. Chill until set. May be garnished with whipped cream and fresh strawberries.

FRUIT PIES

Ingredients for a few varieties of fruit pies are listed in Table 11-5. Fruit pies are made with unbaked pie shells; amounts are sufficient for 9" pies.

Fresh Apple Pie
_____

1. Wash, peel, quarter, core, and slice 4 to 5 apples to make about 5 cups.
2. Place 2 Tbsp water in a 3-qt saucepan; add the apples and 1/8 tsp salt; cover and heat until steaming hot, stirring occasionally; remove from heat.
3. Mix the sugar, cornstarch, 1/8 tsp salt, and spice together until free of lumps.
4. Prepare the bottom crust and fit it into the pie pan.
5. Add the sugar-starch mixture to the apples, mixing until apples are evenly coated; then

pour the apples into the pastry-lined pan.

6. Place the top crust on the pie. A strip of aluminum foil placed around the rim of the pie prevents excessive browning.

7. Bake on lowest rack in preheated oven at 450°F (232°C) about 35 minutes. Apples should be tender when pierced with a fork and filling should be starting to bubble through vent holes.

Table 11-5 Ingredients for Fruit Pies

Fruit		Starch		Sugar[1]	Salt	
Kind	Amount (c)	Kind	Amount (Tbsp)	(c)	(tsp)	Other Ingredients
Fresh apple	4—5	cornstarch	2	1/3	1/8	1 tsp apple-pie spice[2]
Canned apple	2-1/2—3	cornstarch	1	1/3	1/8	1 tsp apple-pie spice[2]
Canned cherry	2-1/2—3	tapioca	3	1/2	1/8	1/2 c cherry juice 1/2 tsp almond extract
Canned crushed pineapple	2-1/2—3	tapioca	3	1/3	1/8	1/4 c water 1/3 c pineapple juice
Canned apricot	2-1/2—3	cornstarch	2	1/4	1/8	1/2 c apricot juice 1/2 tsp almond extract

[1]Sugar may need to be increased if fruit is unsweetened or tart, decreased if fruit is canned in heavy syrup.

[2]Or use 1/2 tsp cinnamon and 1/8 tsp each nutmeg, allspice, cloves, and ginger

Canned Apple Pie

1. Drain the juice from a 20-oz can of pie-sliced apples (not apple-pie filling).
2. Add the sugar, salt, cornstarch, and spice to the juice and mix until smooth.
3. Heat the juice and sugar mixture until steaming hot. If less than 1/3 cup of juice was drained from the apples, omit this step and just mix the juice and the sugar into the apples.
4. If the juice-sugar-starch mixture was heated, then stir it into the apples and follow steps 5 through 7 for Fresh Apple Pie, shortening the cooking time to 30 minutes.

Canned Cherry Pie

1. Drain the juice from a #2-1/2 can of cherries.
2. Measure 1/2 cup of juice and add the tapioca; bring mixture to a boil and remove from heat.
3. Prepare the bottom crust and fit it into the pie pan.
4. Place the drained cherries in the pastry-lined pan.

5. Add the sugar, salt, and almond flavoring to the cherry juice and tapioca, mix well, and pour mixture over the cherries.
6. Follow steps 6 and 7 under Fresh Apple Pie baking about 30 minutes or until filling starts to bubble through the vent holes.

Canned Crushed Pineapple Pie

1. Combine the water and tapioca and allow to set about 5 minutes. (The acid in the pineapple retards hydration of the tapioca.)
2. Drain the juice from a #2-1/2 can of crushed pineapple.
3. Combine 1/3 c pineapple juice and salt with the tapioca and water in a saucepan and heat, stirring constantly, until mixture boils.
4. Remove from heat and stir in pineapple.
5. Prepare the bottom crust and fit it into the pie pan.
6. Stir in the sugar and pour mixture into pastry-lined pie pan.
7. Follow directions for Fresh Apple Pie, baking for 30 minutes or until crust is lightly browned and filling starts to bubble through the vent holes.

Canned Apricot Pie

1. Drain the juice from a #2-1/2 can of apricots (unpeeled, light syrup).
2. Measure 1/2 cup of the juice into a saucepan and add the cornstarch and salt; mix until smooth.
3. Cook the juice-starch mixture over moderately high heat, stirring constantly, until the mixture comes to a boil.
4. Remove from the heat and stir in the sugar and almond flavoring.
5. Arrange the drained, canned apricots in a pastry-lined pie pan; cover with the cooked juice mixture.
6. Place the top crust on the pie.
7. Bake on lowest shelf of preheated oven at 450°F (232°C) for 30 minutes or until crust is lightly browned and filling starts to bubble through the vent holes.

Other fruits and combinations of fruits which can be used with the above proportions and methods include:

Blueberry
Rhubarb
Seedless green grapes and raspberries
Blueberry and peach
Concord grapes
Cranberry and apple

Banana and pineapple
Strawberry and rhubarb
Pineapple and rhubarb
Cherry and banana
Cherry and pineapple
Apricot and pineapple

PUFF PASTRY

Basic Pastry

1 c bread or all-purpose flour with good gluten potential
1/4 tsp cream of tartar
1/4 tsp salt

1 Tbsp + 1/2 c table fat (1/4-lb bar)
1 large egg
2 Tbsp + 1 tsp cold water

1. Combine egg, water, cream of tartar, salt, and 1 Tbsp melted table fat and mix until blended.
2. Add liquid to the flour and mix to form a dough.
3. Cover a bread board with a pastry cloth and flour lightly.
4. Turn the dough out and knead about 20 strokes; round it up into a smooth ball and allow it to rest about 10 minutes.
5. Roll the dough into a rectangle about 8 x 16".
6. Slice the cold 1/4-lb bar of table fat over half the dough; fold the other half over the side covered with table fat and seal on three sides (BF, 261, Fig. 14.11).
7. Roll the dough out again into a rectangle 8 x 16" and fold into thirds (BF, 261, Fig. 14.11).
8. Wrap the dough in foil or plastic wrap and chill in the refrigerator for 30 minutes.
9. Then roll the dough again into a rectangle 8 x 16" and fold into thirds.
10. Repeat steps 8 and 9 three to six times.
11. Allow the dough to rest in the refrigerator for at least 30 minutes before shaping it for baking after the last rolling. It may be refrigerated for up to 24 hours before baking.

Preparation of Pastry for Tarts

1. Roll the dough into a rectangle 8 x 16".
2. Cut it into eight 4"-squares (in half lengthwise and into fourths) with a pastry wheel.
3. Place 1 to 2 Tbsp prepared filling in the center of each square.
4. Mix 1 large egg and 1 Tbsp water together to make egg wash.
5. Moisten the edges of the four sides of each square with the egg wash, using a pastry brush.
6. Fold the pastry over diagonally to form a triangle and press the cut edges of the pastry together firmly with a table fork.
7. With a sharp, pointed knife, cut three "V"-shaped vent holes in the top of each tart.
8. Place the tarts on a baking sheet lined with parchment paper and brush tops with egg wash.
9. Bake at 450°F (232°C) for 25 to 30 minutes until lightly browned.
10. Remove from the oven, cool slightly, and ice, if desired, with Flat Icing (see Index).

FILLINGS FOR TARTS

Apple Filling

1/4 c brown sugar	1 tsp apple pie spice, or 1/2 tsp
1/2 c granulated sugar	cinnamon and 1/8 tsp each nutmeg,
1 Tbsp cornstarch	allspice, cloves, and ginger
1/4 tsp salt	1 20-oz can pie-sliced apples, drained

Combine the sugar, starch, salt, and spice; then mix it into the apples to coat evenly.

Almond Filling

1/2 c cookie crumbs	1 tsp almond flavoring
1/4 c sugar	1/2 tsp cinnamon
1 egg	1/2 c chopped or sliced almonds
1 Tbsp table fat	

1. Place cookies in a plastic bag and roll with a rolling pin to crush.
2. Beat egg and almond flavoring together until blended; add other ingredients and mix well.

Coconut Filling
_____

1/2 c cookie crumbs	1 Tbsp table fat
3/4 c grated coconut	1/2 tsp almond flavoring
1 egg	

1. Crush cookies in a plastic bag with rolling pin.
2. Beat egg and almond flavoring until blended.
3. Add the rest of the ingredients and mix well.

Date Filling
_____

1-1/2 c chopped dates	1/2 c water
2 Tbsp sugar	1/4 c chopped walnuts

1. Combine the dates, sugar, and water in a saucepan and cook over moderate heat, stirring occasionally, until the mixture starts to boil and thickens.
2. Cool and stir in the walnuts.

Apple-Nut Filling
_____

1/4 c graham cracker crumbs	1/8 tsp salt
1/2 c sugar	1/4 c chopped walnuts
1 Tbsp table fat	2 c chopped apples
1 tsp grated lemon rind	1 Tbsp pineapple juice
1/4 tsp cinnamon	

1. Peel, quarter, core, and finely chop 2 apples to yield about 2 cups; mix pineapple juice into chopped apples to prevent enzymatic browning.
2. Add the other ingredients to the apples and mix well.

Coconut-Marmalade Filling
_____

1/2 c angel-flake coconut
1/2 c marmalade

Combine the marmalade and coconut in a bowl.

Note: Left-over fillings may be frozen for later use, except for the Apple-Nut; raw apples do not freeze well.

Apple Strudel
_____

1. Prepare Puff Pastry.
2. Prepare Apple-Nut Filling.
3. Roll the pastry into a rectangle 8 x 16" and brush with melted table fat.
4. Spread the filling over the surface of the dough and make a roll 16" long; seal the edges by pinching them together.
5. Lay the roll of dough on a baking sheet lined with parchment paper with seam side down and bend the roll of dough to form a horseshoe shape; brush it with melted table fat.
6. Bake 20 minutes at 425°F (218°C) and brush again with melted table fat.
7. Bake at 350°F (176.5°C) 10 more minutes.
8. Remove from oven and cool slightly; brush with Flat Icing (See Index).
9. To serve, cut into wide diagonal slices.

UNIT 12   YEAST-LEAVENED PRODUCTS

Suggested reading: Basic Foods, Chapter 16

Objectives

- To learn techniques for the preparation and evaluation of yeast-leavened products
- To prepare a variety of yeast rolls and sweet-dough products

PREPARATION AND EVALUATION
OF YEAST-LEAVENED PRODUCTS

A. General Instructions

1. A flour with good gluten potential will produce the best quality loaves. Enriched refined bread flour or whole-wheat flour from hard wheat is preferred. A second choice is all-purpose enriched refined flour or whole-wheat flour that is part hard wheat. Flours can be tested for gluten potential by the method described in Unit 9.

2. The amount of flour required depends on its water absorption power, which is related to gluten potential. The higher the gluten potential of the flour, the more water is absorbed. Thus, for a given amount of liquid, less flour is required if the flour has high gluten potential. Whole-wheat flour has greater water absorption capacity than white flour because bran has greater water absorption capacity than starch. For these reasons, it is difficult to state exact proportions of liquid and flour and the amounts are approximate.

3. Fresh milk may be used as the liquid in yeast bread. However, it must be scalded and cooled to lukewarm before adding the yeast. This inactivates enzymes in the fresh milk that have a dough-softening effect. Use of water eliminates this step; it also permits the addition of NFDM at the end of the first fermentation (with the sponge method of mixing).

4. The formulas in this unit specify active dry yeast. It must be dissolved in liquid that is 105-115°F (40.5-46°C) to prevent rupture of the yeast cells and loss of yeast activity. Usually water from the hot water tap is approximately this temperature after it is poured into the measuring cup and mixing bowl. It is advisable to check the temperature with a thermometer. If cake yeast is used, have the temperature of the water between 90-95°F (32-35°C). One envelope of active dry yeast contains 1 Tbsp yeast and is equivalent to one cake of yeast.

5. Flours and other ingredients should be at room temperature or slightly warmer. Chilled ingredients cool the dough and slow yeast activity.

6. There are two methods for mixing yeast doughs: the sponge and the straight-dough. The sponge method is fully described in this unit with indications of how to adapt it to the straight-dough method. The sponge method is preferable when such dough-softening ingredients as NFDM, soy flour, or wheat germ are included. It also is advisable for whole-wheat doughs because it permits fuller hydration of the bran in the flour (BF, 286).

7. Temperatures for fermentation should not exceed 100°F (37.5°C), temperatures between 85-95°F (29.5-35°C) are preferable. Higher temperatures destroy yeast cells and the

dough will not rise. If an oven is turned to the "warm" setting for fermenting the dough, check it with a thermometer before, and at frequent intervals during, the fermentation to be sure it does not get too hot.

B. Preparation of Breads

YEAST BREAD: SPONGE METHOD

General Instructions

1. Place a pastry cloth on a bread board and spread about 2 Tbsp all purpose flour in a 12" circle in the center. Use 1 Tbsp of flour on the cloth each time the dough is returned to be kneaded (after first and second fermentations). Use all-purpose flour for kneading even when the dough is made of whole-wheat flour.
2. Have rolling pin ready for shaping the loaves. Flour the rolling pin by rolling it across the floured pastry cloth.
3. Place 1 to 2 tsp oil in a 3—4-qt bowl and spread it around the bowl with a pastry brush.
4. Grease 1 loaf pan (4-1/2 x 8-1/2 x 2-3/4") or 3 pup loaf pans (3-1/4 x 5-3/4 x 2").

Sponge

1-1/3 c bread flour
1 c tap water (105-115°F; 40.5-46.5°C)
1 Tbsp active dry yeast

1 Tbsp sugar
1 Tbsp table fat
1 tsp salt

Plus one of the variations listed below:

White Bread without Milk

1-2/3 c bread flour

White Bread with Milk

1/3 c NFDM
1-1/2 c bread flour

White Bread with Extra NFDM

1/2 c NFDM
1-1/4 c bread flour

White Bread with Soy Flour

1/3 c NFDM
1/3 c soy flour
1 c + 2 Tbsp bread flour

White Bread with Wheat Germ

1/3 c NFDM
1/4 c toasted wheat germ
1-1/2 c bread flour

White Bread with Corn Meal

1/3 c NFDM
1/2 c yellow corn meal
1 c bread flour

Whole-Wheat Bread

Use whole-wheat flour in the sponge, plus:
1/3 c NFDM
1-1/3 c whole-wheat flour

1. Place the hot water in the mixing bowl, check and adjust the temperature; sprinkle the yeast over the top of the water.
2. Immediately stir in the sugar, salt, and table fat.
3. Add 1-1/3 cup of bread flour and mix about 200 strokes by hand or about 2 minutes at high speed with a dough hook and electric mixer.
4. Leave the sponge mixture in the mixing bowl and let it ferment for 30 minutes.
5. Add the ingredients specified in the desired variation, stirring in first the NFDM and the other flours or grains (corn, soy, wheat germ), and then adding the remaining

bread flour gradually to obtain a dough of the correct consistency. The dough should be soft and pliable, but not sticky. One or two Tbsp more (or less) flour may be needed.

6. If a dough hook is being used, mix the dough 5 minutes at high speed; then turn the dough out onto the bread board and knead about 10 strokes into a smooth ball.

7. If the dough is hand mixed, it will be too stiff, so gluten development must be accomplished by kneading. Turn the dough out onto the bread board and knead about 200 strokes or 10 minutes. To knead, flatten the dough by pressing it with the heels of the palms of the hands, then fold it over, make a quarter turn, and press again. Each fold counts as one stroke (See BF, 288, Figs. 16.3-16.4). Round dough into a smooth ball.

8. Place the ball of dough in the oiled bowl and turn it over to oil the top; let dough ferment 30 minutes.

9. Turn the dough out onto the bread board and knead about 10 strokes. If one 1-lb loaf is to be prepared, round the dough into a smooth ball. If pup loaves are to be prepared, divide the dough into three equal parts (can be weighed) and round each part into a smooth ball. Let ball(s) of dough rest about 5 minutes.

10. Flatten the ball of dough by patting it with the palm of the hands; then roll it with the rolling pin into a rectangle as wide as the baking pan is long. (See BF, 291, Figs. 16.8, 16.9).

11. Moisten the top surface of the rectangle of dough lightly with water, using a pastry brush, so that the dough becomes slightly sticky.

12. Roll the dough up, starting at one of the narrow ends.

13. Place the roll of dough, seam side down, in the greased baking pan. (See BF, 291, Fig. 16.10).

14. Brush the top of the loaf with melted table fat. Allow the loaves to rise (proof) for 40 minutes or until the dough is slightly rounded above the top of the pan.

15. Bake in a preheated oven at 425°F (218°C) 25 to 30 minutes for large loaves and 18 minutes for pup loaves (BF, 292).

16. Test for doneness by pressing the side of the loaf lightly with the finger; it is done if the bread springs back after being pressed. Remove from pan immediately and cool on a rack.

Yield: One 1-lb loaf or three pup loaves

YEAST BREAD: STRAIGHT-DOUGH METHOD

1. Prepare the sponge mixture as directed in steps 1 through 3 for the sponge method.

2. Then immediately follow steps 5 through 7 instead of allowing dough to ferment.

3. Place the ball of dough into an oiled bowl and turn it over to oil the top; let it ferment for 30 minutes.

4. Turn the dough out onto the bread board and knead it about 10 strokes; then return it to the oiled bowl and let it ferment for 30 minutes. This "punching down" of the dough is not required with the sponge method.

5. Follow steps 9 through 16 for Yeast Bread: Sponge Method.

YEAST BREAD VARIATIONS

Cornell Formula Bread

1 c hot tap water (105-115°F; 40.5-46.5°C)	2 c bread flour
1 Tbsp active dry yeast	1/3 c soy flour
1 Tbsp sugar	1/3 c toasted wheat germ
1 Tbsp table fat	1/3 c NFDM
1 tsp salt	

1. Measure the hot water into the mixing bowl and check the temperature.
2. Sprinkle the yeast into the water; mix.
3. Add the sugar, table fat, and salt; mix.
4. Add 1-1/3 cups bread flour and follow steps 3 and 4 for Yeast Bread: Sponge Method.
5. Stir the soy flour, toasted wheat germ, NFDM, and remaining bread flour into the sponge.
6. Follow steps 5 through 16 for Yeast Bread: Sponge Method.

Sour Dough French Bread
_____

Starter

1 c water	1/4 c NFDM
1 Tbsp oil	2 c bread flour
1 Tbsp sugar	1 Tbsp active dry yeast
1 tsp salt	

1. Combine the water and oil in a saucepan and bring to a boil; stir in the sugar and salt.
2. Cool the water mixture to 115^OF (46.5^OC) and stir in the yeast and then the NFDM and flour.
3. Place mixture in a clean, sterile jar or bowl. Cover and keep in a warm place ($85-95^O$F; $29.5-35^O$C) 12 to 18 hours.
4. Use in recipe. Remaining starter may be stored in the refrigerator for several days or in the freezer for several months. It should be thawed before using.

French Bread Dough
_____

1 c hot tap water ($105-115^O$F; $40.5-46.5^O$C)	1 tsp salt
	2 Tbsp NFDM
1 Tbsp active dry yeast	3 c bread flour
2 Tbsp starter	1 egg white
1 Tbsp table fat	1 Tbsp water
1 Tbsp sugar	

1. Measure the water into the mixing bowl and check the temperature.
2. Sprinkle the yeast into the water; mix.
3. Add starter, sugar, salt, and table fat.
4. Follow steps 3 through 12 for preparing Yeast Bread: Sponge Method but roll dough into a rectangle 10 x 15" in step 10.
5. Place the roll of dough, seam side down, on a baking sheet.
6. Using kitchen shears, cut diagonal slashes 1/8" deep and about 2" apart along the top of the loaf.
7. Proof for 40 minutes.
8. Bake in a preheated oven at 425^OF (218^OC) 15 minutes with a pan of hot water in the oven to supply steam. (Water should be boiling when the bread is placed in oven.)
9. Brush the top and sides of the loaf with a mixture of egg white and 1 Tbsp water.
10. Bake the bread 5 to 10 minutes longer at 350^OF (176.5^OC).
11. Cool the bread on a rack in a draft to make crust crisp.

Pizza

1 c hot tap water (105-115°F; 40.5-46.5°C)	2 Tbsp table fat
1 Tbsp active dry yeast	1 Tbsp sugar
1 tsp salt	3 c bread flour

1. Measure the hot water into the mixing bowl and check the temperature.
2. Sprinkle the yeast into the water and mix; stir in the salt, oil, and flour to make a stiff dough.
3. Turn onto bread board and knead 50 strokes; divide in half.
4. Grease two 12"-diameter pizza pans or two 10 x 15" baking sheets.
5. Press the dough into the pans with the palms of the hands, forming a rim of dough around the edges.
6. Bake in preheated oven at 400°F (204.5°C) about 8 minutes.
7. Pizza crusts may be cooled, packaged in freezer wrap or plastic bag, and frozen.

Sauce for Pizza

1 8-oz can tomato sauce	1/2 tsp salt
1 6-oz can tomato paste	1/4 tsp oregano, crushed
1/2 c minced onion	1/4 tsp basil, crushed
1 clove garlic, crushed	dash of pepper
1—2 tsp oil	

(1) Place oil in a 1-qt saucepan and add onions; sauté until translucent.
(2) Add remaining ingredients; mix.

   Yield: About 2 cups

Cheese for Pizza

Grate or thinly slice one or more of the following cheeses:

Mozzarella	Swiss
Cheddar	Monterey Jack

Or use grated Romano or Parmesan cheese in combination with any of the cheeses listed above.

Fillings

Many varieties are possible and offer great opportunity for creativity. One or more of the following can be used:

(1) Mushroom: Wash, trim, and slice fresh mushrooms, or drain canned mushrooms
(2) Anchovy: Use drained canned anchovies, whole or pieces
(3) Sausage: Thinly slice pepperoni, linguicia, Italian, or Polish sausage
(4) Pork sausage: Crumble and cook bulk pork sausage; drain and blot with a paper towel
(5) Ground beef: Crumble and cook ground beef until lightly browned; drain off fat and blot crumbles of meat with paper towels
(6) Salami: Slice salami thinly and cut into strips
(7) Shrimp: Drain small canned shrimp
(8) Ham or pastrami: Use thin slices or strips

Garnishes and Flavor Accents

(1) Fresh tomato, peeled and sliced thinly
(2) Thinly sliced rings of green pepper
(3) Sliced black olives or stuffed green olives
(4) Strips of canned pimento
(5) Slices of peeled avocado

Assembling the Pizza (See BF, 297, Fig. 16.18.)

(1) Sprinkle about 1/2 cup grated cheese on baked pizza dough.
(2) Evenly distribute from 3/4 to 1 cup pizza sauce over the cheese-covered dough.
(3) Arrange filling on the pizza.
(4) Add slices of vegetable or garnish.
(5) Top with thinly sliced or grated cheese.
(6) Bake on lowest rack of oven at 425°F (218°C) until cheese is bubbly and filling is heated, about 10 to 15 minutes.

C. Evaluation of Yeast Breads

Table 12-1 is a score sheet for yeast breads. It includes a description of their desirable characteristics. Listed below are some of the causes of poor quality in yeast breads. If breads have defects, try to identify the causes and enter the reasons in the Comments section of the score sheet. Recognition of the causes of poor quality helps in producing better quality the next time.

Causes of poor quality

1. Poor shape: dough not properly shaped, too much dough in the pan; proofed too long or not long enough; excessive amounts of dough-softening ingredients
2. Loaf small, compact, and heavy: too much salt; not enough yeast; fermentation and proofing temperatures too high; not fermented and proofed long enough; flour lacked adequate gluten potential
3. Color too pale: not enough sugar; dough fermented too long; fermentation and proofing temperatures too high; oven not hot enough
4. Color too dark: too much sugar, NFDM, egg, or a combination of these; oven temperature too high for the combination of ingredients
5. Coarse texture inside: dough too soft (not enough flour); fermentation temperature too high; fermentation and/or proofing too long
6. "Moth-eaten" appearance on sides and bottom of loaf: proofed too long
7. Poor flavor: too much yeast; excessive fermentation; rancid ingredients

YEAST ROLLS AND SWEET-DOUGH PRODUCTS

A. Dinner Rolls and Variations

Yeast dinner rolls can be prepared from any of the formulas used for bread, or from a formula with egg, additional sugar, and table fat. This dinner-roll formula can also be used for bread. Combinations of flours and grains can be used in the rolls as well as in the bread.

Table 12-1   Score Sheet for Yeast Breads

Desirable characteristics

- Shape: symmetrical, rounded top; well-proportioned
- Size: large but not airy; neither heavy nor excessively light in proportion to its weight
- Color: even, golden brown
- Texture: fine, thin-walled cells, evenly distributed
- Flavor: neither yeasty nor bitter

Score: Good — 3   Fair — 2   Poor — 1

Type of Bread	Shape	Size	Color	Texture	Flavor	Comments

Yeast Dinner Rolls

3/4 c hot tap water (105–115°F; 40.5–46.5°C)
1 Tbsp active dry yeast
1 large egg
2 Tbsp sugar
2 Tbsp table fat
1 tsp salt
2-2/3 c bread flour (refined or whole-wheat)
1/3 c NFDM

1. Measure hot tap water into mixing bowl, check the temperature, and add the yeast.
2. Stir in the sugar, salt, table fat, and egg.
3. Mix in half the flour and mix 200 strokes by hand or 2 minutes with a dough hook.
4. Let ferment for 30 minutes; then add the NFDM and the remaining flour, adding the last part of the flour gradually to obtain a dough of the correct consistency.
5. If a dough hook is used, mix the dough for 5 minutes. If mixing by hand, turn the dough out onto the bread board, knead 200 strokes, and round into a ball.

6. Dough mixed with the dough hook should be turned out onto the bread board, kneaded about 10 strokes, and rounded into a ball.
7. Place the ball of dough in an oiled bowl and turn it over to oil the top of the dough; let ferment 30 minutes.
8. Turn the dough out onto the bread board and knead about 10 strokes.
9. Let the dough rest for 5 minutes before shaping into rolls.

Shaping Dinner Rolls

(See also Basic Foods, 294-296, Figs. 16.12-17.)

Parkerhouse Rolls: Roll dough out with a
  rolling pin (as for biscuits) to a thickness
  of 1/4 to 1/3". Cut dough with a 3"-diam-
  eter biscuit cutter. Brush the center of
  the small circle of dough with melted table
  fat. Fold each in half and seal the edges.
  Place rolls 1" apart on a greased baking
  sheet (Fig. 12-1).

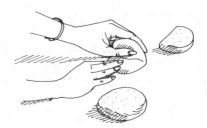

Fig. 12-1: Parkerhouse dinner roll

Bowknots: Cut dough into pieces about the
  size of large walnuts. Roll each piece
  into a strip about 5" long; tie it in a loose
  knot (Fig. 12-2). Place 1" apart on
  greased baking sheet.

Fig. 12-2: Bowknot dinner roll

Crescent Rolls: Roll dough into a circle
  about 1/4 to 1/3" thick. Cut the circle
  of dough into pie-shaped pieces. Starting at the wide end of the pie-shaped
  piece, roll into a strip with the pointed
  end on top (Fig. 12-3). Place strips of
  rolled dough onto a lightly greased baking
  sheet about 2" apart and curve into a
  crescent shape.

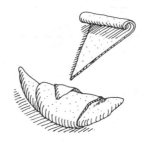

Cloverleaf Rolls: Shape small pieces of
  dough into small balls. Place 3 small
  balls in each cup of greased muffin
  tins (Fig. 12-4).

Fig. 12-4: Cloverleaf roll

<u>Fantans</u>: Roll dough into a sheet about 1/4" thick and cut into strips about 1-1/2" wide. Place 6 strips on top of each other in a stack and cut the stack into 1" pieces. Place on end in greased muffin cups (Fig. 12-5).

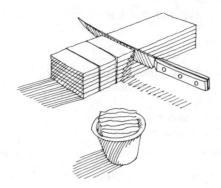

<u>Butterfly Rolls</u>: Prepare crescent rolls; after placing the roll on the baking sheet, press the center of the roll with the handle of a table knife to make an indentation. Or roll the dough into a sheet about 1/4" thick, brush it with melted table fat, and roll it up like a jelly roll. Cut the

Fig. 12-5: Fantan roll

roll into pieces about 2" long and place them on a greased baking sheet about 2" apart. Press the center of the short length with the handle of a table knife to make an indentation.

10. Brush the tops of dinner rolls with melted table fat.
11. Proof the rolls for about 40 minutes at 85-95°F (29.5-35°C).
12. Bake in preheated oven at 425°F (218°C) 10 to 15 minutes.

English Muffins

1 c hot water (105-115°F; 40.5-46.5°C)	2 Tbsp NFDM
	1 tsp salt
1 Tbsp active dry yeast	2 Tbsp table fat
2 tsp sugar	2-2/3 c bread flour

1. Follow steps 1 through 9 for Yeast Dinner Rolls.
2. Roll the dough until about 3/4" thick and cut into 3"-diameter rounds; allow to rise on bread board for 40 minutes.
3. Set the thermostat of electric frying pan or griddle at 275°F (135°C) and grease pan lightly.
4. Place raised muffins on hot griddle with a pancake turner; cook 8 to 10 minutes on each side.
5. Split leftover muffins horizontally and toast before serving.

<u>Yield</u>: About 12 3"-muffins

B. Sweet-Dough Products

Basic Sweet Dough

3/4 c hot tap water (105–115°F;   1 tsp salt
          40.5–46.5°C)   1 egg
1 Tbsp yeast   1/3 c NFDM
1/4 c sugar   2-2/3 c bread flour, white or
1/4 c table fat   whole-wheat

Follow the steps for mixing Yeast Dinner Rolls.

Basic Sweet Dough is used for the following recipes:

Cinnamon Rolls

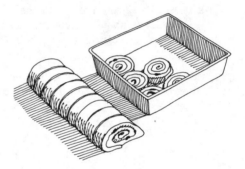

1 c raisins
1/2 c chopped walnuts
1/2 c sugar
1 tsp cinnamon

1. Prepare the Sweet Dough, letting it fer-
    ment as specified.
2. Roll the dough into a rectangle about 1/4"
    thick.
3. Brush the surface of the dough with melted
    table fat.
4. Combine the cinnamon and sugar and
    sprinkle over the surface of the dough.   Fig. 12-6: Cinnamon roll
5. Distribute the raisins and nuts evenly
    over the dough.
5. Roll the dough up like a jelly roll and seal the edge.
7. Cut the roll into 1"-thick slices; place each slice in the greased cup of a muffin tin or
    lay slices side by side in greased baking pan with 1 to 2" sides (Fig. 12-6).
8. Brush tops of rolls with melted table fat and proof for 45 minutes.
9. Bake in preheated oven at 350°F (176.5°C) 20 to 30 minutes.

Raisin Bread

1. Use the same ingredients specified for Cinnamon Rolls.
2. Prepare the Sweet Dough, letting it ferment as specified.
3. Roll the dough into a rectangle no wider than the bread pan is long (8-1/2") and about
    1/3" thick.
4. Brush the surface of the dough lightly with water so that it will stick together when
    rolled up.
5. Combine the sugar and cinnamon and sprinkle it over the dough.
6. Distribute the raisins and chopped nuts over the dough.
7. Follow steps 12 through 14 for Yeast Bread: Sponge Method.
8. Bake in a preheated oven at 375°F (190.5°C) 35 to 40 minutes.
9. Follow step 16 for Yeast Bread: Sponge Method.

Hot Cross Buns

1. Prepare the the Sweet Dough, using the instructions for mixing and fermenting given under Yeast Dinner Rolls.
2. Using kitchen shears, cut the dough into pieces the size of large walnuts.
3. Roll each piece of dough between the palms of the hands to form a ball 1 to 1-1/2" in diameter.
4. Place the balls about 2" apart in a greased 9 x 13" baking dish.
5. Use the kitchen shears to cut a (+) in the top of each roll, making the cut about 1/4" deep (Fig. 12-7).

Fig. 12-7: Cutting the tops of hot cross buns with kitchen shears

6. Brush the rolls with egg wash (1 egg beaten with 1 Tbsp water) and proof for 40 minutes.
7. Bake in a preheated oven at 375°F (190.5°C) 20 to 30 minutes.
8. Cool rolls 5 to 10 minutes; then dribble lemon-flavored Flat Icing (Unit 19) into the gashes in the top of the rolls to form a cross.

Peasant Ring

Date Filling

1 c pitted chopped dates
1/2 c water
1/2 c chopped walnuts

1/4 c sugar
1/2 tsp cinnamon

1. Prepare the Sweet Dough and let it ferment.
2. Combine the dates and water in a saucepan and bring to a boil; simmer 2 to 3 minutes until mixture thickens; cool.
3. Roll the dough into a rectangle about 1/4" thick; brush with melted table fat.
4. Combine the sugar and cinnamon and sprinkle evenly over the surface of the dough.
5. Spread the cooled date mixture evenly over the dough; then distribute the chopped nuts over the dates.
6. Roll up the dough like a jelly roll and seal the edge.
7. Place the roll of dough on a greased baking sheet, seam side down and form a circle, sealing the two ends together (Fig. 12-8a).

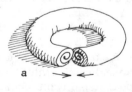

8. Clip the dough with the kitchen shears, cutting from the outside almost to the center into slices about 1" thick and spread slices apart (Fig. 12-8b).
9. Instead of forming a circle with the roll of dough, it can be laid in a straight line on the baking sheet; then cut the slices almost all the way through, alternating the slices on either side (BF, 297, Fig. 16.19).

10. Brush the dough with melted table fat before proofing for 40 minutes.
11. Bake at 350°F (176.5°C) 35 to 40 minutes.

Fig. 12-8: Peasant ring preparation: seal two ends of the ring together (a); clip the dough into slices 1" thick (b)

Stollen

1/2 c chopped blanched almonds	1 c mixed chopped candied citrus peel
1/4 c sliced candied cherries	1 Tbsp grated lemon rind
1/4 c chopped candied citron	melted table fat

1. Prepare the sweet dough, following steps 1 through 3 for Yeast Dinner Rolls.
2. Ferment the sponge for 30 minutes; then stir in the NFDM.
3. Add the chopped fruit and nuts to the flour and mix to coat; then stir the fruit and flour into the sponge and mix well.
4. Follow steps 5 through 9 for Yeast Dinner Rolls.
5. Roll the fermented dough into an oval shape, about 12 x 8", with a rolling pin.
6. Brush the dough with melted table fat and fold in half.
7. Press the folded side of the dough very firmly with the heel of the hand; then place on a greased baking sheet.
8. Brush the top and sides of the stollen with melted table fat and proof for 45 minutes.
9. Bake in a preheated oven at 375°F (190.5°C) 25 to 30 minutes.

Icing or Glaze for Sweet-Dough Baked Products

Use one of the Flat Icings given in Unit 19. Apply the flat icing to the warm, not hot, baked bread. Dribble the icing with a spoon or pour from a small pitcher or liquid measuring cup. If sliced nuts are to be used for garnish, they must be applied to the warm icing immediately so that they will adhere.

Danish Pastry

2/3 c hot tap water (105–115°F; 40.5–46.5°C)	2 eggs
	1/3 c NFDM
1 Tbsp active dry yeast	1/2 tsp vanilla extract
1 tsp salt	1/2 tsp lemon extract
1/4 c sugar	1/2 tsp mace
2 Tbsp + 1/2 c table fat	3 c bread flour

1. Measure the hot water into the mixing bowl and check the temperature.
2. Sprinkle the yeast into the water and mix.
3. Add the sugar, salt, 2 Tbsp table fat, eggs, and flavoring; then follow steps 3 through 6 for Yeast Dinner Rolls.
4. Roll the dough into a rectangle about 8 x 12" with a rolling pin.
5. Slice the 1/2 c table fat over half the dough and fold the dough in half; seal the edges.
6. Roll the dough again to a rectangle 8 x 12"; fold it into thirds; wrap it in foil or plastic wrap and refrigerate for 30 minutes (see BF, 261-263, Fig. 14.10-15).
7. Repeat step 6 two to four more times; after the final rolling, refrigerate dough for at least 1 hour, preferably overnight; it may be refrigerated up to 2 days before shaping for baking.
8. Roll the pastry into a rectangle about 1/4" thick and cut it into 4" squares. Place a tablespoon of filling in the center of each square; moisten the edges with egg wash (1 egg + 1 Tbsp water) and fold in half diagonally; seal the edges.
9. Place tarts on a greased baking sheet, brush with egg wash, proof for 40 minutes.
10. Bake in preheated oven at 400°F (204.5°C) 20 to 25 minutes.

Note: Any of the fillings suggested for Puff Pastry (Unit 11) are suitable for Danish Pastry. Marmalade and fruit preserves can also be used, or the custard-type filling given in Unit 19.

Yeast-Raised Doughnuts

3/4 c hot tap water (105-115° F; 40.5-46.5°C)	1/4 c sugar
1 Tbsp active dry yeast	1 tsp salt
1/4 c table fat	1/4 c NFDM
1 egg	2-3/4 c bread flour

1. Follow the steps for mixing and fermenting Yeast Dinner Rolls.
2. Roll the dough out to a thickness of 1/3".
3. Cut with a floured 3" doughnut cutter.
4. Allow doughnuts to rise (proof) on the pastry cloth-covered bread board for 40 minutes, uncovered so that surface dries out.
5. Lift raised doughnuts with a turner or wide spatula and ease into fat preheated to 375°F (190.5°C). Fry for 1 to 1-1/2 minutes on each side or until lightly browned; turn doughnuts as they rise to the top of the fat. (See Unit 2 for detailed instructions for deep-fat frying.) (See BF, 298, Fig. 16.20.)
6. Lift the doughnuts from the fat with a long-handled cooking fork, being careful not to prick them; drain on absorbent paper.
7. Slightly cooled doughnuts may be sugared by shaking them in a paper bag with granulated sugar, cinnamon sugar, or confectioners' sugar.

UNIT 13   GELATIN COOKERY

Suggested reading: <u>Basic Foods</u>, Chapter 17

Objectives

- To learn techniques for preparing a variety of gelatin mixtures
- To evaluate gelatin mixtures and to compare flavored and unflavored gelatins

PREPARATION OF GELATIN MIXTURES

A. General Instructions

1. Market forms of gelatin vary in quality, that is, in the strength and tenderness of gel they produce. Flavored gelatin mixes also vary in flavor quality. It is often beneficial to compare available brands for these qualities as well as for cost.
2. To obtain maximum gelling strength, the gelatin should be completely dissolved; no grains of undissolved gelatin should adhere to the side of the container.
3. Unflavored gelatin must be softened in cool or warm liquid. The gelatin may be heated over direct heat, in the microwave oven, or boiling liquid may be added to it; it does not have to be boiled to dissolve, although it can withstand a short period of boiling.
4. In flavored gelatin mixtures the gelatin is dispersed in sugar and can therefore be dissolved by direct addition of boiling water.
5. The strength of the gel depends upon one or more of the following factors:
    - The quality of gelatin used
    - The proportion of gelatin and liquid
    - The speed of gelation
    - The addition of solid ingredients

    The amount of liquid used in gelatin mixtures must be adjusted to accommodate these factors. Recipes specifying that fruit or other ingredients be drained prevent excessive ratios of liquid.
6. If a gelatin mixture fails to gel because of excessive proportions of liquid, more gelatin can be added. Soften 1 to 2 tsp unflavored gelatin in 2 to 3 Tbsp water, heat to dissolve the gelatin, and stir the dissolved gelatin into the mixture.
7. Gelatin gels are reversible. If a gelatin inadvertently gels completely before the solid ingredients are added, it may be heated slightly, with stirring, until the proper consistency is obtained.
8. Raw (either fresh or frozen) pineapple, papaya, kiwi, or figs should not be used in gelatin mixtures. These fruits contain enzymes that hydrolyze the gelatin protein and prevent gel formation. These raw fruits should be simmered for 2 minutes before adding to gelatin mixtures; canned fruits do not require heating as they are heated during processing.
9. Techniques for speeding formation of gelatin mixtures include:
    - Placement of the container of gelatin in the coldest part of the food-storage freezer
    - Placement of the container of gelatin in a larger container of ice water
    - Placement of the container of gelatin in a larger container of crushed ice and rock salt.

- Use of a small portion of the liquid to dissolve the gelatin, the remaining liquid to be added to the gelatin after the liquid has been well chilled or partially frozen.
- If a flavored gelatin is being used with water as the liquid, use about 1/4 to 1/3 of liquid for dissolving the gelatin; then crushed ice is put into the measuring cup and the cup filled with water to the desired level to supply the rest of the liquid in the recipe.

10. For ease in unmolding gelatin mixtures, the mold should be lightly oiled before being filled with the partially thickened mixture. For unmolding, container should be dipped in warm water for 5 seconds and the gelatin loosened by running the tip of a sharp knife around the upper edge. The serving dish should be inverted on top of the mold and dish and mold inverted together. If necessary, one side of the mold may be lifted slightly and the tip of a knife inserted to let air into the mold and break the vacuum that forms between the gelled mixture and the mold. To prevent collapse, gelatin should be chilled after unmolding until ready to serve (BF, 308, Fig. 17.5).
11. Gelatin mixtures are at their best if allowed to gel for 4 hours and if used within 24 hours after preparing. Holding for longer periods results in the separation of the liquid from the gel.
12. To dissolve the gelatin in the microwave oven, stir 1 Tbsp unflavored gelatin into 1/4 c water in a glass measure. Cook 1 minute. Flavored gelatin can be heated in 1/2 c water 2-3 minutes.
13. One envelope of unflavored gelatin contains 1 Tbsp of gelatin.

B. Simple Gelatin Mixtures

Cranberry Aspic
_____

1 Tbsp unflavored gelatin	2 Tbsp lemon juice
1-1/2 c cranberry juice cocktail	1/4 c sugar

1. Combine 1/2 c cranberry juice and the gelatin in a saucepan and cook, stirring, until steaming hot; be sure that all granules of gelatin are dissolved.
2. Stir in sugar, lemon juice, and remaining cranberry juice.
3. Chill until the mixture is partially thickened; then pour into a lightly oiled 1-qt mold; chill until set.

Yield: Three 1/2-cup servings

Jellied Cinnamon Applesauce ? p. 22
_____

1 Tbsp unflavored gelatin	1 16-oz can applesauce
1/3 c water	1/4 c cinnamon candies (red hots)

1. Combine the water and gelatin in a saucepan; add the candy.
2. Cook, stirring, until steaming hot and candies and gelatin are dissolved; stir in the applesauce.
3. Chill until the mixture is partially thickened; then pour it into a lightly oiled 1-qt mold; chill until set.

Yield: Four 1/2-cup servings

ɣ Strawberry Whirl

---

1 Tbsp unflavored gelatin	1/4 c sugar
1/2 c water	1 tsp grated lemon rind
1 pt fresh or frozen strawberries	

1. Place about 1/4 of the berries in a blender and liquefy.
2. Add the gelatin to the blender and allow to stand until gelatin granules are moistened.
3. Heat the water to boiling; add to contents of blender, cover, and process at low speed until gelatin dissolves, about 2 minutes. Use a rubber scraper to push granules of gelatin on the sides of the container into the mixture.
4. Add the sugar, lemon rind, and remaining strawberries, and process until smooth. Sweeten to taste.
5. Pour the mixture into a lightly oiled 1-qt mold and chill until set.

Yield: Four 1/2-cup servings

Lemon Whey Jelly

---

1 Tbsp unflavored gelatin	1/4 c lemon juice
1-1/4 c whey	1/3 c sugar

1. To obtain whey, precipitate the casein protein from milk with rennin as described in Unit 14, or use 3 Tbsp powdered whey and 1-1/4 c water.
2. Combine 1/2 c liquid whey and gelatin in a saucepan, and cook, sitrring, until steaming hot and the gelatin is dissolved.
3. Stir in the sugar, lemon juice, and remaining whey.
4. Chill the mixture until partially thickened; then pour it into a lightly oiled 1-qt mold and chill until set.

Yield: Three 1/2-cup servings

C. Gelatin Mixtures with Solid Ingredients

ɣ Ambrosia Gel

---

1 3-oz pkg orange-flavored gelatin	mandarin orange slices, drained
1 c water	banana, sliced
1/2 c low-fat yogurt	1/4 c grated coconut

1. Lightly oil a 1-qt mold and place in the freezer to chill.
2. Bring the water to a boil and stir in the gelatin, mixing until dissolved; stir in the yogurt.
3. Chill the gelatin mixture until partially thickened and stir in the grated coconut. (If desired, stir in mandarin slices and banana. Chill until set.)
4. Working quickly, put a few tablespoons of the thickened gelatin mixture into the chilled mold and tilt the mold to spread the gelatin over the bottom and lower part of the sides. Arrange the mandarin orange slices and bananas in a decorative design and return the mold to the freezer to set the fruit in the gelatin.
5. As soon as the gelatin around the fruit is set, place a few more tablespoons of the partially thickened gelatin mixture in the mold over the fruit and extending part way up the sides; arrange more of the fruit around the sides of the mold; chill until set.
6. Repeat step 5 until the desired design has been obtained and all of the gelatin mixture has been added to the mold; chill until set.

Yield: Four 1/2-cup servings

Spinach Salad Mold
_____

1 Tbsp unflavored gelatin	1/4 c thinly sliced green onions
1-1/4 c water	1 c chopped raw spinach, fresh
1/4 c lemon juice	1/2 c chopped celery
1 Tbsp sugar	1/4 c grated carrots
1/4 tsp salt	

1. Combine 1/2 c water and gelatin in a saucepan and heat, stirring, until mixture is steaming hot and gelatin is dissolved.
2. Add the sugar, salt, lemon juice, and 3/4 c water; mix until dissolved.
3. Chill until the mixture is partially thickened; then stir in the chopped vegetables.
4. Pour into a lightly oiled 1-qt mold and chill until set.

Yield: Four 1/2-cup servings

Orange-Pineapple Whirl
_____

1 Tbsp unflavored gelatin	2 Tbsp sugar
1/4 c undiluted frozen orange juice	1/8 tsp salt
1/2 c boiling water	1/2 c peeled carrot chunks
1/2 c syrup from canned pineapple	1/2 c well-drained pineapple

1. Place 1/2 c pineapple syrup in blender and sprinkle gelatin into it; allow to soften.
2. Add the boiling water to the blender; cover, and process about 1 minute. Scrape down the sides with a rubber scraper and process 1 minute more.
3. Add sugar, salt, and carrot pieces. Process at high speed, turning blender off and on several times to chop the carrots; add the frozen juice and process until blended.
4. Stir in the well-drained crushed pineapple and pour into a lightly oiled 1-qt mold. Chill until set, stirring occasionally to distribute the solid ingredients.

Yield: Four 1/2-cup servings

D. Layered Gelatin Mixtures

Beef Aspic and Tomato Relish
_____

Beef Aspic

1 Tbsp unflavored gelatin	1/2 tsp onion powder
1-1/2 c beef stock	

Tomato Relish

1 Tbsp unflavored gelatin	1 c peeled chopped fresh tomato
1-1/2 c tomato juice	1/4 c chopped green pepper
1/4 tsp salt	1/2 c chopped celery

1. Combine 1/2 c tomato juice, salt, and gelatin in a saucepan and heat, stirring, until mixture is steaming hot and gelatin is dissolved.
2. Stir in 1 c tomato juice and chill until partially thickened; then stir in the tomato, pepper, and celery. Pour into a lightly-oiled 2-qt mold and chill until set.
3. Combine 1/2 c beef stock, onion powder, and gelatin in a saucepan and heat, stirring, until steaming hot and gelatin is dissolved.

4. Add 1 c stock and chill until partially set; then pour into the mold on top of the gelled tomato relish mixture; chill until set.

    Yield: Six servings

Apricot Cheese Mold   ⌐. p. 55

1 Tbsp unflavored gelatin   3 oz Neufchatel cheese
1 16-oz can apricot halves   1/4 c sliced almonds
1/2 tsp almond flavoring

1. Drain syrup from apricots, place in a saucepan, and bring to a boil.
2. Place the apricots and gelatin in the blender and process until smooth; add the boiling syrup and blend 1 minute.
3. Stir in the almond flavoring and pour half the mixture into a lightly oiled 1-qt mold. Chill until set.
4. Add the Neufchatel cheese, crumbled, to the blender and process until smooth; transfer to a bowl and fold in the sliced almonds; chill until partially thickened.
5. Pour the partially thickened cheese-almond mixture on top of the gelled apricot mixture in the mold. Chill until set.

    Yield: Four 1/2-cup servings

Avocado Shrimp Mold

Avocado Mixture

1 Tbsp unflavored gelatin   1/4 c lemon juice
3/4 c water   1/2 c sour half-and-half
1 c mashed avocado   1/8 tsp salt

Shrimp Mixture

1 Tbsp unflavored gelatin   1/2 c chopped celery
1-1/2 c tomato juice   1/4 c chopped pimiento
1 4-1/2-oz can small shrimp   1/8 tsp hot-pepper sauce
1/4 tsp salt

1. Place a small, peeled, ripe avocado in the blender with the lemon juice and blend until smooth.
2. Combine 1/4 c water and the gelatin in a saucepan and heat, stirring, until steaming hot and gelatin is dissolved.
3. Stir 1/2 c water, mashed avocado and lemon, sour half-and-half, and salt into the gelatin mixture, and pour into a lightly oiled 2-qt mold; chill until set.
4. Combine 1/2 c tomato juice and gelatin in a saucepan and heat, stirring, until mixture is steaming hot and gelatin is dissolved.
5. Stir in 1 c tomato juice, hot-pepper sauce, and salt; chill until partially thickened.
6. Stir the drained shrimp, chopped celery, and chopped pimiento into the tomato-gelatin mixture.
7. Pour the shrimp mixture into the mold on top of the completely gelled avocado mixture; chill until set.

    Yield: Eight 1/2-cup servings

↳ Double Chocolate Custard ౸. /౸. 155

---

1 Tbsp unflavored gelatin	1/2 c sugar
1-3/4 c milk	1/3 c cocoa
1 egg	1/8 tsp salt
1 tsp vanilla	

1. Combine sugar, cocoa, and salt; mix until smooth and free of lumps.
2. Combine 1 c milk, 1 egg, and gelatin in a saucepan and mix until blended; stir in the sugar-cocoa mixture.
3. Cook over moderate heat, stirring constantly with a spring stirrer, until mixture is steaming hot and the gelatin and sugar dissolved; do not allow to boil.
4. Place 3/4 c cold milk in the blender and add the hot chocolate mixture; cover, and process at high speed until foamy and light.
5. Pour the mixture into a lightly oiled 1-qt mold; chill until set.

Yield: Four 1/2-cup servings

EVALUATION AND COMPARISON OF GELATIN MIXTURES

A. Evaluations

Desirable characteristics of gelatin mixtures include:

- Appearance: pleasing color combinations; solid ingredients evenly distributed (unless arranged otherwise); no syneresis
- Texture: firm, but tender gel; no leathery layers of gelatin
- Flavor: pleasing blend of flavors; characteristic of ingredients used

Enter evaluations in Table 13-1.

B. Comparison of Flavored and Unflavored Gelatin

Whether one uses the flavored gelatin mixture or unflavored gelatin with appropriate seasoned liquids will depend on several factors.

- The cost can be compared as follows:

1/2 c frozen orange-juice concentrate (2/3 of 6-oz can)	$ .35
1/4 c sugar (varies depending upon acidity of juice)	.06
1 Tbsp unflavored gelatin	.13
Total	$ .54
1 3-oz pkg orange-flavored gelatin	$ .36

- The two products can be prepared and compared for flavor.
- They can also be compared for nutrient contributions. Use the USDA Home and Garden Bulletin No. 72, Nutritive Value of Foods, to fill in the nutrients for the above items in Table 13-2.
- Finally, they can be compared on the basis of the time involved in preparation.

Table 13-1   Score Sheet for Gelatin Mixtures

Score: Good — 3   Fair — 2   Poor — 1

Gelatin Mixtures	Appearance	Texture	Flavor	Comments

Table 13-2   Nutrient Comparison of Gelatin Mixtures

Item No.[1]	Food	Measure	Calories	Protein (g)	Calcium (mg)	Iron (mg)	Vitamin A (IU)	Ascorbic Acid (mg)
297	Frozen orange juice, undiluted	4 oz						
549	Sugar, granulated	1/4 c						
569	Gelatin, unflavored	1 Tbsp						
	Totals							
570	Gelatin dessert powder	3 oz						

[1]Item No. is the number listed beside the item indicated in the Home and Garden Bulletin No. 72

UNIT 14   MILK AND MILK PRODUCTS

Suggested reading: <u>Basic Foods</u>, Chapter 18

Objectives

- To compare various market forms of milk
- To compare a variety of cheeses
- To prepare the milk products cottage cheese and yogurt
- To use milk and cheese in preparing a variety of dishes

MARKET FORMS OF MILK

A. Evaluation of Milk Forms

Compare fluid whole, low-fat, and nonfat milks, buttermilk, and yogurt to the following milks after they have been reconstituted or diluted. Also include imitation and filled milks, if available. Observe flavor and appearance. Chill milks before tasting.

1. Concentrated milk (fresh or frozen): Combine 1-1/3 c concentrated milk with 2-2/3 c water.
2. Canned evaporated whole milk: Combine 1-1/2 c evaporated milk with 1-1/2 c water.
3. Canned evaporated skim milk: Combine 1-1/2 c evaporated milk with 1-1/2 c water.
4. NFDM: Combine 1-1/3 c NFDM with water to make 1 qt.
5. Low-fat dried milk: Combine 1 envelope powdered milk with enough water to make 1 qt.
6. "Mixed" low-fat milk: Combine 2/3 c concentrated milk, 1-1/3 c water, 2/3 c NFDM, 2 c water to obtain 1 qt low-fat milk.

B. Cost Comparison of Milk Forms

Calculate the cost per quart of the milks and enter data in Table 14-1. Compute the cost of milks after reconstitution. Also note which milks are enriched with Vitamins A and D.

VARIETIES OF CHEESE

A. Evaluation of Cheeses

Compare a variety of cheeses for flavor, texture, consistency, and color. Enter observations in Table 14-2. Include such cheeses as:

1. Soft, unripened cheeses: Cottage, Ricotta, Cream, Neufchatel
2. Soft, ripened with molds: Brie, Camembert
3. Hard or Semihard:
    a. Unripened: Mozzarella

Table 14-1 Comparison of Market Forms of Milk

Market Form of Milk	Market Unit		Cost per qt[1] ($)	Vitamins A and D[2]	Observations
	Size	Cost ($)			
Whole fluid milk					
Low-fat fluid milk					
Nonfat fluid milk					
Buttermilk					
Concentrated milk					
Canned evaporated whole milk					
Canned evaporated skim milk					
Low-fat dried milk					
Nonfat dry milk (NFDM)					
"Mixed" low-fat milk[3]					
Yogurt					

[1]Cost per qt of diluted or reconstituted milk.

[2]Write "A" if milk is enriched with Vitamin A, "D" if Vitamin D has been added.

[3]Use the cost of 1/2 qt of concentrated milk after dilution plus the cost of 1/2 qt of NFDM after reconstitution.

Table 14-2   Comparison of Cheese Varieties

Cheese	(1) Protein per 100 g	(2) Market Unit Weight (oz)	(g)	(3) Cost ($)	(4) Protein (g)	(5) Cost per 10 g Protein ($)	Observations
Example: Blue cheese	21.5	4	113.4	1.15	24.4	.471	

b. Ripened with mold: Blue, Roquefort, Gorgonzola
c. Ripened with bacteria: Brick, Edam, Gouda, Gruyère, Liederkranz, Limburger, Muenster, Mysost (Primost), Parmesan, Romano, Cheddar, Port du Salut, Swiss

B. Cost Comparison of Cheeses

Because cheese varies considerably in water content, price comparisons per pound can be misleading. A more equitable method is to compare the cost of that amount of cheese which supplies 10 g of protein (an amount chosen to simplify calculations). Using Table 14-2 calculate the cost of cheese supplying 10 g of protein as follows:

1. Look up the protein content of the cheese for 100-g amounts of cheese. See Basic Foods, Table 18.4, 325, or USDA, Agricultural Handbook No. 8, Composition of Foods, Table 1, and enter amount in Column 1 of Table 14-2.
2. In Column 2 multiply ounces on the purchased package by 28.35 (g per oz) or pounds by 454 (g per lb) to convert to the metric measurement for ease of calculation. Enter

both the English and metric equivalent weight in Column 2.

3. For Column 4: Column 1 ÷ 100 x Column 2 (in grams). For example: 21.5 g of protein ÷ 100 g cheese = 0.215 g of protein per gram of cheese; 0.215 x 113.4 g per pkg = 24.4 g protein per package.

4. For Column 5: Column 3 ÷ Column 4 x 10. For example: $.65 per 4-oz pkg ÷ 24.4 g protein per pkg x 10 = $.266, the cost of the Blue cheese supplying 10 g of protein.

PREPARATION OF COTTAGE CHEESE AND YOGURT

Milks listed in Section 1 for tasting and comparison may be used to make cheese or yogurt, but canned evaporated milk cannot be precipitated with rennin.

Cottage Cheese

1 rennin tablet (Junket)	1 Tbsp buttermilk
1 Tbsp water	2 Tbsp cream
2 c fluid milk	1/8 tsp salt

1. Crush the tablet and mix with water to dissolve.
2. Heat the milk to 95°F (35°C) and stir in the rennin solution and buttermilk.
3. Allow the solution to stand at room temperature, undisturbed, for 20 minutes for clot to form.
4. Cut the clot into 1/2" cubes with a table knife.
5. Heat the curd slowly to 104°F (40°C) and hold at this temperature for 15 minutes; stir at 5-minute intervals to equalize temperature.
6. Line a 1-qt colander or strainer with several thicknesses of cheesecloth; pour the curds and whey into the colander and allow the whey to drain off.
7. When the whey has drained off, mix the curd with salt and cream.
8. The whey may be used to make Whey Jelly (Unit 13) or it may be used in soups, sauces or for cooking cereal grains. It is a good source of nutrients. (It can be frozen for future use.)

   Microwave Oven: In step 2 cook milk in a glass measure 2 minutes.

Yogurt

1-1/2 c NFDM	1/2 c commercial yogurt
3 c warm water	

1. Combine ingredients and pour into small jars or glasses; cover the individual containers.
2. Incubate the milk mixture at 100-115°F (37.5-46°C) 3 to 4 hours. Containers can be placed on a tray in a closed oven with a pilot light (check temperature first), submerged in warm water (to 1" below top of containers), changing the water to maintain desired temperature, or placed over pilot light.

Note: Any kind of milk may be used, but the addition of extra NFDM increases the thickness of the yogurt. Regular-strength milk results in a fluid cultured milk, like buttermilk.

The longer the milk is incubated after it has clotted, the more acidic it becomes. The length of time required for clotting depends upon the concentration of bacteria in the starter (commercial yogurt), the temperature of incubation, and the amount of milk being cultured. Commercial yogurt more than 10 days old may not be a satisfactory starter because of the bacteria's loss of viability. Homemade yogurt can be used as the starter for future batches, if less than 10 days old and if it has been refrigerated. Yogurt, like other milk products, should be refrigerated. For flavored yogurts, use fruit juices or nectars in place of part or all of the water, and sweeten to taste.

COOKING WITH MILK AND CHEESE

A. Milk Dishes

Any kind of milk may be used where just "milk" is specified in a recipe—whole fluid, low-fat fluid, nonfat fluid, concentrated or evaporated (diluted), nonfat or low-fat dry milks (reconstituted). The kind of milk will affect caloric content and cost as well as provide slight differences in flavor and richness.

Condensed Milk Custard

1 can (1-1/3 c) condensed milk, undiluted	1/2 c lemon juice
2 eggs, separated	1 tsp grated lemon rind

1. Stir the egg yolks, juice, and rind into the condensed milk.
2. Beat the egg whites to soft peaks and fold into the milk mixture.
3. Chill before serving. (The mixture thickens when chilled.)

Caramelized Condensed Milk Pudding

1 can condensed milk, unopened

1. Remove the paper wrapper from an unopened can of condensed milk.
2. Place the can of milk in a large pot (at least 3-qt size) and cover with water; bring the water to a boil.
3. Simmer for 3 hours. Do not allow the pot to boil dry or the can will explode.
4. Chill before opening.
5. The contents of the can will have solidified and caramelized; it may be sliced and eaten as pudding.

B. Cheese Dishes

Welsh Rarebit

2/3 c milk	1/8 tsp dry mustard
1 egg	few drops of hot-pepper sauce
1/8 tsp salt	1 c shredded sharp Cheddar cheese

1. Combine milk, egg, and seasonings in a saucepan and mix until blended.
2. Cook over moderate heat, stirring constantly with a spring stirrer, until the mixture is steaming hot and coats the spoon.
3. Remove from heat and stir in the shredded cheese. Do not reheat; prepare just before serving.
4. Serve hot on toast or use as a fondue dip.

   Yield: About 1 cup

Swiss Fondue
———————

2/3 c white stock   1/16 tsp salt
1 Tbsp flour   dash of nutmeg
2 c shredded Swiss cheese

1. Combine the white stock, flour, and seasonings in a saucepan and mix until smooth and free of lumps.
2. Cook over moderately high heat, stirring constantly with a spring stirrer, until the mixture starts to boil.
3. Turn off heat and stir in shredded cheese; do not reheat after adding cheese; wait to add cheese until ready to serve.
4. Transfer fondue to fondue pot to keep warm during service.
5. Serve with cubes of French bread for dips, if desired.

Yield: About 1-1/2 cups

Tomato Rarebit
———————

1 10-3/4-oz can condensed tomato soup, undiluted
2 c shredded Cheddar cheese

1. Heat undiluted condensed tomato soup in a saucepan, stirring constantly, until it starts to boil.
2. Turn off heat and stir in the shredded cheese; do not reheat after adding cheese.
3. Serve over toast or use as a fondue dip.

Yield: About 2 cups

Baked Cheese Fondue
———————

1 c milk   1-1/2 c shredded sharp Cheddar cheese
3 eggs   1/2 tsp salt
1 c soft bread crumbs   dash of pepper

1. Two slices of fresh bread can be processed in a blender for the bread crumbs.
2. Separate the eggs, placing the yolks in one bowl and the whites in another.
3. Add the milk to the yolks and mix until blended; stir in the bread crumbs, cheese, salt, and pepper.
4. Whip the egg whites until soft peaks form; fold the egg-white foam into the yolk-cheese mixture.
5. Pour the mixture into 1-qt casserole; set the casserole into a larger pan and surround the casserole with boiling water.
6. Bake at 350°F (176.5°C) 45 to 50 minutes or until the blade of a table knife inserted in the center comes out clean.
7. Serve hot as soon as baked.

Yield: Four servings

Quiche Lorraine
———————

1 unbaked pastry shell, 9"   1-1/2 c milk
6 slices bacon   4 eggs
1/4 c chopped onion   1/2 tsp salt
1-1/2 c shredded Swiss cheese   dash of pepper and nutmeg

1. Cut the strips of bacon into pieces and sauté until crisp and brown; drain off fat and discard; drain bacon on absorbent paper.
2. Place chopped onion in pan used for cooking bacon and sauté until translucent.
3. Distribute the cooked bacon, shredded cheese, and onion over the bottom of the unbaked pastry shell.
4. Combine the eggs, milk, and seasonings, mixing until smooth.
5. Pour the egg-milk mixture into the pie and bake at 375°F (190.5°C) about 45 minutes or until a knife blade inserted into the center comes out clean.
6. Serve hot.

Yield: Six servings

Carrot Quiche (Crustless)

1 c finely shredded raw carrots	1/2 tsp crushed garlic
4 eggs	1/4 tsp ground ginger
1-1/2 c milk	1/8 tsp white pepper
1/4 c minced onion	1 c grated cheddar cheese
1/2 tsp salt	

1. Steam carrots in 2 Tbsp water on a surface unit until tender, or cooked covered in a glass bowl in the microwave oven 4 minutes without water.
2. Beat eggs until homogenous, add milk, salt, onion, garlic, ginger, and pepper.
3. Stir in the cooked carrots and cheese.
4. Pour into a 9" pie plate; set in a larger pan and surround with boiling water.
5. Bake at 350°F 35 to 40 minutes until a knife inserted near the center comes out clean.
6. Let stand 5 minutes before serving.

Microwave Oven Method:

Pour the mixture into a glass pie plate. Cook 5 minutes, then stir the part that is "set" around the edges into the middle. Cook 5-6 minutes longer until the center "jiggles like jelly." Rest 10-20 minutes before serving.

Cottage Cheese Pudding

2/3 c milk	1/4 tsp salt
1 Tbsp cornstarch	1 tsp vanilla
1 c small-curd creamed cottage cheese	dash of nutmeg
2 eggs	1/4 c + 2 Tbsp sugar

1. Combine the milk, cornstarch, salt, and nutmeg in a saucepan and mix until smooth and free of lumps; cook mixture over moderately high heat, stirring constantly with a spring stirrer, until it comes to a boil; remove from heat.
2. Separate the eggs; place yolks in the blender and whites in a bowl.
3. Add cottage cheese, vanilla, and 2 Tbsp sugar to the blender and process until smooth.
4. Stir the blender mixture into the starch-milk mixture.
5. Beat the egg whites to soft-peak stage, add the 1/4 c sugar, and beat until stiff.
6. Fold the egg-white foam into the milk mixture and transfer the mixture to a 2-quart casserole.
7. Place the casserole in a larger pan and surround with boiling water.
8. Bake at 375°F (190.5°C) about 45 minutes or until a knife blade inserted in the center comes out clean.
9. Serve hot or cold.

Yield: Four servings

Cheese Cake, Baked

1 c graham-cracker crumbs (9 crackers)	2 eggs
1 Tbsp + 1/2c + 2 Tbsp sugar	1-1/2 tsp vanilla
1/4 c melted table fat	1/2 pt (1 c) sour cream or sour
12 oz cream or Neufchatel cheese	half-and-half

1. Place graham crackers in a blender and process to make 1 cup crumbs.
2. Mix 1 Tbsp sugar and melted table fat into the crumbs; press the crumb mixture into the bottom of a 9"-diameter spring form pan or into an 8 or 9"-square baking pan.
3. Combine the softened cream cheese, eggs, 1 tsp vanilla, and 1/2 c sugar, beating until blended; pour into the crumb-lined baking pan.
4. Bake at 375°F (190.5°) 35 to 40 minutes or until filling is firm.
5. Combine the sour cream with 2 Tbsp sugar and 1/2 tsp vanilla and pour over the baked cheese mixture; bake 5 minutes longer at 450°F (232°C).
6. Chill well before serving.

   Yield: Six servings

Cheese Cake, Unbaked

1 c graham cracker crumbs (9 crackers)	1/2 c milk
1 Tbsp + 2 Tbsp + 1/4 c sugar	1 c Ricotta cheese
1/4 c melted table fat	1/8 c finely chopped candied fruits
1 Tbsp unflavored gelatin	(citron, cherries, pineapple)
1/8 tsp salt	1/8 c finely chopped blanched almonds
2 large eggs	1/2 tsp grated lemon rind
1/2 tsp vanilla	

1. Place the graham crackers in a blender and process to make 1 cup crumbs.
2. Combine the crumbs with 1 Tbsp sugar and melted table fat; press into the bottom of a 9"-diameter spring form pan or into an 8 or 9"-square pan.
3. Separate the eggs; place the yolks in a saucepan and the whites in a bowl.
4. Add milk, gelatin, salt, and 2 Tbsp sugar to the yolks and mix until blended.
5. Cook the mixture over moderate heat, stirring constantly with a spring stirrer, until steaming hot or until the mixture coats a spoon; remove from the heat.
6. Beat the Ricotta cheese vigorously until smooth; then stir the cheese, candied fruits, almonds, lemon rind, and vanilla into the custard mixture; chill until partially thickened.
7. Beat the egg whites to soft peaks, add 1/4 c sugar, and beat to stiff peaks. Fold the egg-white foam into the custard mixture and pour into the crumb-lined pan.
8. Chill until firm.

   Yield: Six servings

Blintzes

12-14 7" crepes	1 tsp vanilla
8 oz cream or Neufchatel cheese	1/4 c sugar
2 egg yolks	

1. Combine the softened cream cheese, egg yolks, sugar, and vanilla, mixing until smooth.
2. Place about 1 Tbsp of the mixture off center on a crepe; fold in both sides and the top and roll it up (BF, 257, Fig. 13.8).

3. Place the filled crepes in a greased 5 x 9" baking dish; brush the tops with melted table fat.
4. Bake at 350°F (176.5°C) 30 minutes.
5. Serve hot topped with a Dessert Fruit Sauce or with sour half-and-half.

Yield: Six servings

Questions

1. It is often necessary to substitute one cheese for another for reasons of economy or to reduce calories. Indicate possible substitutions for the following:

   a. A less expensive substitute for

   Roquefort cheese: _____

   Mozzarella cheese: _____

   Ricotta cheese: _____

   Gruyere cheese: _____

   Sharp Cheddar cheese: _____

   b. A lower-calorie substitute for

   Cream cheese: _____

   Creamed cottage cheese: _____

   Cheddar cheese: _____

2. Why should canned evaporated milk not be used for making cottage cheese?
3. Whole milk contains fat; nonfat milk does not. Is there any difference in the cottage-cheese curds obtained from the two types of milk?
4. Why is it necessary to keep the temperature for rennin precipitation and for culturing milk around 100°F (37.5°C)? What would happen if the temperature increased to 125-150°F (51.5-65.6°C)?
5. Why should Welsh Rarebit, Swiss Fondue, and Tomato Rarebit not be heated after addition of the cheese?

UNIT 15   EGGS

Suggested reading: <u>Basic Foods</u>, Chapter 19

Objectives

- To prepare and evaluate eggs cooked in a variety of ways
- To use eggs in the preparation of a variety of dishes
- To compare quality and cost of eggs

PREPARATION AND EVALUATION OF COOKED EGGS

A. Cooked Eggs

Soft-cooked Eggs
_____

    2 eggs

1. Place the eggs, still in their shells, in a small saucepan and cover with water.
2. Cook over high heat until the water starts to boil; then reduce heat to maintain a simmer.
3. Simmer eggs for 3 minutes; remove 1 egg and continue to simmer the other egg for 2 minutes more.
4. As soon as each egg is removed from the water, place it on a small plate and crack it across the middle with a sharp knife.
5. Compare the consistency and firmness of the yolks and whites of the 2 eggs.

Hard-cooked Eggs
_____

    2 eggs

1. Repeat steps 1 and 2 for Soft- cooked Eggs.
2. Simmer the eggs for 10 minutes; remove 1 egg and simmer the second egg for 10 minutes more.
3. As soon as each egg is removed from the water, submerge it in ice water. When it is thoroughly cooled, peel it and slice it in half lengthwise.
4. Compare the color of the yolk and the tenderness of the white of the 2 eggs.

Poached Egg
_____

    1 egg   1 tsp vinegar
    2 c water   1/2 tsp salt

1. Combine water, salt, and vinegar in a 1-qt saucepan and bring to a boil.
2. Break the egg into a small custard cup.
3. Holding the custard dish close to the top of the boiling water, gently pour the egg into the water, turn off the heat, cover, and cook for 3 to 5 minutes, depending on the consistency desired.

4. Remove the egg from the water with a slotted spoon, drain, and serve on buttered toast.

Fried Egg "Sunny Side Up"

3 Tbsp fat
1 egg

1. Heat table fat or bacon drippings in 6—7" frying pan until fat sizzles when a drop of water is placed in it.
2. Break the egg into a small custard cup and ease it into the hot fat.
3. Spoon the hot fat over the egg until the white is coagulated and the yolk has an opaque film of white over it.
4. Lift egg from pan with slotted pancake turner to drain off excess fat.

Fried Egg "Over Easy"

1 Tbsp fat
1 egg

1. Heat table fat or bacon drippings in 6—7" frying pan until sizzling hot.
2. Break the egg into a small custard cup and ease it into the hot fat.
3. Cook the egg over moderate heat for about 1 minute; then turn it over, being careful not to break the yolk.
4. Cook on the second side for 1 to 2 minutes; shorter time yields a softer yolk.

Fried Egg "Steamed"

1 tsp fat
1 egg
1 Tbsp water

1. Heat fat in small frying pan; crack the egg into the hot fat, add the water, cover, and reduce heat. Steam 2 to 3 minutes until the white is coagulated and the yolk is covered with an opaque film.

Scrambled Eggs

1 Tbsp fat   1/8 tsp salt
2 eggs   dash of pepper
2 Tbsp milk

1. Break eggs into a bowl, add milk, salt, and pepper, and beat until blended.
2. Heat the fat in an 8—10" frying pan and add the egg mixture. Cook for about 1 minute, stirring occasionally, over moderate heat, until the egg is coagulated. Turn or stir until all portions are cooked.

Microwave Oven:
1. Spray pan spray into an 8-10 oz glass bowl. Break eggs into the bowl and follow step 1.
2. Cover with a plastic wrap and cook at high power 1-1/2 minutes.
3. Turn over the cooked portion and break into pieces, cover, and cook 1 to 1-1/2 minutes longer.

B. Evaluation of Cooked Eggs

Cooked eggs can be evaluated for tenderness, texture-consistency, and appearance. These characteristics vary according to how the egg is cooked. Desirable characteristics for various cooked eggs are listed below. Enter evaluations in Table 15-1.

1. Soft-cooked eggs: tender white that is opaque and coagulated; translucent yolk, slightly fluid or just coagulated.
2. Hard-cooked eggs: firm, yet tender white; dry, mealy yolk with no dark discoloration.
3. Poached eggs: tender, opaque, coagulated white; translucent yolk, slightly fluid or just coagulated on the interior, with a film of opaque white over the surface; egg compact, not stringy or fragmented.
4. Fried eggs: tender, opaque, coagulated white; translucent yolk, slightly fluid or just coagulated on the interior, with a film of opaque white over the surface; egg compact and high with no frizzled edges or bottom.
5. Scrambled eggs: egg coagulated but moist and tender; no streaks or lumps of either white or yolk; no syneresis (separation of liquid from gel).

Table 15 - 1   Score Sheet for Cooked Eggs
Score: Good — 3   Fair — 2   Poor — 1

Cooking Method	Tenderness	Consistency	Appearance	Comments

PREPARATION OF EGG DISHES

A. Omelets

Basic French Omelet

2 eggs	dash of pepper
2 Tbsp milk	1/3 c shredded sharp Cheddar cheese
1 Tbsp table fat	2 Tbsp thinly sliced green onions,
1/8 tsp salt	including tops

1. Beat together the eggs, salt, pepper, and milk.
2. Heat the table fat in a 10" Teflon frying pan.
3. Pour the egg mixture into the frying pan and cook over moderate heat without stirring until the egg is coagulated.
4. Sprinkle the cheese and onions over the surface of the coagulated egg.
5. Loosen the egg around the edges of the pan with a rubber scraper and roll it up like a jelly roll. Serve with sauce, if desired (See BF, 345, Fig. 19.6).

French Omelet with Egg Substitute

1/2 c egg substitute	1/3 c shredded sharp Cheddar cheese
dash of pepper	2 Tbsp thinly sliced green onions,
1 Tbsp table fat	including tops

1. Mix the egg substitute with pepper or other spices and herbs, if desired.
2. Follow steps 2 through 5 for the Basic French Omelet.

Fillings for Omelets:

- A variety of cheeses, used singly or in combination with each other and with other ingredients
- Chopped ham, corned beef, or dried beef
- Crumbled cooked pork sausage, ground beef, bacon
- Cooked diced shrimp, crab, tuna, or other seafood
- Chopped fruits or vegetables: pineapple, green pepper, carrots, mushrooms, parsley, pimiento, olives, tomato, raw zucchini, green onions, bean or alfalfa sprouts

Sauces for Omelets

Note: The ingredients for other sauces are listed in Table 8-2.

Tomato Sauce

1 8-oz can tomato sauce	1/8 tsp basil, crushed
1 small clove garlic, crushed	1/8 tsp oregano, crushed
2 Tbsp chopped onion	dash of pepper
1 Tbsp oil	2 Tbsp chopped green pepper

Sauté onion, garlic, and green pepper in the oil; add the tomato sauce and seasonings; simmer about 5 minutes.

Yield: 1 cup

Chili Sauce

1 8-oz can tomato sauce	1 tsp chili powder
1 small clove garlic, crushed	dash of pepper
2 Tbsp chopped onion	2 Tbsp canned green chiles, seeded
1 Tbsp oil	and minced
1/8 tsp cumin	

Sauté the onion and garlic in the oil; add the tomato sauce, chiles, and seasonings; simmer about 5 minutes.

Yield: 1 cup

B. Custards

SOFT (STIRRED) CUSTARDS

General Instructions

1. Soft custards may be cooked directly on a surface unit in a pot with a heavy bottom (such as copper-clad or stainless steel). Stirring must be rapid, and continuous, with an implement that removes coagulated protein from the bottom of the pot as soon as it forms (a spring stirrer), and cooking should be discontinued as soon as the custard mixture coats the spoon.
2. Soft custards may also be cooked in the top of a double boiler over simmering water. They still require constant stirring to help equalize the temperature, and cooking must be discontinued as soon as the mixture coats the spoon. It is possible to curdle the custard mixture in a double boiler if it is cooked too long.
3. Aluminum pans are not satisfactory for cooking custard mixtures as the custard is likely to become discolored.
4. Custards, whether soft or baked, are subject to curdling and resulting syneresis when overcooked. In a custard, the protein traps the water in a mesh when heated to a certain temperature; if this temperature is exceeded, the protein shrinks and the water is squeezed out, causing the firm granules of protein and free water characteristic of a curdled custard. Therefore, it is important to discontinue cooking before this stage is reached.
5. Addition of sugar to a custard mixture increases the temperature required for thickening and therefore increases the likelihood of curdling. Adding sugar after the custard is cooked makes curdling less likely.
6. The chalazae in the egg white (BF, 335, Fig. 19.1) often cause lumps in soft custards. The milk-egg mixture may be strained before cooking to remove the chalazae.
7. Since flavoring extracts are volatile, they are best added after the cooking is completed.
8. Pour cooked custard mixtures into chilled dishes to stop cooking action. Cover the cooling custard with plastic film to prevent skin formation. The custard will thicken as it cools.

Microwave Oven:

Mix ingredients together in a glass bowl. Cook 1-1/2 minutes, stir, and cook 1/2 to 1 minute longer until the mixture coats a spoon.

Basic Soft Custard
_____

3/4 c milk	1/2 tsp vanilla
1-1/2 Tbsp sugar	dash of salt
1 large egg	

1. Place the egg in a 1-qt saucepan and beat until blended.
2. Add milk and salt, and mix well.
3. Cook over moderate heat, stirring constantly and rapidly with a spring stirrer, until the mixture is steaming hot and coats a silver spoon. Remove the pan from the heat while checking it to avoid overcooking (BF, 347, Fig. 19.7).
4. Stir in the sugar and vanilla; pour into a chilled dish; cover.
5. Chill before serving.

Yield: Two 1/2-cup servings

Chocolate Soft Custard

3/4 c milk	2 Tbsp sugar	dash of salt
2 Tbsp cocoa	1 large egg	1/2 tsp vanilla

1. Mix the sugar and cocoa together until free of lumps.
2. Place the egg in a 1-qt saucepan and beat until blended.
3. Add the milk, salt, and cocoa-sugar mixture to the egg and mix until smooth.
4. Cook over moderate heat, stirring constantly, until the mixture is steaming hot and coats a silver spoon.
5. Remove from heat and stir in the vanilla.
6. Transfer to a chilled dish, cover, and chill before serving.

Yield: Two 1/2-cup servings

Soft Custard with Egg Substitute

1/4 c egg substitute	1-1/2 Tbsp sugar
2/3 c milk	1/2 tsp vanilla

1. Combine egg substitute and milk in a 1-qt saucepan and cook over moderate heat, stirring constantly, until mixture is steaming hot and coats a silver spoon.
2. Transfer to a chilled dish, cover, chill.

Yield: Two 1/2-cup servings

BAKED CUSTARDS

General Instructions

1. All ingredients of baked custard mixtures must be added at the beginning of cooking. Use of minimum levels of sugar helps reduce the temperature of coagulation, thus preventing possible overheating of the protein.
2. Custard mixtures must be baked surrounded by water to insulate against oven heat. Use of boiling water shortens the cooking time.
3. It is possible to use high oven temperatures if the time is shortened; custard should be baked only until a knife blade inserted just off center comes out clean.
4. The larger the dish of custard, the longer it takes to cook. Dividing the custard mixture into several smaller containers shortens cooking time.
5. Greasing or spraying the custard cups before filling makes them easier to clean after the custard is removed.
6. Scalded milk may be used if desired, but it must be added to the egg gradually to prevent lumping; unheated milk gives very satisfactory results with less effort.

Microwave Oven:

Pour about 1/2 c of the custard mixture into each of two 6-fl oz glass custard cups. Cook 2 minutes, stir gently, cook 1 minute. Rotate each c 1/4 turn and cook 15 seconds. Rest 10-15 minutes, then refrigerate to set.

Baked Custard

3/4 c milk	dash of salt
1 large egg	1/2 tsp vanilla
1-1/2 Tbsp sugar	

1. Combine all ingredients in a blender or mixer and process until blended, about 30 seconds.
2. Divide evenly among three 5-oz custard cups. Place cups in a baking pan; surround with boiling water.
3. Bake at 400°F (204.5°C) 15 to 20 minutes or until a knife blade inserted off center comes out clean.
4. Custard may be served hot or cold.

Yield: Three 1/3-cup servings

Baked Custard with Egg Substitute

2/3 c milk	1-1/2 Tbsp sugar
1/4 c egg substitute	1/2 tsp vanilla

1. Combine and blend all ingredients.
2. Divide evenly among three custard cups; place cups in a baking pan and surround with boiling water.
3. Bake at 400°F (204.5°C) 20 to 25 minutes, or until a knife blade inserted off center comes out clean.
4. Serve hot or cold.

Yield: Three 1/3-cup servings

Butterscotch Custard Pudding

1 c milk	1/16 tsp salt
1 large egg	2 Tbsp table fat
1 Tbsp cornstarch	1 tsp vanilla
1/4 c brown sugar	

1. Break the egg into a 1-qt saucepan and mix until blended.
2. Add milk, cornstarch, and salt; mix until smooth.
3. Cook over moderate heat, stirring constantly, until the mixture starts to boil. (The starch protects the egg and prevents curdling.)
4. Turn off the heat and stir in the sugar, table fat, and vanilla.
5. Transfer to a chilled bowl, cover, chill.

Yield: Two 1/2-cup servings

C. Evaluation of Custards

Custards can be evaluated for flavor, appearance, and consistency or texture. The flavor of custards is slightly sweet and slightly eggy, yet bland, unless such ingredients as chocolate or brown sugar have added specific flavors. The flavor should be natural for the ingredients. Soft custards should appear creamy and smooth. Baked custards should have a soft gel structure, free from syneresis and excessive porosity.

Enter evaluations for custards in Table 15-2.

Table 15-2 Score Sheet for Custards

Desirable characteristics

- Flavor: natural for ingredients used
- Texture: smooth, creamy or soft
- Appearance: smooth and creamy for soft custards; soft gel, no syneresis, minimal porosity for baked custards

Score: Good — 3   Fair — 2   Poor — 1

Custards	Flavor	Texture	Appearance	Observations

D. Miscellaneous Egg Dishes

French Toast

2 slices whole-wheat bread   1 Tbsp milk
1 large egg   1/16 tsp salt

1. Combine egg, milk, and salt, mixing until blended.
2. Trim the crusts from the slices of bread, if desired.
3. Dip the slices of bread into the egg mixture, covering both sides of the bread with the mixture.
4. Fry bread in a lightly greased frying pan, using moderate heat, until browned on each side.
5. Serve hot with jam, jelly, preserves, or syrup.

Yield: One serving

Creole Eggs

1 Tbsp chopped onion	1 Tbsp flour
2 Tbsp chopped celery	1/4 tsp salt
1 Tbsp chopped green pepper	1/4 tsp chili powder
1 Tbsp table fat or oil	dash of cumin
1 8-oz can tomotao sauce	2 hard-cooked eggs, chopped
2 Tbsp canned, drained mushrooms	2 English muffins, split, toasted

1. Sauté the onion, celery, green pepper, and mushrooms in the table fat or oil.
2. Add the flour, salt, chili powder, and cumin; mix well.
3. Stir in the tomato sauce and eggs; heat until bubbly.
4. Serve hot over the toasted English muffins or plain toast.

   Yield: Two servings

Egg Foo Yung

1 Tbsp oil	2 c fresh beansprouts or 1 c canned
1/16 tsp garlic	sprouts
1/4 c chopped onion	2 large eggs (or 1/2 c egg substitute)
1/4 c canned bamboo shoots, chopped	1-1/2 tsp soy sauce
1/4 c canned water chestnuts, sliced	dash of pepper

1. Spread oil in hot frying pan and add the onions, garlic, water chestnuts, bamboo shoots, and bean sprouts, cooking and stirring for about 5 minutes over moderately high heat.
2. Beat the eggs, soy sauce, and pepper together until blended and pour over the vegetables; allow to cook without stirring until egg is set.
3. When eggs are set, cut the mixture into sections and turn to brown lightly on both sides; serve hot with sauce.

   Sauce for Egg Foo Yung

1/2 c chicken stock	1 tsp cornstarch
2 tsp soy sauce	

   Combine ingredients in 1-qt saucepan and heat to boiling, stirring constantly.

   Yield: Two servings

Ranch-style Eggs

Serve fried or poached eggs with Chili Sauce used for omelets.

Fluffy Egg Nest

1 slice hot, buttered toast	2-3 Tbsp shredded sharp Cheddar cheese
1 large egg	salt and pepper to taste

1. Place hot, buttered toast in baking pan.
2. Separate egg, taking care not to break the yolk.
3. Beat the egg white until slightly stiff, but not dry.
4. Pile the egg white foam on the toast and make an indentation in the middle; slide the yolk gently into the middle.
5. Sprinkle with salt and pepper and then with shredded cheese.
6. Bake in 350°F (176.5°C) oven for about 15 minutes until whites are lightly browned. Serve hot.

   Yield: One serving

Eggs Benedict

1 large egg	1/2 split English muffin (or 1 slice bread)
1 thin slice ham	2-3 Tbsp Hollandaise sauce

1. Poach the egg.
2. Toast the split half of the English muffin or slice of bread.
3. Heat the slice of ham slightly in frying pan or oven.
4. Lay the slice of ham on the toasted bread, top with the poached egg, and spoon the Hollandaise sauce over the top.

Deviled Eggs

2 large eggs, hard-cooked	1 Tbsp hotdog relish or 1 tsp prepared
2 Tbsp flaked crab, tuna, shrimp or	mustard and 2 tsp drained pickle
chicken	relish
	1 Tbsp imitation mayonnaise

1. Cut hard-cooked eggs in half lengthwise; scoop out and mash yolks.
2. Combine the flaked or chopped meat, relish, and mayonnaise with the mashed yolks.
3. Fill the egg-white halves with the yolk-meat mixture divided evenly among the four halves and piled up on top.
4. Refrigerate until time to serve.

COMPARISON OF QUALITY AND COST OF EGGS

A. Quality of Raw Eggs

Obtain 6 very fresh eggs and store 5 in the coldest part of the refrigerator, placing 1 egg in the freezer. Remove 1 egg each day from the refrigerator and hold at room temperature during the week prior to the laboratory period in which the eggs will be evaluated. Write on the shell the date the egg was removed from the refrigerator. Keep at least one egg in the refrigerator for a control.

To evaluate the eggs, break them carefully onto flat plates, one for each egg, labeled with the length of time the egg was stored at room temperature. Thaw and display the frozen egg.

Observe the eggs for:
- Spread: how wide an area covered by the white; the diameter of the yolk
- Height: the height of the yolk and white
- Color: transparency of the white; even color of the yolk
- Odor: natural egg odor; off-odors

Enter observations in Table 15-3.

Discard eggs that were held at room temperature.

B. Cost of Eggs

Determine market price of various sizes of eggs and calculate the cost per ounce by dividing cost per dozen by ounces per dozen. Enter calculations in Table 15-4.

Table 15-3   Comparison of Eggs Stored at Different Temperatures

Storage Conditions	Observations
Freezer storage	
Refrigerator storage	
Room temperature for ____ days	
Room temperature for ____ days	
Room temperature for ____ days	
Room temperature for ____ days	

Table 15-4   Cost Comparison for Eggs of Various Size

Size of Eggs	Cost per doz ($)	Oz per doz (oz)	Cost per oz ($)
Extra large		27	
Large		24	
Medium		21	
Small		18	

Example: Large eggs selling for $.66 per doz:
$.66 ÷ 24 = $.0275 per oz

UNIT 16   FOOD FOAMS

Suggested reading: <u>Basic Foods</u>, Chapter 20

Objectives

- To prepare and compare various types of food foams
- To use food foams in a variety of dishes

PREPARATION AND EVALUATION OF FOOD FOAMS

A. Egg White Foams

Egg white foams are evaluated for consistency, appearance, volume, and stability. Stability refers to the ability to retain the foam structure and is measured by the amount of drainage from the foam.

General Instructions

1. Use exactly 30 ml of raw egg white for each variation listed below; use kitchen shears to snip the egg white so that it can be measured accurately.
2. Place the egg white in a pint-sized graduated liquid measure and beat to the stage specified in the variation. Each variation should be prepared in the same type of container and with the same type of beater, hand or electric. The beater(s) should be moved around the bowl and the foam should be checked frequently until the specified stage has been reached.
3. When beating is completed, knock or scrape the foam from the beaters and pack the foam into the measure and mark a line on the measuring cup with a felt pen at the top of the foam. Remove the foam from the cup and fill the cup to the line with water. Measure the water in a graduated cylinder. Record under volume in Table 16-1.
4. Place a funnel in a 25-ml graduated cylinder. Fill a 1/2-cup nested measuring cup carefully with the foam and level it off. Transfer the foam to the funnel and cover top with plastic wrap to prevent drying. Allow the foam to drain for one hour and measure the amount of drainage. Record in Table 16-1.
5. Observe and record the following characteristics in the foams:
   - Fluidity or rigidity
   - Peaks: standing up or folding over
   - Air bubbles: small or large
   - Appearance: moist or dry; smooth or curdled

Preparation of Egg White Foams (See BF, 356, Fig. 20.2.)

1. Foamy stage: Beat the egg white until it is frothy, but still fluid; at this stage it will not hold a peak.
2. Soft-peak stage: Beat the egg white until soft peaks form; the peaks of egg white should fold over when the beaters are removed; the foam should flow in the bowl.
3. Stiff-peak stage: Beat the egg whites until stiff peaks form; when the beaters are

removed, the peaks stand up straight. A spatula cut through the foam leaves a "canyon" with straight sides.

4. Dry-foam stage: The foam breaks instead of forming peaks and is very rigid, dry, and curdled.

5. Stiff-peak stage with sugar: Beat egg white to soft-peak stage, then add 2 Tbsp sugar and beat to stiff-peak stage.

6. Stiff-peak stage with cream of tartar: Add 1/8 tsp cream of tartar and beat to stiff-peak stage.

Table 16-1   Comparison of Egg White Foams

Egg White Foam	Volume of Foam (ml)	Drainage from Foam (ml)	Observations
Foamy stage			
Soft-peak stage			
Stiff-peak stage			
Dry foam			
Stiff peak + 2 Tbsp sugar			
Stiff peak + 1/8 tsp cream of tartar			

B. Milk Foams

Milk foams are evaluated for flavor, consistency, appearance, stability, and volume of foam obtained.

General Instructions

1. Prepare the milk foams as specified for each variation.
2. Measure the volume of the foams in graduated liquid measures of the appropriate size; mark a line on the cup with a felt pen at the top of the foam. Transfer the foam to a glass bowl and allow it to set for an hour. Fill the measuring cup to the line with water and measure the volume of the water in a graduated cylinder. Record in Table 16-2.
3. At the end of an hour observe the volume and drainage of the foams and record in Table 16-2.
4. Taste the foams and observe flavor and consistency.
5. Compare the cost per cup of the various milk foams based on the volumes of whipped foam obtained in these variations. Enter calculations in Table 16-3. The volume of foam obtained will depend partly on whipping conditions and will influence cost slightly (BF, 361, Table 20.1).

Table 16-2   Comparison of Volume, Flavor, and Consistency of Milk Foams

Kind of Milk	Volume of Foam (ml)	Drainage from Foam (ml)	Observations
Whipping cream			
Concentrated milk			
Canned whole evaporated milk			
Canned skim evaporated milk			
Nonfat dry milk (NFDM)			

a. Convert the market-unit size into cups: 1 qt fluid milk = 4 c; 1 lb NFDM = 454 g and 1 c NFDM = 68 g; 454 ÷ 68 = 6.676 c per lb. Enter cups in market unit in column 2.

b. Enter amount of milk (in cups) used to prepare foam in column 4.

c. Multiply column 3 by column 4 and divide by column 2. Example: $10.79 x .5 c ÷ 66.76 = $.0808

d. Divide the millilitres of foam recorded in Table 16-2 by 237 to obtain the cups of foam. Example: If the NFDM whipped into 600 ml foam, then 600 ml ÷ 237 ml per c = 2.53 c of foam. Enter the cups of foam obtained in column 6.

e. Divide column 5 by column 6 to get the cost per cup of foam and enter in column 7.

6. Compare the caloric content of the various foams and enter in Table 16-3.

a. Calories per cup of unwhipped milk are listed in column 8 of Table 16-3.

b. Amount of milk used to prepare the foam is listed in column 4.

c. Multiply column 8 by column 4 and enter in column 9. Example: 245 calories per c x .5 c = 122.5 calories in 1/2 c milk used to prepare the foam.

d. Volume of foam is entered in column 6.

e. Divide column 9 by column 6 and enter calories per cup of foam in column 10. Example: 122.5 calories ÷ 2.53 c of foam = 48 calories per cup of foam.

PREPARATION OF MILK FOAMS

Whipped Cream

1/2 pt (1 c) whipping or all-purpose cream

Whip chilled cream at high speed in small bowl of electric mixer until soft peaks form.

Whipped Concentrated Milk

1/3 c undiluted concentrated fresh
    or frozen milk
1 Tbsp water

1/4 tsp unflavored gelatin
1/2 tsp cream of tartar

1. Combine all ingredients in a 1-qt saucepan and cook over moderate heat, stirring constantly with a spring stirrer, until mixture is steaming hot and the gelatin is dissolved.

Table 16–3 Comparison of Cost and Caloric Content of Milk Foams

	1	2	3	4	5	6	7	8[1]	9	10
		Market Unit		Amount used for foam (c)	Cost of milk in foam ($)	Volume of foam (c)	Cost of foam per c ($)	Calories per c of milk	Total calories in foam	Calories per c of foam
Kind of Milk	As purch.	Cups (c)	Cost ($)							
Example:										
Nonfat dry milk	4 lb	26.75	6.00	0.5	.11	2.53	.044	245	122.5	48
Canned evaporated whole milk								345		
Canned evaporated skim milk								194		
Concentrated milk								477		
Whipping cream								715		

[1]Calories for milks were obtained from Basic Foods, Table 20.1, p. 361 and from USDA Home and Garden Bulletin No. 72, Nutritive Value of Foods.

2. Transfer the mixture to the bowl in which it will be whipped and chill in the freezer until partially frozen.
3. Whip to soft-peak stage; then add cream of tartar and whip at highest speed to stiff peaks.

Whipped Evaporated Milk with Gelatin

1/3 c undiluted whole or skim evaporated milk
1/4 tsp unflavored gelatin

1. Combine the milk and gelatin in a 1-qt saucepan and cook over moderate heat, stirring constantly with a spring stirrer, until the mixture is steaming hot and the gelatin is dissolved.
2. Transfer to the bowl in which it will be whipped and chill in the freezer until partially frozen (see BF, 362, Fig. 20.9).
3. Whip at highest speed until soft peaks form.

Whipped Evaporated Milk with Lemon Juice

1/3 c undiluted whole or skim evaporated milk
2 tsp lemon juice

1. In the freezer, chill milk in the bowl in which it is to be whipped until partially frozen.
2. Whip at highest speed until soft peaks form; add lemon juice and whip until stiff. (see BF, 364, Fig. 20.14).

Nonfat Dry Milk Foam with Lemon Juice

1/2 c instant NFDM   2 tsp lemon juice
1/3 c ice-cold water

Combine water and NFDM in large bowl of the mixer and whip at highest speed until soft peaks form; add lemon juice and whip until stiff. (see BF, 363, Fig. 20.13).

Nonfat Dry Milk Foam

1/2 c instant NFDM
1/3 c ice-cold water

Combine water and NFDM in large bowl of the mixer and whip at highest speed until stiff. (see BF, 364, Fig. 20.15).

Note: If milk foams are to be used as toppings, they may be sweetened to taste after the foam is formed. Toppings that contain lemon juice may be flavored with lemon extract and are satisfactory for topping fruit mixtures and bread and rice puddings. Toppings that do not contain lemon juice or other acid may be flavored with vanilla or almond extracts and are suitable for topping chocolate mixtures.

C. Gelatin Foams

Lemon Whip

1/4 c water   1 c ice-cold water
1 Tbsp unflavored gelatin   1/4 c lemon juice
1/2 c sugar

1. Combine the 1/4 cup water and gelatin in a 1-qt saucepan and cook over moderately high heat, stirring, until mixture is steaming hot and the gelatin is dissolved.
2. Remove from the heat and stir in the sugar until dissolved; then stir in the lemon juice and ice water.
3. Transfer mixture to the large bowl of the electric mixer and chill until it is partially thickened—about the consistency of raw egg white.
4. Whip at high speed to soft-peak stage; if it fails to whip, chill a little longer and try again.
5. Pour into a lightly oiled mold and chill until set.

Yield: Four servings

Cranberry Soufflé Salad

1-1/4 c pineapple juice	2 Tbsp grated orange rind
1/3 c sugar	1/4 c walnuts, chopped
1/8 tsp salt	1 c canned whole cranberry sauce
1 Tbsp unflavored gelatin	1/2 c pippin apple, unpeeled, cored, chopped
1/2 c imitation mayonnaise	1/2 c orange, peeled, chopped

1. Combine 1/2 cup pineapple juice, sugar, salt, and gelatin in a 1-qt saucepan and cook over moderately high heat, stirring, until the mixture is steaming hot and the gelatin is dissolved (or heat in the microwave oven about 2 minutes).
2. Remove from heat and stir in remaining juice and the mayonnaise; blend.
3. Transfer the mixture to the large bowl of the electric mixer and chill until partially thickened—the consistency of raw egg white; then beat it at highest speed until fluffy.
4. Fold in the drained cranberry sauce, apple, orange, and walnuts.
5. Pour the mixture into a lightly oiled mold and chill until set.

Yield: Six servings

USE OF FOOD FOAMS

A. Gelatin-Milk Foams

Apricot Bavarian Cream

1 #2 can (16 oz) apricot halves	3 Tbsp NFDM
1 Tbsp unflavored gelatin	2-1/2 Tbsp cold water
1/2 tsp almond extract	

1. Drain and reserve the juice from the canned apricots.
2. Place the apricots in the blender and process until smooth; transfer the puréed apricots to a 2-cup graduated measure.
3. Place 1/4 cup of the juice from the apricots in the blender and process to rinse the blender; add to the puréed apricots.
4. Add additional apricot juice to the puréed apricots to make a total of 1-1/4 cups; chill while preparing the gelatin.
5. Combine 1/4 cup apricot juice (or water) with the gelatin in a saucepan and cook over moderately high heat, stirring constantly, until mixture is steaming hot and the gelatin is dissolved.
6. Add the sugar and almond extract to the gelatin, combine with the puréed apricots, and place in large bowl of electric mixer; chill until partially thickened (consistency of raw

egg white).

7. Place the 3 Tbsp NFDM and 2-1/2 Tbsp water in the small bowl of the mixer and beat to soft-peak stage.
8. Using the same beaters without washing, beat the gelatin mixture until foamy.
9. Fold the two foams together; transfer to a lightly oiled mold and chill until set.

Yield: Six servings

Strawberry Bavarian Cream

1 16-oz pkg frozen strawberries, thawed	1/3 c undiluted concentrated milk
1 Tbsp unflavored gelatin	1 Tbsp water
sugar to taste	1/4 tsp gelatin
	1/2 tsp cream of tartar

1. Combine milk, water, and gelatin in a saucepan and heat, stirring constantly, until steaming hot.
2. Transfer the mixture to a mixing bowl and chill until partially frozen.
3. Drain the juice from the frozen, thawed strawberries and place in a saucepan with 1 Tbsp unflavored gelatin.
4. Heat gelatin and juice until mixture is steaming hot and gelatin is dissolved.
5. Stir in the thawed berries and sweeten to taste. Chill until partially thickened.
6. Whip the milk mixture at high speed to soft peaks; add the cream of tartar and whip until stiff.
7. Fold the partially thickened strawberry gelatin mixture into the milk foam.
8. Pour the mixture into a lightly oiled mold and chill until set.

Yield: Six servings

Pineapple Angel Whip

1/3 c whole or skim evaporated milk, undiluted	1/2 c sugar
1 Tbsp unflavored gelatin	1 Tbsp lemon juice
1/4 c water	1 16-oz can crushed pineapple

1. Place milk in the large bowl of the electric mixer and chill in the freezer until partially frozen.
2. Combine water and gelatin in a saucepan and heat, stirring, until mixture is steaming hot and gelatin is dissolved.
3. Stir the sugar into the hot gelatin mixture and add pineapple, including juice; chill until partially thickened.
4. Whip the partially frozen evaporated milk to soft peaks; add the lemon juice and whip until stiff.
5. Fold the pineapple into the milk foam.
6. Pour the mixture into a lightly oiled mold and chill until set.

Yield: Six servings

B. Gelatin-Egg Foams

Chocolate Spanish Cream

1-3/4 c milk	3 Tbsp cocoa
2 eggs	1/16 tsp salt
1 Tbsp unflavored gelatin	1/2 tsp vanilla
1/4 c + 1/4 c sugar	

1. Mix the cocoa and 1/4 c sugar together until free of lumps.
2. Separate eggs; place yolks in a 1-qt saucepan and whites in a bowl.
3. Stir the milk into the egg yolks, mixing until blended; then stir in the cocoa mixture, gelatin, and salt.
4. Cook over moderate heat, stirring constantly with a spring stirrer, until mixture is steaming hot and gelatin is dissolved.
5. Add the vanilla and chill until partially thickened.
6. Beat the egg whites to soft peaks, add 1/4 c sugar, and beat to stiff peaks.
7. Fold partially thickened gelatin mixture into the foam, pour into a lightly oiled mold and chill until set.

Yield: Four servings

Lemon Chiffon Custard

1/3 c + 3 Tbsp water	1/4 c + 1/4 c sugar
1 Tbsp unflavored gelatin	1/3 c lemon juice
2 eggs	1/3 c NFDM
1/16 tsp salt	

1. Separate the eggs; place the yolks in a 1-qt saucepan and the whites in a bowl.
2. Add 1/3 c water to the yolks and mix until blended; then stir in the gelatin and salt.
3. Cook over moderately high heat, stirring constantly, until the mixture is steaming hot and gelatin is dissolved.
4. Remove from heat and stir in 1/4 c sugar and lemon juice. Chill until partially thickened.
5. Add 3 Tbsp water and 1/3 c NFDM to the egg whites and beat at high speed to soft peaks; add 1/4 c sugar and beat to stiff peaks.
6. Fold the gelatin mixture into the foam and pour the mixture into a lightly oiled mold; chill until set.

Yield: Six servings

Pumpkin Chiffon Cheesecake

1-1/4 c graham cracker crumbs	3 eggs, separated
1-1/4 c sugar	2 8-oz pkgs cream cheese
1/4 c (1/2 cube) table fat	1 15-oz can pumpkin
1-1/2 Tbsp unflavored gelatin	1 tsp pumpkin pie spice
1/3 c cold water	1/2 c finely chopped walnuts

1. Combine graham cracker crumbs, 1/4 c sugar and table fat; press into the bottom of an 8" diameter spring-form pan and chill.
2. Soften the gelatin in the cold water and then combine with egg yolks and 2/3 c sugar in a saucepan; heat over moderate heat, stirring constantly, until thickened.

(Better, combine in a glass bowl and cook in the microwave oven 1 minute, or until steaming hot.)

3. Gradually blend in the softened cream cheese, pumpkin, spice, and nuts.
4. Beat egg whites to a soft peak stage, add 1/3 c sugar and beat until stiff.
5. Fold the egg white foam into the pumpkin mixture and transfer to the prepared spring-form pan. Chill to set.

C. Puffy Omelets

Basic Puffy Omelet

2 eggs	1 small green onion, thinly sliced
2 Tbsp milk or light cream	1 slice bacon, chopped, fried crisp
1/8 tsp salt	

1. Separate eggs, placing yolks in one bowl and whites in another.
2. Add the milk and salt to the yolks and mix until blended.
3. Beat egg whites to soft-peak stage; fold the yolk mixture into the foam with a French whip.
4. Pour the foam into a well-greased 6" frying pan and cook over moderate until lightly browned on the bottom.
5. Place the omelet in a 350°F (176.5°C) oven for about 15 minutes; test for doneness with a clean knife blade; if the blade comes out clean when inserted in the center, the omelet is cooked.
6. Score the top of the omelet by cutting a gash 1/2" deep across the middle of the top.
7. Sprinkle the onion and bacon pieces over one-half the omelet and fold in half.
8. Serve while hot; may be topped with sauce or another filling used. (See fillings and sauces for French Omelets in Unit 15.)

Puffy Omelet with Egg Substitute

1/2 c egg substitute	1/16 tsp cream of tartar
1/16 tsp salt	

1. Combine all ingredients in small bowl of electric mixer and beat at high speed for 5 to 10 minutes.
2. Follow steps 4 through 8 for Basic Puffy Omelet.

   Yield: One serving

D. Soufflés

Cheese Soufflé

1/2 c milk	2 eggs
1 Tbsp cornstarch	3/4 c (3 oz) grated sharp Cheddar cheese
1/4 tsp salt	

1. Combine milk, cornstarch, and salt in a 1-qt saucepan and mix until smooth.
2. Cook mixture over moderately high heat, stirring constantly with a spring stirrer, until it starts to boil.
3. Remove from heat and stir in cheese (see BF, 357, Fig. 20.3).
4. Separate the eggs and stir the yolks into the cheese sauce.

5. Beat the egg whites to soft-peak stage and fold into the cheese mixture with a French whip (see BF, 357, Fig. 20.4).
6. Pour the mixture into a 1-qt casserole; place the casserole in a pan and surround with boiling water.
7. Bake at 400°F (204.5°C) about 30 minutes; test with clean knife blade inserted in center; when soufflé is cooked, the blade comes out clean (see BF, 358, Fig. 20.5).
8. Serve immediately.

Yield: Two servings

Roulade

2 c milk	4 large eggs
1/2 c flour	1 tsp sugar
1/4 tsp salt	1/4 tsp cream of tartar

1. Grease a 10 x 15 x 1" jelly roll pan; line with wax paper or parchment paper; grease and flour the paper.
2. Combine milk, flour, and salt in a 1-1/2-qt saucepan and stir until smooth.
3. Cook mixture over moderately high heat, stirring constantly with a spring stirrer, until it starts to boil; remove from heat.
4. Separate the eggs; place whites in a large bowl and add the cream of tartar; beat to soft-peak stage.
5. Add yolks and sugar to the cooled starch mixture and mix until blended.
6. Fold the foam into the starch mixture with a French whip.
7. Spread the mixture evenly in the prepared pan.
8. Bake at 350°F (176.5°C) 40 minutes until lightly browned.
9. Lay a piece of wax paper or parchment paper on bread board and sprinkle bread crumbs over the paper. Invert the baked roulade on the crumb-covered paper; lift off the pan and immediately peel off the paper that was used to line the pan.
10. If the edges seem dry and brown, they may be trimmed off with a sharp slicing knife so that the roulade is easier to roll.
11. Spread the filling (see below) over the roulade and roll it up like a jelly roll; heat about 15 minutes at 350°F (176.5°C), then slice into eight equal pieces and serve hot (BF, 359, Fig. 20.6). Top with a dollop of sour half-and-half, if desired.

Note: The filled roll can be frozen or stored in the refrigerator for several days. Heat to serve. Individual slices may be heated.

Mushroom Filling

1 c chopped onions	1/4 c sour half-and-half
1 lb fresh mushrooms	2 Tbsp thinly sliced green onions
1 Tbsp table fat	2 Tbsp lemon juice

1. Melt table fat in frying pan and add the chopped onions; sauté until translucent.
2. Wash, trim, and slice mushrooms.
3. Add mushrooms to onions and cook until dry in texture.
4. Add the sliced green onions, lemon juice, and sour half-and-half.
5. Use as filling for roulade.

Chicken Filling

3/4 c chicken stock	1 tsp lemon juice
3 Tbsp flour	1/3 c low-fat yogurt
3/4 tsp curry powder	1/4 c finely minced chutney
salt and pepper to taste	1 c flaked or chopped cooked chicken meat

1. Stir the flour and curry powder into the chicken stock and mix until smooth.
2. Cook mixture over moderately high heat, stirring constantly, until it starts to boil.
3. Turn off heat and stir in the chicken, lemon juice, chutney, and yogurt; season to taste with salt and pepper.
4. Use as filling for roulade.

E. Meringues

Coconut Kisses (Macaroons)

1/4 c egg white	1/2 tsp vanilla or almond extract
1/8 tsp cream of tartar	1 c angel-flake coconut
1/2 c sugar	

1. Beat egg white to soft-peak stage; add sugar, cream of tartar, and flavoring extract; beat to stiff peaks.
2. Fold in the coconut.
3. Cut parchment paper or heavy brown wrapping paper to fit baking sheet.
4. Drop meringue by teaspoonfuls about 1" apart on the paper-lined baking sheet.
5. Bake at 375°F (190.5°C) 8 to 10 minutes or until lightly browned.
6. As soon as the pan is removed from the oven, slide the paper with the cookies off the pan and spread a damp towel out on the pan. Place the paper of cookies over the damp cloth on the hot pan. This steams the cookies from the paper. Allow to steam for 1 minute.
7. Lift cookies off the paper with a wide spatula or turner; do not allow them to cool before removing.

Yield: About 30 macarooms

Hard Meringue Shells

1/4 c egg white	1/2 c sugar
1/8 tsp cream of tartar	1/2 tsp vanilla or almond extract

1. Beat egg whites to soft-peak stage; add the cream of tartar, sugar, and flavoring extract; beat until stiff peaks form.
2. Cut parchment paper or heavy brown paper to fit the baking sheet.
3. Use about 1/2 c foam for each shell. Place the foam in mounds about 1" apart and 4" in diameter on paper-lined baking sheet and shape with the back of a teaspoon so that they are high on the rim and a depression is formed in the center.
4. Bake at 275°F (135°C) 1 hour; turn off the oven; leave the meringue shells in the oven to cool and dry out.
5. Serve filled with custard filling, whipped cream or milk, or ice cream, or topped with nuts and/or fresh or preserved fruits.

Note: Shells can be stored for several days at room temperature loosely wrapped. Do not store in air-tight containers.

Yield: Four shells

UNIT 17   ANGEL, SPONGE, AND CHIFFON CAKES

Suggested reading: <u>Basic Foods</u>, Chapter 22

Objective

- To prepare and evaluate a variety of foam-type cakes

PREPARATION OF ANGEL CAKES

Note that it is easy to cut foam-type cakes into smooth, even slices with a nonserrated, thin-bladed knife. Dip the knife into water before each slice and wash the crumbs off the blade after each cut.

Basic Angel Cake

For 8" tube pan	For 10" tube pan
2/3 c sifted cake flour	1 c sifted cake flour
1/3 c sugar	2/3 c sugar
1/4 tsp salt	1/2 tsp salt
1 c egg white	1-1/2 c egg white
1 tsp cream of tartar	1-1/2 tsp cream of tartar
3/4 c sugar	1 c sugar
1 tsp vanilla or almond extract	1-1/2 tsp vanilla or almond extract

1. Sift and measure the flour, add salt and sugar (1/3 c for small cake; 2/3 c for large), and mix well with French whip.
2. Beat egg whites and cream of tartar in the large bowl of the electric mixer at high speed to soft-peak stage.
3. Add sugar to the foam (3/4 c for small cake; 1 c for large) and beat to stiff-peak stage; beat in extract (see <u>BF</u>, 370, Fig. 21.2).
4. Knock the foam from the beaters into the mixing bowl; using the French whip, fold the flour mixture into the foam, adding the flour mixture in 3 parts.
5. Transfer the batter gently to the tube pan; cut through the batter with a table knife to eliminate large air pockets.
6. Bake at 400°F (204°C) 30 minutes for the 10" cake and 25 for the 8" cake; test for doneness by pressing near the middle of the cake lightly with the finger; if cake springs back, it is done.
7. Invert the tube of the cake pan over an inverted funnel so that the cake may hang to cool.
8. Cool the cake thoroughly before cutting it out of the pan.

Chocolate Angel Cake
_____

For 8" tube pan	For 10" tube pan
1/2 c + 1 Tbsp sifted cake flour	3/4 c + 1 Tbsp sifted cake flour
1/3 c sugar	2/3 c sugar
1/4 tsp salt	1/2 tsp salt
3 Tbsp cocoa	1/4 c cocoa
1 c egg white	1-1/2 c egg white
1 tsp cream of tartar	1-1/2 tsp cream of tartar
3/4 c sugar	1 c sugar
1 tsp vanilla	1-1/2 tsp vanilla

1. Sift and measure the flour; add salt, cocoa, and first sugar, and mix until smooth; if necessary, sift to remove lumps.
2. Follow steps 2 through 8 for Basic Angel Cake, working very quickly and baking as soon as the cocoa mixture is added to prevent excessive loss of volume from the effects of cocoa on the egg foam.

Marble Angel Cake
_____

1. Prepare Basic Angel Cake batter and Chocolate Angel Cake batter.
2. Alternate spoonfuls of each batter in 2 tube pans, until all of the batter has been used.
3. Twirl a table knife in the batter to "streak" the two mixtures together.
4. Follow steps 6 through 8 for Basic Angel Cake.

Coconut Angel Cake
_____

1. Prepare Basic Angel Cake, but add 1 c angel-flake coconut in step 1, coating the flakes of coconut with the flour mixture.

WHOLE EGG AND YOLK SPONGE CAKES

Whole Egg Sponge Cake (I)
_____

For use with a mixer with a wire whip and hypocycloidal beating action:

For 8" tube pan	For 10" tube pan
1 c sifted cake flour	1-1/2 c sifted cake flour
1 c sugar	1-1/2 c sugar
1/4 tsp salt	1/2 tsp salt
1 c whole eggs	1-1/2 c whole eggs
1-1/2 tsp cream of tartar	2-1/4 tsp cream of tartar
1 tsp vanilla or lemon extract	1-1/2 tsp vanilla or lemon extract

1. Sift and measure cake flour; combine flour, half the sugar, and salt, mixing with a French whip.
2. Beat the eggs and cream of tartar at highest speed in mixer with wire beater for 8 to 10 minutes.
3. Add remaining sugar and flavoring and beat for 30 seconds.
4. Remove the beater and knock foam from beater into the bowl.
5. Use a French whip to fold the sugar-flour mixture into the foam, adding the flour in 3 parts.

6. Pour the batter into the tube pan and bake immediately at 375°F (190.5°C) 30 to 35 minutes for the small cake and 40 minutes for the large. Test for doneness by pressing top of cake lightly with fingertip; if the cake springs back, it is done.
7. Invert the baked cake with the tube over an inverted funnel and cool completely before cutting the cake from the pan.

Whole Egg Sponge Cake (II)

For use with twin beater mixer:

For 8" tube pan	For 10" tube pan
1 c sifted cake flour	1-1/2 c sifted cake flour
1 c sugar	1-1/2 c sugar
1/4 tsp salt	1/2 tsp salt
6 large eggs	8 large eggs
3/4 tsp + 3/4 tsp cream of tartar	1-1/4 + 1 tsp cream of tartar
2 Tbsp water	2 Tbsp + 2 tsp water
1 tsp vanilla or lemon extract	1-1/2 tsp vanilla or lemon extract

1. Sift and measure the flour; combine flour, salt, and half the sugar with a French whip, mixing well.
2. Separate the eggs; place the yolks in the small bowl of the mixer and the whites in the large bowl.
3. Combine whites and cream of tartar (3/4 tsp for the small cake; 1-1/4 tsp for the large), beat at high speed to soft-peak stage.
4. Add remaining sugar and beat at high speed to stiff peaks.
5. Using the same beaters, beat the yolks, water, and cream of tartar (3/4 tsp for the small cake; 1 tsp for the large) to soft peaks or foamy stage.
6. Remove the beaters and knock the egg foam from the beaters into the bowl.
7. Fold the flour-sugar mixture into the yolk foam, then fold into the egg white foam.
8. Follow steps 5 through 7 of Whole Egg Sponge Cake (I).

Egg Yolk Sponge Cake

A satisfactory product is only possible if a wire whip on the hypocycloidal type mixer is used; mixers with twin beaters do not form foams of sufficient volume.

For 8" tube pan	For 10" tube pan
1 c sifted cake flour	1-1/2 c sifted cake flour
1 c sugar	1-1/2 c sugar
1/4 tsp salt	1/2 tsp salt
12 large egg yolks	16 large egg yolks
6 Tbsp water	1/2 c water
1-1/2 tsp cream of tartar	2-1/4 tsp cream of tartar
1 tsp vanilla or lemon extract	1-1/2 tsp vanilla or lemon extract

1. Sift and measure the flour; combine flour, salt, and half the sugar with a French whip.
2. Combine egg yolks, water, and cream of tartar in the mixer bowl and beat at high speed with wire whip to soft-peak stage.
3. Add remaining sugar and flavoring; beat for 30 seconds.
4. Follow steps 4 through 7 for Whole Egg Sponge Cake (I).

Jelly Roll

1 c sifted cake flour	3/4 c whole egg (4 large eggs)
3/4 c sugar	1-1/8 tsp cream of tartar
1/4 tsp salt	1 Tbsp + 1 tsp water
1 tsp vanilla	

1. Sift and measure the flour; combine flour, 1/4 c sugar, and salt, mixing well with a French whip.
2. Separate the eggs, placing the whites in the large bowl of the mixer and the yolks in the small bowl.
3. Add 1/2 tsp cream of tartar to the whites and beat to soft-peak stage.
4. Add 1/2 c sugar to the egg white foam and beat to stiff peaks.
5. Add the water and 5/8 tsp cream of tartar to the yolks and beat to soft-peak stage with the same beater used for the whites.
6. Knock the foam from the beaters and fold the yolk foam into the white foam with a French whip.
7. Add the flour-sugar mixture in 3 parts, folding in with the French whip.
8. Line a jelly-roll pan (15-1/2 x 10-1/2 x 1") with parchment or waxed paper and spread the batter evenly in the lined pan.
9. Bake at 375°F (190.5°C) 12 to 15 minutes or until it tests done.
10. As soon as the cake is removed from the oven, run a table knife around the edges to loosen the cake from the pan.
11. Place a clean towel over the cake and lay a baking sheet over the towel; invert the cake onto the towel-covered baking sheet.
12. Lift off the baking pan and peel the paper off the cake.
13. Trim the edges from the cake and spread the cake with any of the fillings given in Unit 19.
14. Starting at the narrow end, roll the cake; then roll it in a towel and cool. The cake is easier to roll while warm; it may crack if cold.
15. Slice into 3/4 to 1" thick slices to serve.

Almond Sponge Cake

1. Finely chop or grind 1 c blanched almonds.
2. Prepare the Yolk or Whole Egg Sponge Cake; add the ground nuts to the flour mixture and mix well to coat the nuts with the flour.

CHIFFON CAKES

Basic Chiffon Cake

2 c cake flour	1/2 c oil
1-1/2 sugar	5 egg yolks
2 tsp SAS baking powder	1 tsp vanilla or other flavoring
1/2 tsp salt	1 c egg whites
3/4 c milk	1 tsp cream of tartar

1. Stir the cake flour, fill the cup lightly, and level; sifting the flour before measuring is not necessary with this cake.
2. Combine the flour, 1 c sugar, baking powder, and salt, and mix well with a French whip.
3. Beat the oil and egg yolks together; stir in the milk and flavoring.
4. Combine the liquid and dry ingredients and mix just until smooth.

5. Beat the egg whites and cream of tartar to the soft-peak stage; add 1/2 c sugar and beat to stiff-peak stage.
6. Fold the batter mixture into the egg white foam with a French whip.
7. Pour the batter into a 10" tube pan and bake at 375°F (190.5°C) 40 minutes, or until cake tests done when pressed with finger tip.
8. Invert tube pan over an inverted funnel and allow the cake to hang during cooling.
9. Cool the cake completely before cutting it out of the pan.

Lemon Chiffon Cake

2 c cake flour	1/4 c lemon juice
1-1/2 c sugar	1/2 c oil
2 tsp SAS baking powder	5 egg yolks
1/2 tsp salt	1 c egg whites
1 Tbsp finely grated lemon rind	1 tsp cream of tartar
1/2 c milk	

1. Follow steps 1 and 2 for Basic Chiffon Cake, adding the lemon rind to the flour mixture in step 2.
2. Beat the oil and egg yolks together; then stir in the milk and lemon juice.
3. Follow steps 4 through 9 for Basic Chiffon Cake.

Pineapple Chiffon Cake

2 c cake flour	1/2 c crushed pineapple, drained
1-1/2 c sugar	1/2 c oil
2 tsp SAS baking powder	5 egg yolks
1/2 tsp salt	1 c egg whites
1/2 c pineapple juice	1 tsp cream of tartar

1. Follow the recipe for Basic Chiffon Cake, adding the pineapple and juice in place of the milk and flavoring in step 3.

Banana Chiffon Cake

2 c cake flour	1 Tbsp pineapple juice
1-1/2 c sugar	1/2 c oil
2 tsp SAS baking powder	5 egg yolks
1/2 tsp salt	1 tsp vanilla
1/3 c milk	1 c egg whites
3/4 c mashed banana	1 tsp cream of tartar

1. Follow steps 1 through 3 for Basic Chiffon Cake.
2. Mash the banana and mix it well with the pineapple juice to prevent enzymatic browning.
3. Add the mashed banana and pineapple juice to the liquid ingredients and follow steps 4 through 9 for Basic Chiffon Cake.

Chocolate Chiffon Cake

2 c cake flour	5 egg yolks
1/3 c cocoa powder	3/4 c milk
1-1/2 c sugar	1 tsp vanilla
2 tsp SAS baking powder	1 c egg whites
1/2 tsp salt	1/2 tsp cream of tartar
1/2 c oil	

1. Follow the recipe for Basic Chiffon Cake, combining the cocoa with the flour mixture in step 2.

Whole-Wheat Spice Chiffon Cake

	1/2 c finely chopped walnuts
1-3/4 c whole-wheat pastry flour	5 egg yolks
1/2 tsp salt	1/2 c oil
2 tsp SAS baking powder	3/4 c milk
1 c brown sugar	1 tsp vanilla
1 tsp cinnamon	1 c egg whites
1/4 tsp nutmeg	1 tsp cream of tartar
1/4 tsp allspice	1/2 c sugar

1. Stir the whole-wheat pastry flour, spoon it lightly into cup and level.
2. Stir the salt, baking powder, and spices into the flour.
3. Pack the brown sugar into the cup and level; then crumble it into the flour mixture and mix well with a French whip; press out lumps of sugar so that it is finely dispersed in the flour mixture.
4. Stir the nuts into the flour-sugar mixture.
5. Follow steps 3 through 9 for Basic Chiffon Cake.

Orange Chiffon Cake

2-1/4 c cake flour	5 egg yolks
1-1/2 c sugar	1/2 c oil
2 tsp SAS baking powder	3/4 c orange juice
1/2 tsp salt	1 c egg whites
1/3 c nonfat dry milk	1 tsp cream of tartar
1 Tbsp grated orange rind	

1. Follow steps 1 and 2 for Basic Chiffon Cake, adding the nonfat dry milk and grated orange rind to these dry ingredients.
2. Beat the oil and egg yolks together, then stir in the orange juice.
3. Follow steps 4 through 9 for the Basic Chiffon Cake.

EVALUATION OF CAKES

Enter evaluations on score sheet, Table 21-1.

A. Causes of Poor Quality

1. Volume too small, cake heavy for size: egg foam underbeaten; grease in mixing bowls, on beaters, or in baking pans; batter overmixed during incorporation of flour mixture; baking temperature too low.
2. Sunken cake: too much sugar used in the cake; pan not inverted and allowed to hang during cooling; cake removed from pan before being completely cooled.
3. Soggy cake: too much liquid used in chiffon and sponge cakes; too much sugar; foam underbeaten before addition of flour mixture; cake not baked long enough.
4. Tough cake: not enough sugar or cream of tartar used in cake; foam underbeaten before addition of flour mixture; batter overmixed while incorporating the flour mixture; cake baked too long.

B. Desirable Characteristics

1. Color: bright white for angel cakes; appropriate for ingredients in other cakes.
2. Grain: small, thin-walled cells; no large air spaces; no compact layer of cells; elastic or springy crumb.
3. Texture: tender and moist, not compact or soggy.
4. Shape: straight sides and top; not sunken in middle.
5. Flavor: natural for ingredients; no chemical taste.

Table 21-1 Score Sheet for Foam-Type Cakes

Score: Good — 3   Fair — 2   Poor — 1

Type of Cake	Color	Grain	Texture	Shape	Flavor	Comments

C. Comparison of Angel Cake Mixes with Prepared Cakes

Two types of angel cake mixes are available: one contains a packet of egg whites and a packet of flour and is mixed in the same way as the homemade variety of angel cake; the other contains only one packet of ingredients and is mixed in one bowl at one time.

1. Prepare the two types of mix according to package directions. Compare them to the prepared angel cakes and enter scores in Table 21-1, considering appearance, texture, tenderness, and flavor.
2. Compare costs of mixes and prepared cakes by calculating the cost of the ingredients used in making the prepared cakes. Even though only the egg whites are used, the cost of the yolks is included in the cost of the eggs. Consult Basic Foods, Appendix 1-Table 9 (pp. 596-611) for yields, noting that 1 doz large eggs supplies about 1-1/2 c egg white, that 1 lb cake flour equals about 4-1/2 c sifted before measuring, and that 1 lb granulated sugar contains about 2-1/4 c. Enter calculations for cost comparisons in Table 21.2.

D. Nutrient Composition of Foam-type Cakes

Basic Foods, Table 21.2 (p. 372), compares the nutrients in foam-type cakes with those in shortened cakes.

Questions

1. What ingredients in the whole egg and yolk sponge cakes are responsible for the higher iron and Vitamin A content of these cakes? *egg yolk*
2. What ingredient in shortened cakes is responsible for their higher caloric content? *fat*
3. Which cake would you recommend for low-fat diets? For lowest calories? *Angel*

Table 21-2   Cost Comparison of Angel Cakes

Type of Cake	Ingredients	Market Unit Measure	Cost ($)	Amt. in Recipe Measure (c)	Cost ($)	Total cost ($)	Total weight (g)	Cost per 100 g ($)

UNIT 18   SHORTENED CAKES

Suggested reading: Basic Foods, pages 265-272

Objective

- To prepare and evaluate a variety of shortened cakes

PREPARATION OF SHORTENED CAKES

General Instructions

1. Recipes are for two 9"-diameter layer cake pans unless otherwise specified.
2. Prepare pans before mixing the cake batter:
   a. Cut out parchment paper liners to fit the bottom of pan. Trace the outline of the pan on the paper with a pencil and cut inside the line; check to be sure the paper lies flat in the pan; trim where needed.
   b. Grease and flour the pan; then lay one paper liner in the pan and grease and flour it. Pan spray may be used for grease.
3. Center oven shelves and preheat oven to 350°F (176.5°C).
4. Use cake flour and sift before measuring, unless specified otherwise. Measure whole-wheat pastry flour by stirring it and then spooning it lightly into the cup. Use 2-1/4 c sifted cake flour for 2 c whole-wheat pastry flour.
5. Use shortening containing an emulsifier (mono- or diglycerides); 1/4 tsp butter flavor may be used if desired; it is not specified in the recipes.
6. Bake layers 25 to 30 minutes or until they test done:
   a. Cake springs back when lightly touched with finger tip.
   b. A food pick inserted in the center comes out clean.
7. Allow cakes to cool 5 minutes in the pan set on a cake rack.
8. Remove cake from the pan by inverting the rack over the top of the pan, inverting pan and rack together, lifting off the pan, and removing the paper liner.
9. Cool thoroughly before icing. See Unit 19 for recipes and instructions for icings and fillings.

Microwave Oven:

1. Use two 9" diameter glass cake dishes; grease dishes and paper liners; do not use flour.
2. Fill the dishes no more than 1/3 full; some of the batter may be left over.
3. Tape together 3" wide strips of aluminum foil long enough to extend around the circumference of the dishes; tape ends together.
4. Fold the foil down over the top of the dish so that it extends out over the batter about 1-1/2" and shields it from overcooking.
5. Cook one layer at a time on high power 6 minutes, turning the dish one-quarter turn every 2 minutes.
6. Remove the foil and cook 2-4 minutes longer, turning at the end of 2 minutes.

7. Cake may be moist on top when done, but it should spring back when pressed lightly with your finger.
8. Cook the cake in the dish 15 minutes, then invert it onto a plate.

A. Plain, Standard, and Rich Cake Formulas

Conventional Method of Mixing $\frac{1}{3}$ dry $+\frac{1}{2}$ l. $+\frac{1}{3}$ dry $+\frac{1}{2}$ l $+\frac{1}{3}$ dry

1. Place the shortening and sugar in the large bowl of the mixer and beat at high speed until light and fluffy.
2. Add the eggs and beat until the consistency of whipped cream (BF, Fig. 15.3, p. 270).
3. Measure the milk and add to it the vanilla (or other flavoring).
4. Sift and measure the flour and stir in the baking powder and salt.
5. Beat 1/3 the flour mixture into the creamed mixture, mixing about 30 seconds.
6. Mix in 1/2 the milk mixture, mixing about 15 seconds.
7. Repeat steps 5 and 6, adding another 1/3 of the flour and remaining milk.
8. Add the remaining flour mixture and beat 30 seconds.
9. Divide the batter evenly between the two prepared pans.
10. Position the pans in the oven as illustrated in Basic Foods, Fig. 3.5, p. 67, with one pan on each shelf and at opposite corners of their respective shelves, unless the oven is wide enough to place the pans side by side on the same shelf.
11. Bake and cool as specified under General Instructions.

Table 18-1 lists the ingredients for these three cake variations.

Table 18-1   Formulas for Plain, Standard, and Rich Shortened Cakes

Ingredients	Plain Cake	Standard Cake	Rich Cake
Cake flour, sifted	2 c	2 c	2 c
SAS baking powder	2 tsp	2 tsp	2 tsp
Salt	1/2 tsp	1/2 tsp	1/2 tsp
Sugar	2/3 c	1 c	1-1/3 c
Shortening	1/4 c	1/2 c	3/4 c
Eggs, large	1	2	3
Milk	2/3 c	2/3 c	2/3 c
Vanilla	1 tsp	1 tsp	1 tsp

B. Variations of Shortened Cakes

Gold Cake

2/3 c shortening	3/4 c orange juice	1/2 tsp salt
1-1/4 c sugar	2 c sifted cake flour	2 tsp finely grated orange
6 large egg yolks	2 tsp baking powder	rind

1. Follow steps 1 and 2 for Conventional Method of Mixing.
2. Measure the orange juice.
3. Sift and measure the flour and add the baking powder, salt, and orange rind, mixing well so that the orange rind is evenly distributed in the flour.
4. Follow steps 6 through 11 using orange juice instead of milk.

White Cake

1/2 c shortening	2/3 c milk	2 tsp baking powder
1-1/4 c sugar	1 tsp vanilla	1/2 tsp salt
4 large egg whites	2 c sifted cake flour	

1. Follow Conventional Method of Mixing.

Coconut Cake

Prepare White Cake; add 1 c coconut to the flour mixture in step 4 and mix well to coat the coconut.

Chocolate Cake

2 squares(oz) unsweetened chocolate	2 large eggs	3/4 tsp baking soda
1/2 c shortening	1 c buttermilk	1/2 tsp salt
1-1/3 c sugar	1 tsp vanilla	1 tsp cinnamon
	2 c sifted cake flour	

1. Melt chocolate by one of the following methods:
   a. Place squares of chocolate in a small glass dish and cook in the microwave oven 1-2 minutes.
   b. Place squares of chocolate in a small saucepan and heat on a surface unit; stir and watch to prevent scorching.
   c. Place the dish containing the squares of chocolate in a pan of water and heat on a surface unit.
2. Add the melted chocolate to the shortening and sugar in step 1 for the Conventional Method of Mixing.
3. Follow steps 2 through 4, adding the cinnamon to the flour mixture in step 4; then follow steps 5 through 11.

Pumpkin Cake

1/c shortening	1/2 tsp vanilla	1-1/2 tsp pumpkin-pie spice
1-1/3 c brown sugar	2 c whole-wheat pastry flour	or 1 tsp cinnamon; 1/4 tsp
2 large eggs	or 2-1/4 c sifted cake flour	nutmeg; 1/4 tsp allspice
3/4 c buttermilk	1 Tbsp SAS baking powder	1/2 c chopped walnuts
3/4 c canned pumpkin	1/2 tsp salt	

1. Follow steps 1 and 2 for Conventional Method of Mixing.
2. Combine pumpkin, buttermilk, and vanilla.
3. Stir the whole-wheat pastry flour and spoon it lightly into the cup; level it off to measure.
4. Combine flour, baking powder, salt, spice, and nuts; follow steps 5 through 11.

Carrot Cake

2/3 c shortening	2 c whole-wheat pastry flour or
1-1/3 brown sugar	2-1/4 c sifted cake flour
4 large eggs	2 tsp SAS baking powder
1/2 c milk	1/2 tsp salt
1 tsp vanilla	1/2 tsp cinnamon
1-1/2 c peeled and finely grated carrots	1/2 c chopped walnuts

1. Follow steps 1 through 3 for Conventional Method of Mixing.
2. Stir the flour, spoon it lightly into the cup, and level; combine flour, baking powder, salt, cinnamon, and walnuts.
3. Follow steps 5 through 11, stir the carrots into the batter in step 8.

Banana Nut Cake
_____

1/2 c shortening	1 Tbsp pineapple juice
1 c sugar	2 c sifted cake flour
2 large eggs	2 tsp SAS baking powder
1/2 c buttermilk	1/2 tsp salt
1 tsp vanilla	1/2 c chopped pecans
1 c mashed banana	

1. Follow steps 1 and 2 for Conventional Method of Mixing.
2. Mash the bananas and mix with the pineapple juice to prevent enzymatic browning; combine the mashed banana, buttermilk, and vanilla.
3. Follow step 4, adding the chopped nuts to the flour mixture.
4. Follow steps 5 through 11.

Pineapple Cake
_____

1/2 c shortening	1/2 c crushed pineapple, drained
1-1/4 c sugar	2 c sifted cake flour
2 large eggs	3/4 tsp baking soda
1/2 c pineapple juice	1/2 tsp salt

1. Follow steps 1 and 2; combine pineapple and juice and use   instead of milk and vanilla in step 3.
2. Follow steps 4 through 11, using pineapple instead of milk.

Wheat-Germ Spice Cake
_____

2/3 c shortening	1 c toasted wheat germ
1-1/2 c brown sugar	2 tsp SAS baking powder
4 large eggs	3/4 tsp salt
3/4 c milk	1-3/4 tsp apple-pie spice or 1 tsp cinnamon;
2 tsp vanilla	1/4 tsp each nutmeg, allspice, cloves
1-1/4 c whole wheat pastry flour or	1/2 c chopped pecans or
1-3/8 c sifted cake flour	1/4 c sesame seeds

1. Follow steps 1 through 4 for Conventional Method of Mixing, adding the wheat germ, pecans, and spice to the flour mixture.
2. Follow steps 5 through 11.

C. Conventional Sponge Method of Mixing

The conventional sponge method of mixing shortened cakes is called for when table fat or shortening without emulsifier is used.

1. Measure and combine the flour, salt, leavening, and other dry ingredients.
2. Measure the liquid and combine with flavoring extract.
3. Separate the eggs.
4. Cream together the egg yolks, 1/2 the sugar, and the fat.
5. Add the flour mixture and the liquid ingredients alternately to the creamed mixture.
6. Beat the egg whites to soft peaks, add 1/2 the sugar, and beat to stiff peaks.
7. Fold the egg-white foam into the batter and bake as directed for Conventional Method of Mixing.

EVALUATION OF SHORTENED CAKES

A. Causes of Poor Quality

1. Cake sunken in center: too much sugar, fat, or leavening; not enough liquid; not mixed enough after addition of flour mixture; pan too small for the amount of batter; oven temperature too low; cake not baked long enough.

2. Humped, cracked top and tunnels: not enough fat and/or sugar; mixed too much after addition of flour mixture; pan too deep for the amount of batter; oven temperature too high.

3. Uneven shape of layers: wrinkled paper liner in baking pan; layers not centered in oven; uneven oven temperatures.

4. Coarse crumb texture: too much sugar or leavening; oven temperature too low; not mixed enough after addition of flour mixture.

5. Heavy compact texture, low volume: not enough leavening, gas lost from batter before baking started; too much liquid, fat, or sugar; poor-quality shortening (lacked emulsifier); lack of air in creamed mixture; overmixed after addition of flour mixture; oven temperature too low; pan too small for amount of batter.

7. Lack of tenderness, dry crumb: not enough fat, sugar, or liquid; too much flour or egg; overmixed after addition of flour mixture.

8. Sugary, crispy top: too much sugar, fat, or leavening.

B. Desirable Characteristics

1. Appearance: straight sides, slightly rounded top; no cracks or peaks on top surface; even golden brown.

2. Grain: Small, thin-walled cells, evenly distributed, with no tunnels.

3. Texture: tender, smooth, moist crumb; neither soggy nor crumbly.

4. Flavor: characteristic of ingredients used, with no bitterness nor chemical off-flavors.

Enter evaluations on Table 18-2.

Table 18-2   Score Sheet for Shortened Cakes
   Score: Good — 3   Fair — 2   Poor — 1

Type of Cake	Appearance	Grain	Texture	Flavor	Comments

C. Comparison of Commercial Mixes with Prepared Cakes

Quality Comparisons

Prepare and bake several brands of shortened cake mixes and compare with comparable cakes, i.e., compare chocolate cakes with chocolate, white with white.

Cost Comparisons

Calculate cost of ingredients used in preparing a cake with the cost of comparable mixes of different brands, using Table 18-3.

Table 18-3   Cost Comparison of Shortened Cakes

Type of Cake	Ingredients	Market Unit		Amt. in Recipe		Total[1] cost ($)	Total[2] weight (g)	Cost per 100 g ($)
		Measure	Cost ($)	Measure	Cost ($)			

[1]Enter the total cost of all the ingredients for the prepared cakes and the cost of the mixes in this column.

[2]Obtain the total weight of both layers of the cakes after they are baked and cooled to room temperature.

Questions

1. Is baking soda a quick-acting, slow-acting, or double-acting leavening agent? *quick-acting*
2. What precautions must be observed when baking soda is used as the leavening agent?
   + acid

UNIT 19   FROSTINGS AND FILLINGS

Suggested reading: <u>Basic Foods</u>, pages 472-478

Objectives

- To prepare a variety of frostings and fillings
- To learn techniques for icing and decorating cakes

PREPARATION OF FROSTINGS AND FILLINGS

A. Flat Icings

Cream Glaze
_____

    1 c sifted confectioners' sugar   1 tsp honey

    1 Tbsp half-and-half or milk   1/2 tsp vanilla or almond extract

Mix together all of the ingredients; dribble over slightly cooled, baked sweet-dough products, or apply with a pastry brush to cookies or breads.

    <u>Yield</u>: Icing for top of one 8 or 9" layer

Fruit Juice Glaze
_____

    1 c sifted confectioners' sugar

    1 Tbsp juice (lemon, lime, orange, pineapple)

    1/4 tsp butter flavor

Combine all ingredients into a smooth mixture and use on baked breads and cookies.

    <u>Yield</u>: Icing for top of one 8 or 9" layer

Fruit Purée Glaze
_____

    1 c fruit purée   1/3 c light corn syrup

    1/3 c granulated sugar   1/4 tsp butter flavor

1. Process fresh, frozen, or canned drained fruits (berries, apricots, peaches, plums, persimmons) in a blender to prepare purée, adding 1 tsp lemon or pineapple juice to apricots and persimmons to prevent enzymatic browning.
2. Combine 1 c purée, sugar, and corn syrup in a 1-qt saucepan and bring to a boil; simmer about 3 minutes.
3. Use on baked cookies and breads as a glaze.

    <u>Yield</u>: About 1 cup

Cocoa Glaze

3 Tbsp water	1 c sifted confectioners' sugar
2 Tbsp table fat	1 tsp honey
1/4 c cocoa powder	1/2 tsp vanilla

1. Combine the water and table fat in a 1-qt saucepan and bring to a boil.
2. Remove from heat and stir in the cocoa, mixing until smooth. The mixture should form a ball at this point.
3. Add sugar, honey, and vanilla, mixing until smooth.

   Yield: Icing for one 8 or 9" layer

B. Broiled Frostings

Basic Broiled Frosting

3 Tbsp table fat, melted	1 c angel-flake coconut, chopped nuts, or
3/4 c brown sugar	combination
1/4 c half-and-half or milk	1—3 Tbsp sesame seeds (optional)

1. Combine all ingredients and spread on slightly cooled coffee cake still in its baking pan.
2. Place the pan low under the broiler and broil until the frosting is bubbly.

   Yield: Frosting for two 8 or 9" layers, or one 9 x 13" oblong

Peanut Butter Broiled Frosting

2 Tbsp table fat, melted	1/4 c half-and-half or milk
1/4 c peanut butter	1/2 c chopped peanuts or chocolate or
3/4 c brown sugar	butterscotch bits or mixture

1. Mix the melted table fat and peanut butter together until smooth, then stir in the other ingredients.
2. Spread the mixture on the cake and broil until bubbly.

   Yield: Frosting for two 8 or 9" layers, or one 9 x 13" oblong

C. Uncooked Frostings

Butter Cream Frosting I

4-1/2 c (1 lb) sifted confectioners' sugar	1/2 tsp salt
1 c (1/2 lb) table fat or shortening	2 tsp vanilla or almond extract
1/4 tsp butter flavor (optional)	2—3 Tbsp milk or cream

1. Combine fat, sugar, salt, and flavoring with about 2 Tbsp of the milk or cream and beat with an electric mixer.
2. Add additional milk while beating, 1 tsp at a time, until the frosting is smooth and fluffy and a good consistency for spreading.

   Yield: Frosting for two 8 or 9" layers, or one 9 x 13" oblong

This frosting is suitable for use in a pastry tube for forming cake decorations. It may also be used to frost a cake.

Butter Cream Frosting II

4-1/2 c (1 lb) sifted confectioners' sugar
1/2 c table fat or shortening
1/2 tsp salt

1/3 c half-and-half
2 tsp vanilla or almond extract
1/4 tsp butter flavor (optional)

Mix as described for Butter Cream Frosting I.

Yield: Frosting for two 8 or 9" layers or one 9 x 13" oblong

Chocolate Butter Cream Frosting

4-1/2 c (1 lb) sifted confectioners' sugar
1 c (1/2 lb) table fat or shortening
1/2 c cocoa powder, sifted
1/2 tsp salt

1/4 tsp butter flavor (optional)
1-1/2 tsp vanilla
1/2 to 1 tsp red food coloring
3 Tbsp milk or cream

1. Combine all ingredients and beat with electric mixer until smooth and fluffy.
2. Add additional milk if needed to obtain good spreading consistency.

Yield: Frosting for two 8 or 9" layers or one 9 x 13" oblong

Mocha Butter Cream Frosting

4-1/2 c (1 lb) sifted confectioners' sugar
1/2 c table fat or shortening
1/2 tsp salt
1/2 c cocoa powder, sifted

1/3 c half-and-half
1 tsp vanilla extract
1/4 tsp butter flavor (optional)
1 tsp instant coffee

Combine all ingredients and mix with electric mixer until smooth and fluffy, adding additional milk if needed to obtain spreading consistency.

Yield: Frosting for two 8 or 9" layers or one 9 x 13" oblong

Pineapple Cream Frosting

4-1/2 c (1 lb) sifted confectioners' sugar
1/2 c table fat or shortening
1/2 tsp salt

1/3 c crushed pineapple, drained
1/4 tsp butter flavor (optional)
1 tsp vanilla

Combine all ingredients and mix with an electric mixer until smooth and fluffy, adding pineapple juice as needed to obtain spreading consistency.

Yield: Frosting for two 8 or 9" layers or one 9 x 13" oblong

Lemon Butter Cream Frosting

4-1/2 (1 lb) sifted confectioners' sugar
1/2 c shortening or table fat
1/2 tsp salt
1 tsp finely grated lemon peel

2 Tbsp milk
1 Tbsp lemon juice
1 tsp vanilla or lemon extract
1/4 tsp butter flavor (optional)

Combine all ingredients and mix with an electric mixer until smooth and fluffy; add more milk or lemon juice if needed to obtain spreading consistency.

Yield: Frosting for two 8 or 9" layers or one 9 x 13" oblong

Cream Cheese Frosting

4-1/2 c (1 lb) sifted confectioners' sugar	2 Tbsp milk
1 3-oz package cream or Neufchatel cheese	1/2 tsp salt
	1 tsp vanilla
2 Tbsp table fat	1/4 tsp butter flavor (optional)

1. Combine the softened cheese, soft table fat, milk, salt, and flavoring; mix with electric mixer.
2. Add the sugar and mix until smooth and fluffy, adding more milk if needed to obtain spreading consistency.

   Yield: Frosting for two 8 or 9" layers or one 9 x 13" oblong

Creamy Decorative Frosting

2 c sifted confectioners' sugar	1/8 tsp salt
2 Tbsp shortening or table fat	1/2 tsp vanilla or almond extract
1 egg white	1/4 tsp butter flavor (optional)

1. Combine sugar, fat, salt, and flavoring; mix with electric mixer.
2. Add egg white and beat until smooth; add additional sugar if needed to get correct consistency. The frosting should be soft enough to pass through the decorator tip easily but firm enough to hold its shape.

Ornamental Icing

3 egg whites	4-1/2 c (1 lb) sifted confectioners' sugar
1/2 tsp cream of tartar	1 tsp vanilla

1. Combine the egg whites and cream of tartar in large bowl of electric mixer and beat at high speed to soft-peak stage.
2. Add the vanilla and sugar and beat until very stiff.
3. This icing crystallizes very fast and has a tendency to clog the tips of the decorating tubes. Place only a small amount of the icing in the pastry bag at a time, and wrap a wet towel around the outside of the bowl holding the icing.

Note: This icing dries to a hard consistency and is not suitable for frosting cakes. Decorations made from it are quite permanent, especially for hot climates.

D. Cooked Frostings

Seven-Minute Frosting

2 egg whites	1/2 Tbsp light corn syrup
1-1/2 c granulated sugar	1 tsp vanilla, lemon, orange, or almond extract
1/4 c + 1 Tbsp water	

1. Place the egg whites, water, sugar, and corn syrup in the top of a glass or stainless-steel (not aluminum) double boiler.
2. Cook over, not in, boiling water while beating constantly with a hand electric mixer for 7 minutes, or longer, until frosting holds a peak.
3. Beat in flavoring and color if desired.

4.   Keep warm over the hot water while frosting the cake.

     Yield: Frosting for two 8 or 9" layers or one 9 x 13" oblong

Maple Frosting

1/4 c milk   1/2 tsp maple flavoring
3/4 c dark brown sugar   1/2 tsp vanilla
1/4 c table fat   1/4 tsp salt
4-1/2 c (1 lb) sifted confectioners' sugar

1.   Combine the milk and sugar in a 1-qt saucepan and heat to boiling, stirring constantly.
2.   Place the table fat in a large mixing bowl and pour the hot milk mixture over it; beat
     the mixture with an electric mixer until smooth.
3.   Add the flavoring and salt. Add the confectioners' sugar, a little at a time, beating
     continuously with the electric mixer.
4.   Beat for 2 minutes after all the sugar has been added.
5.   If frosting appears too stiff, add a little milk and beat well.

     Yield: Frosting for two 8 or 9" layers or one 9 x 13" oblong

E. Fillings

Cream or Custard Filling

1 c half-and-half   1/4 tsp salt
1 Tbsp cornstarch   1/3 c sugar
2 egg yolks

Flavor Variations

a.   1 tsp vanilla
b.   1/2 tsp vanilla, 1/2 tsp almond extract, 1/2 c chopped almonds
c.   1 tsp vanilla, 1/2 c chopped dates, 1/4 c chopped walnuts
d.   1 c angel-flake coconut, 1/2 tsp almond flavoring

1.   Combine the egg yolks, half-and-half, and cornstarch in a 1-qt saucepan and mix until
     smooth; cook over moderate heat, stirring constantly with a spring stirrer, until the
     mixture comes to a boil.
2.   Remove from the heat and stir in the sugar, salt, and one of the flavor variations.
3.   Chill well before using as filling between cake layers or for sweet-dough products.

     Yield: 1-1/4 cup filling

Clear Fruit Filling

2/3 c water   2 Tbsp table fat
3 Tbsp cornstarch   1/2 c sugar
1/4 tsp salt

Flavor Variations

a.   1/3 c concentrated frozen lemonade, 1/2 tsp finely grated lemon rind
b.   1/3 c concentrated frozen orange juice, 1/2 tsp finely grated orange rind
c.   2/3 c pineapple juice instead of water, 1/2 c well-drained crushed pineapple

1. Combine the water, cornstarch, and salt in a 1-qt saucepan and mix until smooth.
2. Cook over moderately high heat, stirring constantly with spring stirrer, until mixture starts to boil.
3. Stir in the table fat, sugar, and one of the variations.
4. Cool before using as filling between cake layers or for sweet-dough products.

Yield: About 1 cup

Cocoa Whipped Cream

4 tsp cold water	dash of salt
1 tsp unflavored gelatin	1 c (1/2 pt) whipping cream
1/3 c cocoa powder	1/4 tsp vanilla
1/2 c sifted confectioners' sugar	

1. Place cold water in small metal measuring cup and add gelatin; allow to soften about 5 minutes; then place cup in container of hot water to dissolve the gelatin.
2. Press cocoa and confectioners' sugar through a sieve to remove lumps; add salt and mix until blended.
3. Whip cream until stiff, add the vanilla and warm gelatin, and beat to combine.
4. Add the cocoa-sugar mixture and beat until stiff enough to spread.
5. Use as filling between cake layers or for a cake roll.

Yield: About 2 cups

STEPS IN FROSTING AND DECORATING CAKES

A. Coloring the Frosting

1. Since table fats are slightly yellow in color, it is difficult to make table fat-frostings any color other than yellow, orange, or yellow-green. If other colors are desired, the frosting should be made with shortening. Addition of butter flavor to frostings prepared with shortening provides a pleasant flavor.
2. Colors are usually matched to the flavor used in the frosting: yellow for lemon, orange for orange flavor, pink for peppermint. Coconut is most often used with pure white frostings, which necessitates use of shortening in making the frosting.
3. Pale colors are more attractive than intense colors in frostings. It is advisable to combine a drop or two of the color with a tablespoon of the frosting and then mix portions of the colored frosting with the rest of the frosting to obtain the desired tint. Blends of colors, such as lavender, are obtained in this way.

B. Applying the Frosting

1. Cool layers or loaf cakes to room temperature; this can be accomplished by placing the cake, uncovered, in the freezer for 10 to 15 minutes.
2. In order to obtain a level cake, when working with layers, slice the rounded top off the layers so that the cake is level with the edge of the pan; a thin, long-bladed slicing knife or a sturdy string can be used (BF, 487, Fig. 25.4).
3. Brush loose crumbs from the sides and bottoms of layers with fingers or a pastry brush.
4. Place the first layer, cut side down, on a level plate. Place folded strips of waxed paper around the edge of the cake between the cake and the plate. These can be removed

easily after the cake is frosted, leaving the plate clean and attractive for serving.

5. Use 1/2 c to 1 c of the frosting or of a filling that blends in flavor with the cake and the frosting; spread it evenly over the bottom layer of the cake.

6. After brushing the top layer of the cake free of loose crumbs, place it on top of the lower layer so that the cut surface (top of the cake) is next to the filling.

7. If the layers are uneven, that is, higher on one side than on the other, try to place the thickest side of the top layer over the thinnest side of the lower layer.

8. Spread a thin layer of frosting over the sides and top of the two layers to bind the crumbs.

9. Chill the cake in the freezer 10 to 20 minutes, uncovered, before applying the final coat of icing.

10. To finish, place a mound (1/2 c) of frosting on the top of the cake to frost the sides of the cake, working from the bottom up and using additional frosting as needed until the sides are covered.

11. Frost the top of the cake and blend it into the sides.

12. If decorations are to be used on the cake, smooth the frosting. Dip a metal spatula in hot water, shake off the excess water, and quickly smooth over the sides and top. Avoid excessive strokes that may melt the frosting.

13. If Seven-Minute Frosting has been used, omit the smoothing and swirl designs onto frosting (BF, 486, Fig. 25.3) or stripe it in one or more directions with the back of a spoon or the tines of a fork (BF, 488, Fig. 25.8).

C. Decorations

1. Use Butter Cream Frosting I, Creamy Decorative Frosting, or Ornamental Icing. Divide into small bowls according to the number of colors needed. Color according to instructions for tinting frosting.

2. Use a separate pastry bag for each color and for each kind of tip to be used. Parchment paper or heavy brown paper shaped into cones are easily made (Fig. 19-1):

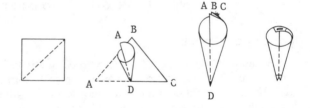

Fig. 19-1: Making a pastry bag from a piece of parchment paper cut into a triangle and rolled into a cone

  • Cut a 12" square of parchment paper into triangles as shown.
  • Roll up the triangle so that the tip of the cone is at D and points A, B, and C all come together at the top.
  • Fold over the points twice and staple to keep the cone from coming apart.

3. Cut off the tip of the cone to press icing through the hole for writing and similar decorating tasks, or insert a tip through the hole in the tip of the bag.

4. Fill the bag no more than half full and fold the top down over the icing to keep it feeding through the tip and not out the top.

5. Practice with various tips, making designs on waxed paper, to become familiar with the designs produced by each kind of tip, the angle at which to hold the tip, and the amount of pressure to use on the bag.

UNIT 20   COOKIES AND FRUIT-NUT BREADS

Suggested reading: Basic Foods, pages 275-282

Objective

- To prepare and evaluate a variety of cookies and fruit-nut breads

PREPARATION OF COOKIES

General Instructions

1. Place oven shelves on two center runners in the oven.
2. Preheat oven to specified temperature.
3. Measure flour by stirring it, spooning it lightly into the cup, and leveling it off, unless otherwise specified.
4. If cookies appear to be getting too brown on the bottom, move the pan to the top shelf; if too brown on top, move to lower shelf; if they become too brown in the back of the oven, reverse the baking pan; color does not always indicate doneness. A test cookie can be baked to check cooking time and temperature and how much the cookie will spread. After the cookie is baked, break it open to see if the interior is properly cooked. Most bar cookies can be tested for doneness by pressing lightly with a finger tip; if the cookie springs back, it is done.
5. Except for bar cookies, remove cookies from the pan as soon as they are baked and cool on a cake rack or in a single layer on waxed or parchment paper on the counter top.
6. Bar cookies are left in the pan to cool completely, but many are cut into bars and squares while still warm.

A. Drop Cookies

Oatmeal Drop Cookies
_____

3/4 c table fat or shortening	1/2 tsp salt
1 c brown sugar, firmly packed	1 tsp SAS baking powder
1 large egg	2 c rolled oats, uncooked
1 tsp vanilla	1/2 tsp apple-pie spice or cinnamon
1 c raisins	
1 c all-purpose or whole-wheat pastry flour	

1. Cream together the shortening, sugar, and egg.
2. Combine flour, salt, baking powder, and spice.
3. Add the vanilla to the creamed mixture; then stir in the oats, raisins, and flour mixture.
4. Drop by teaspoonfuls onto greased baking sheet.
5. Bake at 350°F (176.5°C) about 15 minutes.
   Yield: About 5 doz cookies

Chocolate Chip Cookies

1/2 c table fat or shortening
1/3 c granulated white sugar
1/3 c brown sugar, firmly packed
1 large egg
1 tsp vanilla

1 c all-purpose or whole-wheat pastry flour
1 tsp SAS baking powder
1/2 tsp salt
1 6-oz pkg chocolate chips

1. Cream together the shortening, sugars, and egg.
2. Combine flour, salt, and baking powder.
3. Add the vanilla to the creamed mixture; then stir in the chocolate chips and the flour mixture.
4. Drop by teaspoonfuls onto greased baking sheets.
5. Bake at 375°F (190.5°C) about 10 minutes.

Yield: About 4 doz cookies

Sesame Seed Cookies

1/3 c table fat or shortening
3/4 c brown sugar, firmly packed
1 large egg
1 tsp vanilla

2/3 c all-purpose or whole-wheat pastry flour
1/2 tsp SAS baking powder
1/2 tsp salt
1/3 c sesame seed

1. Cream together the shortening, sugar, and egg.
2. Stir the vanilla into the creamed mixture.
3. Combine flour, salt, and baking powder.
4. Add sesame seeds and flour mixture to the creamed mixture.
5. Drop by teaspoonfuls onto greased baking sheet.
6. Bake at 375°F (190.5°C) about 10 minutes.

Yield: About 4 doz cookies

Salted Peanut Macaroons

1/2 c table fat
1 c brown sugar, firmly packed
1 large egg
1 tsp vanilla
1/2 c salted peanuts, coarsely chopped

1 c all-purpose or whole-wheat flour
1/2 tsp salt
1 tsp SAS baking powder
1 c rolled oats, uncooked
1/2 c wheat flakes

1. Cream together table fat, sugar, and egg; stir in the vanilla and peanuts.
2. Combine flour, salt, and baking powder; then stir in the rolled oats.
3. Stir the flour mixture and wheat flakes into the creamed mixture.
4. Drop by teaspoonfuls onto a greased baking sheet.
5. Bake at 375°F (190.5°C) about 15 minutes.

Yield: About 4 doz cookies

Cottage Cheese Cookies

1/4 c table fat
1/2 c sugar
1/2 c small-curd cottage cheese
1/2 tsp vanilla

1 c cake flour
1 tsp SAS baking powder
1/4 tsp salt

1. Cream together the table fat and sugar; stir in the cottage cheese and vanilla.
2. Stir the cake flour and spoon lightly into the measuring cup and level.
3. Combine flour, baking powder, and salt.
4. Stir the flour mixture into the cottage cheese mixture.
5. Drop by teaspoonfuls onto a greased baking sheet.
6. Bake at 375°F (190.5°C) about 12 minutes.

Yield: About 3 doz cookies

B. Molded Cookies

Walnut Bon Bons
_____

1 c table fat	2 c sifted cake flour
1 c sifted confectioners' sugar	1/4 tsp salt
2 tsp vanilla	1 c finely chopped or ground nuts

1. Using an electric mixer, cream together the table fat and sugar; stir in the vanilla.
2. Add flour, salt, and nuts, and mix well.
3. Chill the dough in the freezer for 20 minutes.
4. Shape the dough into small balls, about 1" in diameter, and place them 1" apart on an ungreased baking sheet.
5. Bake at 375°F (190.5°C) about 9 minutes.

Yield: About 3 doz cookies

Peanut Butter Crisps
_____

1/2 c table fat	1 c + 2 Tbsp all-purpose or
1/2 c peanut butter	whole-wheat pastry flour
1 c brown sugar, firmly packed	1 tsp SAS baking powder
1 large egg	1/4 tsp salt
1 tsp vanilla	

1. Cream together the table fat, peanut butter, sugar, and egg; stir in the vanilla.
2. Combine flour, salt, and baking powder; stir the flour mixture into the creamed mixture.
3. Chill the dough in the freezer for 20 minutes.
4. Shape the dough into 1"-diameter balls and place about 3" apart on a greased baking sheet.
5. Flatten each ball with a fork dipped into flour, making the tines go in both directions on the cookie to form a checked design.
6. Cookies should not be more than 1/4" thick after being flattened.
7. Bake at 375°F (190.5°C) about 10 minutes.

Yield: About 3 doz cookies

Cream Cheese Pompoms
_____

1 c table fat	1 large egg yolk	1/2 tsp SAS baking powder
1 3-oz pkg Neufchatel or cream cheese	1 tsp vanilla	1/2 c chopped walnuts
	2-1/4 c all-purpose flour	1 egg white
1 c sugar	1/2 tsp salt	3/4 c finely ground nuts

1. Cream together the table fat, cheese, sugar, and egg yolk; stir in the vanilla.
2. Combine flour, salt, baking powder, and chopped walnuts.
3. Stir the flour mixture into the creamed mixture.
4. Chill the dough in the freezer for 20 minutes.
5. Shape the dough into balls 1" in diameter.
6. Beat the egg white until it is frothy.
7. Dip the balls of dough into the egg white and then roll in the finely ground nuts.
8. Place the nut-covered balls onto a greased baking sheet about 2" apart.
9. Bake at 350°F (176.5°C) about 15 minutes.

Yield: About 5 doz cookies

Almond Tea Cookies

1 c table fat	1/2 c finely chopped almonds
1/4 c honey	2 c all-purpose flour
1 tsp almond extract	1/4 tsp salt
1 c chopped raisins	1/2 tsp SAS baking powder

1. Cream together the table fat, honey, and almond extract; stir in the raisins and almonds.
2. Combine flour, salt, and baking powder, and stir into the raisin-almond mixture.
3. Chill the dough in the freezer for 20 minutes.
4. Shape the dough into small balls 1" in diameter and place them 2" apart on an ungreased baking sheet.
5. Bake at 350°F (176.5°C) for about 15 minutes.

Yield: About 3 doz cookies

C. Rolled Cookies

Gingerbread Cookies

1/2 c table fat or shortening	2 tsp SAS baking powder
3/4 c brown sugar, firmly packed	1/2 tsp salt
1/2 c dark molasses	1/2 tsp ginger
1 large egg	1/2 tsp cinnamon
1/2 tsp vanilla	1/4 tsp ground cloves
3 c all-purpose flour or 2-2/3 c whole-wheat pastry flour	

1. Cream together the shortening, sugar, molasses, and egg; stir in the vanilla.
2. Combine flour, salt, baking powder, cinnamon, ginger, and cloves.
3. Stir the flour mixture into the creamed mixture.
4. Roll out one-half the dough at a time on a lightly floured, pastry-cloth covered bread board to a thickness of 1/8".
5. Cut into desired shapes with cookie cutters or pastry wheel and place 1" apart on a greased baking sheet.
6. Bake at 350°F (176.5°C) about 10 minutes.

Yield: About 3 doz cookies

Cinnamon Sugar Cookies

1/2 c table fat
1 c sugar
1 large egg
1 tsp vanilla
2 c cake flour

1-1/2 tsp SAS baking powder
1/2 tsp salt
1 egg white
cinnamon sugar

1. Cream together the table fat, sugar, and egg; stir in the vanilla.
2. Combine flour, salt, and baking powder, and stir the flour mixture into the creamed mixture.
3. Chill the dough in the freezer for 20 minutes.
4. Roll out one-half the dough at a time on a lightly floured, pastry-cloth covered bread board to a thickness of 1/8".
5. Cut into desired shapes with cookie cutters or a pastry wheel. Brush tops with egg white; sprinkle with cinnamon sugar. Place 1" apart on a greased baking sheet.
6. Bake at 375°F (190.6°C) about 9 minutes.

Yield: About 4 doz cookies

D. Refrigerator Cookies

Cherry Coconut Cookies

1/2 c table fat
1/4 c sugar
1 Tbsp maraschino cherry juice
1/2 tsp vanilla
1/3 c chopped maraschino cherries

1/3 c finely chopped almonds
1/3 c grated coconut
1 c all-purpose flour
1/2 tsp SAS baking powder
1/4 tsp salt

1. Cream together the table fat, sugar, cherry juice, and vanilla.
2. Stir in the chopped fruits and nuts, flour, baking powder, and salt.
3. Pack the dough firmly into empty 6-oz frozen orange juice or similar containers.
4. Chill overnight if possible in the refrigerator; or place in coldest part of the freezer and chill 30 minutes or longer, rotating the container of dough at intervals to speed chilling.
5. Peel off the cardboard carton and slice the cookies about 1/4" thick.
6. Place cookies on an ungreased baking sheet 1" apart.
7. Bake at 375°F (190.5°C) for about 9 minutes.

Yield: About 3 doz cookies

Butterscotch Nut Chips

1/2 c table fat
1 c brown sugar, firmly packed
1 large egg
1/2 tsp vanilla
1-3/4 c whole-wheat pastry flour or 2 c all-purpose flour

1-1/2 tsp SAS baking powder
1/4 tsp salt
1/2 c finely chopped walnuts or pecans

1. Cream together the table fat, brown sugar, and egg; stir in the vanilla.
2. Combine the flour, baking powder, salt, and nuts; stir the flour mixture into the creamed mixture.
3. Follow steps 3 through 5 for Cherry Coconut Cookies, slicing cookies only 1/8" thick.

4. Follow steps 6 and 7 for Cherry Coconut Cookies.

    Yield: About 5 doz cookies

Chocolate Refrigerator Cookies
_____

1/2 c table fat	1/2 tsp vanilla
1-1/2 squares (1-1/2 oz) unsweetened chocolate	1-3/4 c whole-wheat pastry flour or 2 c all-purpose flour
1 c sugar	1 tsp SAS baking powder
1 large egg	1/4 tsp salt

1. Cream together the table fat, melted chocolate, sugar, and egg; stir in the vanilla.
2. Combine flour, baking powder, and salt; stir the flour mixture into the creamed mixture.
3. Follow steps 3 through 5 for Cherry Coconut Cookies, slicing the dough only 1/8" thick.
4. Follow steps 6 and 7 for Cherry Coconut Cookies.

    Yield: About 5 doz cookies

E. Pressed Cookies

Spritz Cookies
_____

1 c shortening	2-1/4 c sifted all-purpose flour
3/4 c sugar	1/4 tsp salt
1 large egg	1/2 tsp SAS baking powder
1 tsp lemon extract	

1. Cream together the shortening, sugar, and egg; stir in the lemon extract.
2. Sift and measure the flour; combine flour, salt, and baking powder.
3. Chill the dough in the freezer for 10 minutes.
4. Pack the dough into the cookie press with the desired disc in place.
5. Press the cookies out onto an ungreased baking sheet, spacing 1" apart.
6. Bake at 400°F (204.5°C) about 8 minutes.

    Yield: About 6 doz cookies

Orange Tea Cakes
_____

1/2 c shortening	1 tsp orange extract
1 c sugar	1-3/4 sifted all-purpose flour
1 large egg	1 tsp SAS baking powder
2 Tbsp milk	1/2 tsp salt

1. Cream together the shortening, sugar, and egg; stir in the milk and orange extract.
2. Sift and measure the flour; combine flour, baking powder, and salt.
3. Stir the flour mixture into the creamed mixture.
4. Follow steps 3 through 6 for Spritz Cookies.

    Yield: About 6 doz cookies

Peanut Krinkles

1/2 c peanut butter
1/4 c shortening
1/2 c brown sugar, firmly packed
1/2 c granulated sugar
1 large egg

1/2 tsp vanilla
3/4 c all-purpose flour
1 tsp SAS baking powder
1/4 tsp salt

1. Cream together the peanut butter, shortening, sugars, and egg; stir in the vanilla.
2. Combine flour, baking powder, and salt; stir the flour mixture into the creamed mixture.
3. Follow steps 3 through 6 for Spritz Cookies.

Yield: About 6 doz cookies

Cream Cheese Cookies

1/2 c shortening
1 3-oz pkg cream or Neufchatel cheese
1/2 c sugar
1 large egg yolk

1-1/2 tsp orange extract
1-1/2 c sifted all-purpose flour
1/2 tsp salt
1/2 tsp SAS baking powder

1. Cream together the shortening, cheese, sugar, and egg yolk; stir in the orange extract.
2. Sift and measure the flour; combine flour, salt, and baking powder; stir the flour mixture into the creamed mixture.
3. Follow steps 3 through 6 for Spritz Cookies.

Yield: About 5 doz cookies

F. Bar Cookies

Brownies

1/3 c table fat
2 squares (2 oz) unsweetened chocolate
1 c sugar
2 large eggs
1 tsp vanilla

3/4 c all-purpose or whole-wheat
               pastry flour
1/2 tsp SAS baking powder
1/2 tsp salt
1/2 c chopped walnuts

1. Place the table fat and chocolate in a 2-qt saucepan and melt them over moderate heat, stirring occasionally.
2. Remove pan from heat and stir in the sugar, eggs, and vanilla.
3. Combine flour, baking powder, salt, and nuts, and stir the flour mixture into the chocolate mixture.
4. Pour the batter into a greased 8 x 8" baking pan.
5. Bake at 350°F (176.5°C) about 25 minutes or until brownies spring back when touched lightly with the finger near the center.
6. Cool slightly and cut into squares.

Microwave Oven:

1. A glass 8" x 8" baking dish may be used, but a round one is preferable.
2. The baking dish should be greased, then the ingredients can be mixed in the baking dish and spread into an even layer.
3. Prepare a 3" wide strip of aluminum foil to be placed around the circumference of the dish, as described for shortened cakes (p. 180).

4. Cook at high power 6 minutes, turning dish one-quarter turn every 2 minutes.
5. Remove the foil and cook 2-4 minutes longer.
6. Brownies will be moist on top, but will spring back when pressed lightly with your finger.
7. Cool in a dish until cool to the touch, then cut into squares.

Date Nut Bars

3/4 c brown sugar	1-1/2 c chopped dates	1 tsp SAS baking powder
2 large eggs	3/4 c chopped walnuts	1/2 tsp salt
1 tsp vanilla	3/4 c all-purpose or whole-wheat pastry flour	

1. Cream together the sugar and eggs; stir in the vanilla.
2. Combine flour, baking powder, and salt; add the flour mixture, nuts, and dates to the egg mixture.
3. Spread the batter evenly into a greased 9 x 9" baking pan.
4. Bake at 325°F(162.5°C) about 30 minutes.
5. Cut into squares as soon as bars are baked, but cool completely before removing squares from the pan.

Microwave Oven:

Follow instructions for Brownies.

Wheat Germ Butterscotch Brownies

1/3 c table fat	1/2 c wheat germ
1 c brown sugar, firmly packed	1 tsp SAS baking powder
2 large eggs	1/4 tsp salt
1 tsp vanilla	1/2 c chopped cashews
3/4 c all-purpose or whole-wheat pastry flour	

1. Cream together the table fat, sugar, and eggs; stir in the vanilla.
2. Combine flour, wheat germ, baking powder, and salt.
3. Stir the flour mixture and cashews into the creamed mixture.
4. Pour the mixture into a greased 8 x 8" baking pan.
5. Bake at 350°F (176.5°C) 25 minutes or until brownies spring back when touched lightly in the center with the finger tip.

Microwave Oven:

Follow instructions for Brownies.

Nut Chews

1 c brown sugar, firmly packed	1/2 tsp SAS baking powder
2 large eggs	1/8 tsp salt
1 tsp vanilla	1 c chopped Brazil nuts or almonds
1/3 c all-purpose or whole-wheat pastry flour	

1. Beat together the sugar, eggs, and vanilla.
2. Combine flour, baking powder, and salt.
3. Stir the flour mixture and chopped nuts into the egg mixture.
4. Spread the mixture into a well-greased 9 x 9" baking pan.
5. Bake at 350°F (176.5°C) about 25 minutes.
6. Invert the pan immediately on a cake rack as soon as it is baked.
7. Cool before cutting into squares or bars.

Microwave Oven:

Follow instructions for Brownies.

G. Filled Cookies

Kolachky
_____

1/2 c table fat	1 c sifted all-purpose flour
1 3-oz pkg Neufchatel or cream cheese	preserves or thick jam
1/8 tsp salt	confectioners' sugar
1 Tbsp sugar	

1. Using an electric mixer, cream together the table fat and cheese.
2. Sift and measure the flour; stir the salt and sugar into the flour.
3. Stir the flour mixture into the cheese mixture to form a ball of dough.
4. Roll out the dough to a thickness of about 1/16" on a lightly floured pastry cloth.
5. Cut dough with 2"-diameter round cutter.
6. Spread each circle of dough with jam or preserves and fold two opposite edges of the circle to the center, overlapping slightly.
7. Place filled cookies on a lightly greased baking sheet about 1" apart.
8. Bake at 375°F (190.5°C) for 15 minutes.
9. Sift confectioners' sugar over top of warm cookies.

Yield: About 3 doz cookies

Cookie Tarts
_____

1. Prepare recipe for rolled Cinnamon Sugar Cookies, omitting the cinnamon.
2. Roll the dough to 1/6" thickness and cut with a 3"-diameter cutter, or cut into 3" squares with a pastry wheel.
3. Prepare one of the fillings for Puff Pastry Tarts (Unit 11).
4. Place 1 Tbsp filling in the center of each circle or square.
5. Moisten the edges of the circle or square of cookie dough with water or egg wash (1 egg mixed with 1 Tbsp water or milk).
6. Fold the circle or square in half and press the outer edges of the tart together to retain the filling; use the tines of a fork to seal the edges for a decorative effect.
7. Prick the top of the tart several times with a blunt fork.
8. Transfer the filled cookie tarts to a greased baking sheet with a wide spatula or pancake turner, placing 2" apart.
9. Bake at 375°F (190.5°C) about 10 minutes or until lightly browned.
10. Allow tarts to cool on the baking sheet for about 5 minutes, then transfer to a cake rack to finish cooling.

Pastry Tarts

---

1. Prepare recipe for single-crust pastry (Unit 11). Use of table fat provides a rich flavor in the pastry.
2. Follow directions for Cookie Tarts.

EVALUATION OF COOKIES

Cookies can be evaluated for their general appearance, texture, and flavor. Because of the great variety possible with cookies, it is difficult to establish specific characteristics that apply to all types of cookies.

A. Appearance

1. The size varies with the type of cookie.
    a. Cookie should be thin enough to bite through easily but not so thin that it crumbles or falls apart.
    b. The diameter should be small enough for cookie to be handled and consumed easily.
2. The shape should be uniform for the type of cookie. Bar cookies should hold the shape in which they are cut; rolled cookies should hold the shape of the cutter; pressed cookies should hold the shape and imprint of the template used.
3. The color of the cookie should be characteristic of the ingredients used, lightly browned; not excessively dark.
4. The cookies should hold together and not crumble into pieces.

B. Texture

1. Texture should be characteristic for the type of cookie.
2. Cookies should be tender. Some are moist and cakelike, some are crisp, and some are chewy.

C. Flavor

1. Flavor should be characteristic of the ingredients used.
2. Cookies should be free of bitter or off-flavors caused by using rancid flour, fat, chocolate, nuts, or other ingredients, or excessive leavening, or insufficient acid for the amount of baking soda used.
3. Cookies should have adequate but not excessive amounts of salt, flavoring extract, or spices.

Score cookies for these characteristics in Table 20-1.

Table 20-1   Score Sheet for Cookies

Score: Good — 3   Fair — 2   Poor — 1

Type of Cookie	Appearance	Texture	Flavor	Comments

PREPARATION OF FRUIT-NUT BREADS

General Instructions

Ingredients for a variety of fruit-nut breads are listed in Table 20-2. Amounts will make one 4-1/2 x 8-1/2 x 2-3/4" loaf or three pup loaves 3-1/4 x 5-3/4 x 2".

Spice Nut Bread

1. Preheat oven to 375°F (190.5°C).
2. Brush bottom and sides of loaf pan(s) with melted table fat or shortening, applying generously.
3. Cream together the sugar and table fat in the large bowl of the electric mixer; add the egg and flavoring and beat until light.
4. Stir the flour and spoon it lightly into the measuring cup.
5. Combine flour, baking powder, salt, and spices. If the baking soda or baking powder contain lumps, press them through a sieve.
6. Stir the chopped nuts into the flour mixture.
7. Add the milk to the creamed mixture and mix with electric mixer about 2 seconds.
8. Add the flour mixture and mix only until combined; scrape down the bowl as needed. This step should require about 15 seconds of mixing with an electric mixer.

9. Pour the batter into the large loaf pan or divide it evenly among the pup loaf pans.
10. Bake large loaf about 55 minutes and small loaves about 35 to 40 minutes.
11. Cool the loaves in the pans about 5 minutes; cut the bread from the sides of the pan if necessary, and complete cooling of the breads on a cake rack.
12. Do not try to slice the breads until they are completely cooled; cooling can be hastened by placing the breads in a plastic bag in the freezer.
13. Slice thin and serve with softened cream cheese, table fat, or plain.

Microwave Oven:

1. Use a glass loaf pan of the above dimensions; grease, line the bottom with parchment paper and grease the paper.
2. After placing the batter in the loaf pan, arrange a 3" strip of aluminum foil over each end of the loaf pan and folded so that about 1-1/2" of the foil shields the batter at the end of the pan.
3. Cook at high power for 4 minutes, turning the pan a quarter turn every 2 minutes.
4. Remove the foil and cook 2-4 minutes longer, turning every 2 minutes.
5. The bread should spring back when pressed lightly with your finger.

Orange Nut Bread

1. Follow steps 1 through 6 for Spice Nut Bread.
2. Add the undiluted thawed orange-juice concentrate and the orange rind or candied orange peel with the milk in step 7; then follow steps 8 through 11.

Coconut Almond Bread

1. Follow steps 1 through 6 for Spice Nut Bread.
2. Stir the coconut and almonds into the flour mixture in step 6.
3. Follow steps 7 through 11.

Date Nut Bread

1. Place chopped, pitted dates and milk in a 1-qt saucepan and heat, stirring occasionally until steaming hot. Chill in freezer.
2. Follow steps 1 through 6 for Spice Nut Bread.
3. Add the date-milk mixture in place of milk in step 7; then follow steps 8 through 11.

Banana Nut Bread

1. Mash bananas and measure 3/4 cup; stir the pineapple juice into the mashed banana to prevent enzymatic browning.
2. Follow steps 1 through 6 for Spice Nut Bread.
3. Add the mashed banana to the milk in step 7 and follow steps 8 through 11.

Apple Nut Bread

1. Wash, peel, and core about 2 apples; grate on coarse grater and measure 3/4 cup; stir the pineapple juice into the grated apple to prevent enzymatic browning.
2. Follow steps 1 through 6 for Spice Nut Bread.
3. Add the grated apple to the milk in step 7 and follow steps 8 through 11.

Table 20-2   Ingredients for Fruit-Nut Breads

Ingredients	Spice Nut	Date Nut	Banana Nut	Apple Nut	Orange Nut	Coconut Almond
Granulated sugar (c)	—	—	1/2	1/2	1/2	1/2
Brown sugar (c)	2/3	1/3	—	—	—	—
Table fat (c)	1/4	1/4	1/4	1/4	1/4	1/4
Large egg	1	1	1	1	1	1
Vanilla extract (tsp)	1	1	1/2	1	—	—
Buttermilk	1 c + 2 Tbsp	—	1/2	1/2	—	—
Milk (c)[1]	—	3/4	—	—	1/2	1 c + 2 Tbsp
All-purpose flour (c)[2]	2-1/4	2-1/4	2-1/4	2-1/4	2-1/4	2-1/4
SAS Baking powder (tsp)	1	1	1	1	1	3
Baking soda (tsp)	1/2	1/2	1/2	1/2	1/2	—
Salt (tsp)	1/2	1/2	1/2	1/2	1/2	1/2
Walnuts (c)[3]	1/3	1/3	1/3	1/3	1/3	—
Apple-pie spice (tsp)[4]	2	1/2	—	—	—	—
Other ingredients		1/2 c chopped dates	3/4 c mashed banana 2 Tbsp pine-apple juice	3/4 c grated apple 2 Tbsp pine-apple juice	1/3 c frozen orange-juice 2 tsp grated orange rind[5]	1 tsp almond extract 2/3 c grated coconut 1/3 c sliced almonds

[1]Milk can be nonfat, low-fat, whole, fresh milk, or reconstituted dried or canned milk.

[2]Two cups whole-wheat pastry flour can be used instead of all-purpose.

[3]Other nuts can be used and the amount increased.

[4]Apple-pie spice is a mixture of spices: 1/2 tsp cinnamon, 1/8 tsp nutmeg, 1/8 tsp cloves, 1/8 tsp ginger, and 1/8 tsp allspice.

[5]Or 1/2 c chopped candied orange peel. Orange peel should be finely grated, not shredded, using the colored part of the peel only.

EVALUATION OF FRUIT BREADS

Desirable Characteristics

- Shape: straight sides, slightly rounded top, free from peaks; a cracked top is acceptable
- Color: golden brown
- Texture: moist, tender; not soggy, crumbly, or dry
- Grain: compact, small cells, free from tunnels
- Flavor: characteristic of ingredients used; no bitter or off-flavors

Enter evaluations on Table 20-3.

Table 20-3   Score Sheet for Fruit-Nut Breads

Score: Good — 3   Fair — 2   Poor — 1

Type of Bread	Shape	Color	Texture	Grain	Flavor	Comments

Questions

1. Why should fruit-nut breads containing baking soda be mixed and baked as quickly as possible?
2. Why do all of the fruit breads except the Coconut Almond and Danish Fruit use baking soda?
3. Why is it necessary to use baking powder in the fruit breads containing baking soda?
4. Account for the different amounts of milk used in the different breads.

UNIT 21   MEAT PREPARATION

Suggested reading: Basic Foods, Chapter 22

Objectives

- To compare costs of lean meat from various retail cuts and grades of ground meat
- To identify retail and wholesale cuts of meat
- To prepare meats using dry-heat and moist-heat methods
- To prepare ground meat in a variety of ways

YIELD AND COST OF VARIOUS MEATS

A. Retail Cuts of Meat

Use such cuts as rib steak, T-bone steak, sirloin steak, full-cut round steak, top or bottom round steak, chuck steak, or flank steak; lamb loin, rib or shoulder chops; pork shoulder or loin chops; and veal round steak.

1. Weigh the piece of meat to the nearest gram; record the weight in Table 21-1, column 2, and record the cost per pound of the meat in column 1.
2. Using a sharp paring knife and razor blade, carefully cut connective tissues and fat from the lean meat and separate both from the bones.
3. Obtain the weight of the lean meat and record it in column 8 of Table 21-1. Record the weight of the bone in column 6 and the weight of the fat and connective tisues in column 4.
4. Calculate the percentage of connective tissue and fat: column 4 ÷ column 2 x 100 = column 5.   Example: 95 g fat ÷ 794 g meat x 100 = 11.96%, which rounds off to 12% fat and connective tissue.
5. Calculate the percentage of bone: column 6 ÷ column 2 x 100 = column 7. Example: 24 g bone ÷ 794 g meat x 100 = 3.02%, or 3% bone.
6. Calculate the percentage of lean meat: column 8 ÷ column 2 x 100 = column 9. Example: 675 g lean meat ÷ 794 g x 100 = 85% lean meat.
7. Calculate cost of piece of meat used for dissection: column 1 ÷ 454 x column 2 = column 3. Example: $2.30 ÷ 454 x 794 = $3.90, the cost of the cut of meat and therefore the cost of the lean meat obtained from the cut.
8. Calculate the cost of 100 g lean meat: column 3 ÷ column 8 x 100 = column 10. Example: $3.90 ÷ 675 x 100 g = $0.58, the cost of 100 g lean meat.

B. Grades of Ground Beef

Use samples of beef ground from various retail cuts.

1. Weigh out exactly 100 g ground meat.
2. Crumble the sample into a 6" frying pan. Heat the surface unit and cook the meat over moderately high heat, stirring, for exactly 4 minutes.

208 / Meat Preparation

X Table 21-1   Yield and Cost Comparisons of Various Retail Cuts

Cut of Meat	Cost per lb ($)	Weight of cut (g)	Cost of cut ($)	Connective tissue-fat (g)	(%)	Bone (g)	(%)	Lean (g)	(%)	Cost of lean per 100 g ($)
	1	2	3	4	5	6	7	8	9	10
Example: Round steak, entire, bone in, choice	2.30	794	3.90	95	12	24	3	675	85	0.58
Round steak	2.29									
Top Round	3.29									
chuck	2.49									
Short ribs	1.39									
Sirloin steak	3.29									
Brisket	1.19									
Ribeye	2.79									
Flank	3.99									

3. Pour the cooked meat into a strainer to separate the cooked meat from the fat; press the meat with a spoon or rubber scraper to remove as much fat as possible.
4. Weigh the lean meat to the nearest gram and record the weight in column 2 of Table 21-2; record the cost per pound of meat in column 1.
5. Calculate the cost of the cooked meat: column 1 ÷ 454 x 100 = column 3.   Example: $1.60 ÷ 454 x 100 = $0.35.
6. Calculate the cost of 100 g of cooked lean meat: column 3 ÷ column 2 x 100 = column 4. Example: $0.35 ÷ 58 x 100 = $0.61.

Table 21-2 Yield and Cost Comparisons of Ground Meat

Sample Number	Cost per lb ($) 1	Cooked Lean (g) 2	Cost of Cooked Lean ($) 3	Cost of 100 g of Cooked Lean ($) 4
Example	1.60	58	0.35	0.61
Regular	1.94			
Round	2.49			

IDENTIFICATION OF RETAIL AND WHOLESALE CUTS OF MEAT

A. Beef

Identify the wholesale or primal cuts of beef indicated by numbers in Figure 21-1. For each primal cut, name one or more retail cuts according to the Uniform Retail Meat Identity Standards.

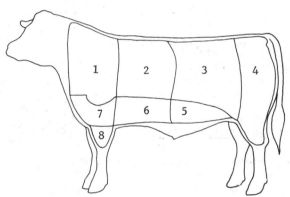

Fig. 21-1: Wholesale (primal) cuts of beef

Wholesale (primal) cuts

1. _____ :
2. _____ :
3. _____ :
4. _____ :
5. _____ :
6. _____ :
7. _____ :

Retail cuts

_____ , _____
_____ , _____
_____ , _____
_____ , _____
_____
_____
_____

B. Lamb

Indicate the primal cut from which these retail cuts are obtained:

Loin chop: _____

Blade chop: _____

Leg of lamb: _____

Rib chop: _____

Arm chop: _____

Square-cut shoulder roast: _____

C. Pork

Indicate the primal cuts from which these retail cuts are obtained:

Blade steak or roast: _____

Loin chop: _____

Picnic shoulder ham: _____

Smoked ham: _____

MEAT COOKERY

Generally, one serving of meat equals about 4 oz boneless lean or slightly marbled meat. If meat includes bones or large amounts of fat, the amount per serving must be increased accordingly. Use of textured vegetable protein, egg, cheese, beans, and other meats in a particular dish decreases the amount of meat per serving.

A. Dry-Heat Method: Roasting

Low-Temperature Roasting (BF, 392-393)

This method is suitable for beef rump, round, round-bone chuck; lamb shoulder; and veal shoulder.

1. Trim fat and connective tissue from the meat.
2. Oil the outer surface of the roast unless it is very well marbled.
3. Place the roast on a rack in a roasting pan.
4. Place a meat thermometer so that the tip is in the center of the roast touching neither fat nor bone (BF, 393, Fig. 22.12).
5. Roast the meat uncovered in a 200°F (93.5°C) oven until the desired internal temperature is reached. Allow about 70 minutes per lb for rare meat (140°F; 60°C) and about 95 minutes per lb for medium or well done (160-165°F; 71.5-74°C). These cuts of meat lose tenderness when cooked to the well-done stage.
6. Check the internal temperature of the meat 1 to 2 hours before expected serving time, depending on the size of the roast. If the meat appears to be cooking too quickly, reduce the oven temperature to 150-175°F (65.5-79.5°C) to keep it warm until serving

time. If it appears to be cooking too slowly, increase the oven temperature to 225–250°F (107–121°C).

Moderate-Temperature Roasting

This method is suitable for rib, loin, and sirloin beef roasts; pork loin, shoulder, and fresh leg roasts and hams; lamb shoulder, rib, loin, and leg roasts; and veal leg, loin, and rib roasts.

1. Trim exterior visible fat from the roast, and lightly oil surface.
2. Place the roast on a rack in a roasting pan.
3. Place a meat thermometer so that the tip is in the center of the roast touching neither fat nor bone.
4. Roast uncovered at 325°F (162.5°C) until the desired internal temperature is obtained. Allow about 30 minutes per lb for rare meat and about 40 to 45 minutes per lb for medium to well done.

B. Dry-Heat Method: Broiling

This method applies to beef rib, T-bone, or sirloin steaks; lamb and pork chops; and ground-meat patties.

Broiling Tender Meats

1. Place broiler shelf 2-3" below the heat source if meat is from 3/4-1" thick, and 3-5" below the heat source if the meat is 1-2" thick. Broilers vary in heat output so these distances are approximate.
2. Trim visible fat and connective tissue from meat.
3. Arrange the meat on the rack of the broiler pan (Fig. 21-2). To facilitate cleaning, rack and pan may be coated with pan spray, or aluminum foil may be placed in the pan under the rack.
4. Set the heat control regulator to broil; the unit need not be preheated.
5. Brown the meat on the top side for 5 to 10 minutes; then season it with salt and pepper. Meat may be brushed with melted table fat or barbecue sauce before broiling, but it should not be salted.
6. Turn the meat over with tongs and brown the second side.
7. Test for the desired degree of doneness. A thermometer may be used in thick steaks (2"): roasting temperatures apply to broiled meat. For thinner cuts of meat, cut a small slit in the center of the meat or near the bone and check the color.

Fig. 21-2: A stainless steel pan and rack for broiling and roasting small amounts of meat

Tenderized Beef Round Steak

 round steak, at least 3/4" thick
 papain
 barbecue sauce

1. Trim the steak of connective tissue and fat.
2. Pierce the steak repeatedly on both sides with a sharp fork.

3. Sprinkle each side of the steak with papain (meat tenderizer) and rub it into the meat with the fingers.
4. Brush a light coating of barbecue sauce on each side of the steak and place the meat on the rack of the broiler pan; let stand at room temperature 30 minutes.
5. Broil the meat on each side to the desired degree of doneness; this cut of meat loses tenderness if cooked beyond the rare stage.

Beef Kabobs

1/2-1 lb beef round or sirloin, 1-2" thick	1/4 tsp basil, crushed
2 Tbsp soy sauce	1/2 tsp cornstarch
1/4 c wine or meat stock	1 tsp oil
1 small clove garlic, crushed	1/8-1/4 lb fresh mushrooms
1/4 c minced onion	1/4-1/2 lb pearl onions
1/4 tsp oregano, crushed	6-8 cherry tomatoes

1. Trim the meat of fat and connective tissue and cut into 1-2" cubes.
2. Combine soy sauce, wine or stock, garlic, minced onion, oregano, basil, cornstarch, oil, and meat; marinate in the refrigerator overnight, if possible.
3. Place the meat on skewers about 2" below heat source and broil to the desired degree of doneness, turning once with tongs.
4. Wash, dry, and dip the mushrooms in the meat marinade or in French dressing; thread on skewers.
5. Place pearl onions in saucepan and cover with water; bring to a boil; boil 3 minutes; drain; cool in cold water; peel, and thread on skewer.
6. Cherry tomatoes may be skewered and broiled, or placed on the ends of the skewers of meat as a garnish.
7. The skewers of mushrooms and onions can be placed on the broiler pan with the meat, but the time required to cook them may differ from the time required for the meat, depending on their size and on how well done the meat is to be.

Yield: 4 servings per lb lean meat

Lamb Shish Kabob

1/2-1 lb lamb shoulder or leg	Optional:
1 small onion, sliced	
1 small clove garlic, crushed	1 green pepper
1/8 tsp thyme, crushed	1 tomato
1/8 tsp rosemary, crushed	1 whole onion
1/2 tsp salt	

1. Trim the meat of fat and connective tissue and cut it into 1-1/2-2" cubes.
2. Combine the cubes of meat with the sliced onion, garlic, thyme, rosemary, and salt; marinate in the refrigerator overnight, if possible.
3. Skewer the meat and broil to the desired degree of doneness, turning once. Pieces of green pepper, tomato, and onion may be alternated with the meat on the skewers.

Yield: 4 servings per lb lean meat

Beef Teriyaki

1/2 lb beef round	1 tsp onion powder
2 Tbsp soy or teriyaki sauce	1 tsp crushed ginger
1/4 c wine or beef stock	1/2 tsp cornstarch
1 small clove garlic, crushed	

1. Partially freeze a 2 x 2 x 4" piece of beef round so that it will remain rigid for slicing. Slice it into 2 x 2" slices about 1/8" thick.
2. Combine the soy sauce, wine or stock, garlic, onion powder, ginger, cornstarch, and sliced beef; marinate overnight if possible.
3. Thread the strips of meat on skewers by bending the pieces back and forth as the skewer is pierced through them. Several pieces can be placed on one skewer.
4. Place the meat on rack of broiler pan and broil about 2" below the heat source, turning once.

Yield: 3 servings

Beef Roulade

1/2 lb lean beef round, trimmed	1/4 c grated Parmesan cheese
1 small green onion, including top	1/4 c grated Monterey Jack cheese
1 Tbsp finely chopped celery	1/4 c fresh bread crumbs
2 Tbsp chopped canned mushrooms	1 Tbsp liquid from canned mushrooms
1 tsp table fat	or milk
1/8 tsp salt	

1. Partially freeze a 2 x 2 x 4" piece of beef round so that it will remain rigid for slicing. Slice it into eight or nine 2 x 4" slices.
2. Slice the onion.
3. Melt the table fat in the frying pan and sauté the onion, celery, and mushrooms.
4. Mix the vegetables with the salt, cheeses, bread crumbs, and liquid.
5. Spread filling on each slice of meat.
6. Starting at the narrow end, roll up each slice and fasten with a food pick.
7. Place the rolls of meat on a broiler pan about 2" below the heat source and broil 3-5 minutes on each side.
8. Carefully remove the food picks before serving.

Yield: 3 servings

C. Dry-Heat Method: Pan Broiling

Pan-Broiled Lamb or Pork Chops

2 chops	1 Tbsp flour
1/2 c water	seasoning to taste

1. Trim visible fat and connective tissue from the chops.
2. Spray the frying pan lightly with pan spray, or spread about 1 tsp fat over bottom of pan.
3. Place the chops in the pan and cook over moderate heat, uncovered, turning occasionally to cook evenly until well done.
4. Drain off any accumulated fat.
5. Season the chops and keep warm while preparing the gravy.
   a. Add water and flour to the juices in the pan, mixing until smooth and free of lumps.

b. Heat to boiling, stirring constantly. Season to taste.

c. The chops can be heated in the gravy to serving temperature, or the gravy can be served over cooked noodles or mashed potatoes.

Yield: 2 servings

D. Dry-Heat Method: Pan Frying

For flour mixtures, egg dips, or crumbs used for coating pieces of meat, the amounts shown in the recipes are approximate. Left-over crumbs may be frozen in an airtight container for later use.

It is also difficult to specify the amount of fat needed for sautéing. More is required in a large pan than in a small one. It is preferable to use as little as possible.

Chicken-Fried Steak
_____

1/2 lb round steak, 1/3-1/2" thick	1/8 tsp pepper
1/4 c flour	1-2 Tbsp oil
1/2 tsp salt	

1. Combine the flour, salt, and pepper in a flat pan or on waxed paper.
2. Trim the fat and connective tissue from steak and cut into pieces.
3. Pound each piece on both sides with a meat pounder until meat is about 1/4" thick.
4. Dredge meat on both sides in flour mixture.
5. Put oil into frying pan and heat until a drop of water placed in the pan sizzles.
6. Place the meat in pan and brown on each side over moderate heat.

Yield: 2 servings

Pan-Fried Beef Liver and Onion
_____

1/3-1/2 lb beef liver, sliced 3/4" thick
1 Tbsp table fat
1 small onion

1. Remove the membranes from the liver.
2. Melt the table fat in a small frying pan and lay slices of liver in a single layer in the pan.
3. Cook the liver over moderate heat 2 to 3 minutes on each side. The meat should be slightly pink on the interior and juice should run out when the meat is cut.
4. Remove the liver to a hot serving plate and keep warm.
5. Peel the onion, cut in half lengthwise, and slice.
6. Place onion in pan and cook, covered, over low heat until translucent.
7. Serve liver topped with sautéed onion.

Yield: 2 servings

Breaded Veal Cutlets
_____

1/2 lb veal round steak	1 egg
1/4 c flour	1 Tbsp milk
1/2 tsp salt	1-1/2 c bread crumbs
1/8 tsp pepper	2 Tbsp oil

1. Trim the fat and connective tissue from the veal and cut into 2 pieces.
2. Pound each piece with a meat pounder until about 1/4" thick.
3. Combine the flour, salt, and pepper, and dredge meat in mixture.
4. Beat the egg and milk together and dip the floured veal into the egg mixture; then cover both sides with crumbs.
5. Heat the oil in the frying pan, add the veal, and cook over moderate heat, browning both sides.

Yield: 2 servings

Sautéed Stuffed Veal

1/2 lb veal round, 2 x 2 x 4", trimmed	seasoning salt
3 slices (2-1/4 oz) Swiss cheese	1/4 c flour
1 oz prosciutto ham, thinly sliced or other smoked ham or sausage	1 Tbsp oil

1. Slice the veal into six 2 x 4" slices. Lay the slices between sheets of wax paper and pound with the flat side of the meat pounder to about 1/8" thickness.
2. On each of three slices of veal place a slice of Swiss cheese, then a slice of prosciutto, and then another slice of veal.
3. Press the two pieces of veal together, encasing the cheese and ham; fasten the ends with food picks.
4. Sprinkle the veal, top and bottom, with seasoned salt; dredge in flour.
5. Heat the oil in a frying pan and sauté the stuffed veal over moderate heat, until browned on each side.

Yield: 3 servings

Veal or Beef Parmigiana

1/2 lb veal or beef round, 2 x 2 x 4"	1 small onion, peeled, chopped
1 egg	1 tsp + 1 Tbsp oil
1 Tbsp milk	1 c (8 oz) tomato sauce
1/4 c grated Parmesan cheese	1/8 tsp oregano, crushed
2 Tbsp cereal flake crumbs	2 oz Mozzarella cheese
1/2 c mushrooms, sliced	

1. Trim fat and connective tissue from meat and slice into four 2 x 4" slices.
2. Pound each piece with meat pounder to about 1/4" thickness.
3. Beat together egg, salt, and milk.
4. Combine the Parmesan cheese and cereal crumbs.
5. Sauté the onion and mushroom in 1 tsp oil; add the tomato sauce and oregano.
6. Slice or coarsely grate the Mozzarella cheese.
7. Dip the pieces of pounded meat into the egg mixture and then coat with crumb mixture.
8. Heat 1 Tbsp oil in a frying pan and fry the coated pieces of meat, browning on both sides.
9. Place the browned meat in a single layer in a baking pan. Divide the Mozzarella cheese into four parts and place each on top of a meat slice.
10. Spoon the tomato sauce over the cheese-topped meat.
11. Bake in 400°F (204.5°C) oven until cheese is melted, about 15 to 20 minutes.
12. If desired, serve topped with a sprinkling of Parmesan cheese and minced parsely.

Yield: 3 servings

E. Moist-Heat Method: Pot Roasting

Basic Pot Roast

2-3 lb roast from chuck, arm, brisket, or rump	1 Tbsp oil
2 Tbsp flour	1/2 c water, brown stock, or dry red wine
1 tsp salt	additional flour and water for gravy
1/8 tsp pepper	

1. Trim visible fat and connective tissue from the roast.
2. Combine 2 Tbsp flour, salt, and pepper, and rub the mixture into the roast, covering all sides.
3. Heat oil in heavy saucepan or Dutch oven, place the meat in the pan, and brown it slowly over moderate heat; turn to brown all sides.
4. Add liquid, cover tightly, and cook over very low heat 2 to 3 hours or until easily pierced with a fork.
5. Add more liquid during cooking if needed.
6. Peeled potatoes, carrots, onions, or other vegetables may be added during the last 30 to 45 minutes of cooking.
7. Remove meat and vegetables to serving dishes and prepare gravy. For each cup of pan juice, combine 2 Tbsp flour and 1/4 c water; mix well or shake together in a small jar.
8. Add the flour-water mixture to the pan juices and cook over moderately high heat, stirring constantly with a spring stirrer, until the gravy starts to boil. Turn off heat.

Yield: 2 to 3 servings per lb

Beef Tongue

1 fresh beef tongue, 3 lb or less	1/2 lb potatoes
2 c water	1/2 lb carrots
1 tsp salt	1 onion, peeled and quartered

1. Wash beef tongue under running water, pat dry, and trim off visible fat, connective tissue, and the taste buds that run along the side of the tongue at the edge of the skin area.
2. Place the water, tongue, and salt in the pressure saucepan, close cover, and start heating.
3. When steam starts coming out the vent in the top, time it for one minute; then place the pressure control weight on the vent.
4. Adjust the heat under the pot to maintain a pressure of 10 lb.
5. Allow the tongue to cook at 10 lb pressure for 55 minutes; cool under cold tap water, remove the pressure control weight, open lid.
6. Remove the tongue and skin it; keep it warm in oven.
7. Place onion and peeled potatoes and carrots, cut into 1" cubes, in pressure saucepan.
8. Cook the vegetables at 15 lb pressure for three minutes; cool under cold tap water; remove pressure control weight; open lid.
9. Remove vegetables to serving dish.
10. Prepare gravy as for Basic Pot Roast, steps 7 and 8.

Yield: 2 to 3 servings per lb

F. Moist-Heat Method: Braising

Sour half-and-half is suggested in a number of the following recipes as it is lower in calories and less expensive than sour cream, which provides a richer flavor. For even fewer calories, yogurt may be used, but it does not yield exactly the same flavor and consistency.

A number of recipes suggest serving the meat with cooked noodles or rice. Allow 1 oz uncooked noodles per serving, and cook noodles in about 1/2 c water so that all water is absorbed. If cooking 3 oz or more, reduce proportion of water (see BF, Table 9.1, p. 208). Allow 1/4-1/3 c raw rice per serving, and cook in twice the volume of water, adding a little extra water if cooking less than 1 c rice.

Veal Ragout
_____

1/2 lb boneless veal leg, shoulder, or round	1 c mushrooms, sliced
	1/4 c chopped onion
1/4 c flour	1/2 c white stock
1/2 c tsp salt	1/8 tsp thyme
1/8 tsp pepper	1/4 c sour half-and-half
1 Tbsp oil	

1. Trim fat and connective tissue from veal and cut into 1/2" cubes.
2. Combine flour, salt, and pepper, and coat cubes with flour mixture.
3. Heat the oil in an electric frying pan, add veal, and brown on all sides.
4. Add the onions and mushrooms, and sauté a few minutes.
5. Add stock and thyme; simmer, covered, about 5 minutes.
6. Just before serving, add the sour half-and-half. Do not boil after adding cultured milk.
7. Serve over hot, cooked noodles.

Yield: 2 servings

Beef Stew
_____

1/2 lb boneless beef chuck	1/2 lb potatoes
1/4 c flour	1/2 lb carrots
1/2 tsp salt	1 medium onion
1/8 tsp pepper	2 c brown stock
1 Tbsp oil	1 bay leaf

1. Trim fat and connective tissue from meat; cut into 1 to 1-1/2" cubes.
2. Combine flour, salt, and pepper, and dredge pieces of meat in the mixture.
3. Heat the oil in an electric frying pan; add the meat and brown on all sides.
4. Add the stock and bay leaf, cover, and simmer about 40 minutes or until the meat is almost tender. Or cook at 10 lb pressure in the pressure saucepan for 20 minutes; then reduce the pressure.
5. Remove the bay leaf.
6. Peel the potatoes, carrots, and onion. Cut onion into quarters and potatoes and carrots into 1 - 2" cubes.
7. Add the vegetables to the meat and simmer about 25 minutes or until tender, or cook in the pressure saucepan at 15 lb pressure for 3 minutes.
8. The flour left from dredging the meat can be mixed with water to a smooth paste and added to the meat and vegetables to thicken the juices.
9. Season to taste.

Yield: 2 servings

Swiss Steak
_____

1/2 lb beef round steak, 1/2" thick	1/4 tsp basil, crushed
1/4 c flour	2 c tomato juice
1/4 tsp salt	1/2 c celery
1/8 tsp pepper	1 small onion
1 Tbsp oil	

1. Trim steak of fat and connective tissue; cut in half.
2. Pound both sides of the steaks with a meat pounder to about 1/4" thickness.
3. Dredge the meat in a mixture of the flour, salt, and pepper.
4. Heat the oil in an electric frying pan, add the floured meat, and brown on both sides.
5. Add 1 c of tomato juice and crushed basil; cover and simmer about 40 minutes or until meat is tender.
6. Peel the onion and cut into quarters; cut celery into 1" lengths.
7. Add the celery and onion to the meat; add more tomato juice if needed, and simmer about 15 minutes until the vegetables are tender.
8. Combine the remaining flour mixture with a small amount of water and use to thicken juices, if needed.
9. Serve with mashed potatoes.

Yield: 2 servings

Microwave Oven:

1. Follow steps 1 through 3 above.
2. Combine only 1 c of tomato juice with basil and pour half into a 1-1/2-q glass casserole.
3. Place floured meat in a casserole and pour the rest of the juice on top.
4. Cover the casserole with a plastic wrap and puncture three or four times with a sharp knife to vent.
5. Cook at medium power 25 minutes; test meat; it should be fork-tender; if not, cook longer.
6. When tender, add celery and onions; leave uncovered and cook at high power 2-3 minutes, until vegetables are tender.

Beef Stroganoff
_____

1/2 lb beef round, 2 x 2 x 4"	1/8 lb fresh mushrooms or 2-oz
1/4 c flour	can mushroom pieces
1/4 tsp salt	1 c brown stock
1/8 tsp pepper	1 tsp lemon juice
1 Tbsp oil	1/2 c sour half-and-half
1 small onion	

1. Trim fat and connective tissue from the steak and cut into 1/4" slices.
2. Combine flour, salt, and pepper, and dredge the meat in the mixture.
3. Heat the oil in an electric frying pan and add the meat in a single layer; brown the pieces on both sides, using moderate heat.
4. Peel the onion, cut it in half lengthwise, and slice it into 1/4" thick slices.
5. Wash the mushrooms and slice from the stem end through the cap, or drain the canned mushrooms and add the liquid to the stock.
6. Remove meat from frying pan and add mushrooms and onions; cover pan and steam until onions are translucent (about 3 minutes), stirring occasionally.

7. Combine the remaining flour and brown stock, mixing until smooth.
8. Cook the stock-flour mixture with the onions and mushrooms, stirring constantly, until the mixture starts to boil.
9. Return the meat to the pan and heat to simmering; add the sour half-and-half and lemon juice just before serving; do not boil after adding the cultured milk.
10. Serve hot over cooked noodles.

Yield: 2 servings

Microwave Oven:

1. Follow steps 1 and 2 above.
2. Combine the stock and the remaining flour and mix until smooth in a 1-1/2-q glass casserole; add floured meat and stir to coat each piece with liquid.
3. Add sliced onion and lemon juice and stir.
4. Cover with a plastic wrap and puncture with a sharp knife to vent.
5. Cook at medium power 10 minutes; meat should be fork-tender; if not, cook longer.
6. Stir in the drained mushrooms or fresh mushrooms and cook 1 to 2 minutes at high power.
7. Stir in the sour half-and-half.

G. Combination Meat Dishes

Sweet and Sour Pork
___

1/2 lb boneless pork shoulder or leg	2 Tbsp brown sugar
2 Tbsp cornstarch	1 Tbsp soy sauce
1/4 tsp salt	2 Tbsp catsup
1 Tbsp oil	1/2 c pineapple juice
1 small onion	1/3 c green pepper
1 tsp wine vinegar	1/2 c pineapple chunks, drained

1. Trim the fat and connective tissue from the pork; cut into 1" cubes.
2. Combine cornstarch and salt and dredge pork in the mixture.
3. Heat the oil in an electric frying pan, add the pork cubes, and brown them on several sides.
4. Peel the onion, cut in half lengthwise, and slice into 1/4" thick slices.
5. Add the onion to the pork and sauté lightly; turn off the heat.
6. Add the vinegar, brown sugar, soy sauce, catsup, and pineapple juice to the frying pan and mix well. (If pineapple juice is sweetened, only 1 Tbsp brown sugar may be needed.)
7. Cover the pan and simmer until meat is tender, about 20 minutes. More juice or water should be added if evaporation is excessive.
8. Wash the green pepper, remove the seeds, and cut into 1" squares.
9. Add the pepper squares and pineapple chunks to the pork and cook until the green pepper is just barely done; do not overcook.
10. Serve over steamed hot rice.

Yield: 2 servings

Chop Suey

1/2 lb boneless pork shoulder or leg	3/4 c diagonally sliced celery
2 tsp oil	3/4 c water
1 small onion	1 Tbsp cornstarch
1/4 lb fresh bean sprouts	2 Tbsp soy sauce

1. Trim the pork of fat and connective tissue; cut into 1/2" cubes.
2. Heat the oil in a frying pan, add the pork, and brown, stirring occasionally.
3. Peel the onion, cut in half lengthwise, and slice into 1/4" thick slices.
4. Add onion, celery, and bean sprouts to the browned meat, cover, and steam for about 5 minutes, stirring occasionally.
5. Combine the water, cornstarch, and soy sauce and add to the meat and vegetables; heat until sauce thickens.
6. Serve hot over steamed rice.

   Yield: 2 servings

Lamb Curry

1/2 lb boneless lamb shoulder	1/4 tsp salt
1/3 c chopped onion	1/8 tsp ginger
1/2 c chopped apple	1-1/2 c brown stock
1 tsp curry powder	1 Tbsp cornstarch
1/4 tsp crushed garlic	

1. Trim lamb of fat and connective tissue; cut it into 3/4" cubes.
2. Place lamb cubes in an electric frying pan and brown, using moderate heat; blot excess fat with paper towels.
3. Add the chopped onions and sauté.
4. Stir in apple, curry powder, garlic, salt, ginger, and 1 c stock.
5. Cover and simmer the meat and seasonings about 1 hour or until the meat is tender.
6. Mix 1/2 c brown stock and cornstarch until smooth; stir into the meat mixture and heat to boiling.
7. Serve over steamed rice.

Note: Condiments that can be served with curries include thinly sliced green onions, minced parsley, chopped salted peanuts, raisins, pineapple tidbits, grated hard-cooked egg, coconut, and chutney, each served in a small dish (BF, 412, Fig. 23.10).

   Yield: 2 servings

Creole Liver

1/2 lb beef liver, sliced	1 Tbsp oil
2 Tbsp flour	1 small onion, sliced
1/8 tsp salt	1/2 small green pepper
1/8 tsp pepper	1/2 c canned tomato sauce

1. Remove all membranes from liver.
2. Combine flour, salt, and pepper; dredge liver slices in mixture.
3. Heat the oil in an electric frying pan and add meat.
4. Brown the meat and turn the pieces over.
5. Place the onion slices around the liver and brown meat on the second side.

6. Add the tomato sauce and the seeded green pepper, cut into 1" pieces.
7. Cover and simmer about 5 minutes.

Yield: 2 servings

GROUND MEAT DISHES WITH TEXTURED VEGETABLE PROTEIN

Seasoned Hamburgers

1/2 lb ground beef	2 Tbsp finely chopped onion
1 Tbsp chili sauce	salt and pepper

1. Mix the chili sauce, onion, and beef; shape into two patties about 3/4" thick.
2. Apply a very thin coating of oil or pan spray to the frying pan and place meat patties in pan.
3. Cook meat patties over moderate heat until browned on the bottom; turn patties over, season the top with sprinkling of salt and pepper, and finish cooking.

Microwave Oven:

1. Follow step 1 above.
2. Place patties on a rack in a glass dish.
3. Brush about 1 tsp soy sauce on top of each pattie for color.
4. Cook at high power 3 minutes; turn patties over and coat the other side with soy sauce.
5. Cook 2 to 3 minutes longer until browned on the bottom.

Yield: 2 servings

Meat Loaf

1/2 lb ground beef	1/2 tsp Worcestershire sauce
3/4 c fresh bread crumbs	1/4 c minced celery
1/4 c NFDM	1/4 c catsup or chili sauce
1/4 tsp. seasoned salt	1 egg
1 Tbsp dehydrated onion	

1. In the large bowl of the mixer, combine the bread crumbs, NFDM, seasoned salt, and dehydrated onion.
2. Add remaining ingredients and mix.
3. Press the meat mixture into a pup loaf pan, 3 x 5-1/2 x 2-1/4".
4. Bake at 350°F (176.5°C) 30 to 35 minutes; pour off and discard the accumulated fat.
5. Cut the meat loaf in half or slice and serve hot with baked potatoes.

Microwave Oven:

1. Follow steps 1 and 2 above.
2. The loaf will bake best in a round dish: use a one-half q casserole and press the mixture into a ring, leaving a 1-1/2" to 2" hole in the center.
3. Cook at high power 2 minutes, turn dish a quarter turn and cook 2 minutes longer.
4. Use a paper towel to blot the fat that renders out into the center hole.

5. Repeat step 3; blotting up the fat and turning the dish at each 2-minute interval.
6. A meat thermometer can be used to check to see if it is done; it should register 190°F (88°C) when done.

Yield: 2 servings

Chili Beans

1/2 lb ground beef	1 8-oz can tomato sauce
1/4 c chopped onion	1/4 tsp salt
1/2 tsp crushed garlic	1/8 tsp pepper
1 tsp chili powder	1 16-oz can red or kidney beans
1/2 tsp cumin	

1. Crumble the meat into an electric frying pan and cook over high heat, stirring and turning occasionally until browned.
2. Turn off the heat and drain off and discard the fat rendered from the meat.
3. Blot the meat with paper towels to remove as much of the fat as possible.
4. Add the remaining ingredients, including the liquid from the canned beans, to the browned meat.
5. Cover the pan and simmer on low heat 20 minutes, stirring occasionally, to blend the flacors.
6. Serve hot over steamed brown rice.

Yield: Three servings

Microwave Oven:

1. Crumble the meat into a 2-q glass casserole; cook at high power 2 minutes.
2. Pour off the fat and juices rendered from the meat into a custard cup; stir and break up the meat, moving cooked portions to the center.
3. Cook at high power 2 minutes and repeat step 2.
4. Cook at high power 1 minute and repeat step 2.
5. Add all remaining ingredients, cover with a plastic wrap and puncture to allow for ventilation.
6. Cook at medium power 5 minutes to blend the flavors.

UNIT 22   POULTRY AND SEAFOOD

Suggested reading: Basic Foods, Chapter 23

Objectives

- To learn to disjoint and bone chicken and to evaluate market forms of poultry
- To prepare shellfish and to compare market forms of shellfish
- To cook poultry and seafood in a variety of ways

PREPARATION AND EVALUATION OF POULTRY

A. Preparation of Poultry

Disjointing Chicken (BF, 405-407, Figs. 23.1-7)

1. Remove the giblets and neck from the body cavity of a whole, drawn chicken fryer.
2. Wash the fryer, inside and out, and the giblets and neck.
3. Pat dry with paper towels.
4. Remove the wings by bending each wing up and back, away from the body; then cut from the underside through the joint at the shoulder.
5. Remove the legs by bending the leg back away from the body; then slit the skin and cut through the flesh to expose the joint of the hip and thigh bones. Cut through this joint and through the flesh that joins the back and thigh.
6. Separate the lower leg and thigh by cutting through the skin and flesh on the inside of the leg to the joint; then cut through the joint and the flesh and skin on the other side.
7. After separating the legs and wings from the body, separate the back from the breast by cutting through the rib joints on each side, beginning at the hole just under the shoulder joint where the wing was removed.
8. Bend the back and breast backwards, away from each other, and cut the bones apart at the shoulder with the knife held parallel to the bones of the joint. Unlike other joints, the shoulder cannot be separated by cutting across the joint.
9. The back and breast can each be cut into two pieces, if desired. Hold the back with the neck end in one hand and the tail end in the other hand so that the thumbs are resting in the center of the back. Press down with the thumbs and pull up on the two ends to break the backbone; then cut through the skin and flesh.
10. Cut down through the skin and flesh of the breast just above the end of the keel bone. Then take the breast in the hands, placing the thumbs in the center inside, and press with the thumbs as the two ends of the breast are bent together to break the bones; then complete cutting through the flesh and skin on either side.
11. Cut off wing tips and tail and add to stock pot.

Boning Chicken

---

1. Bone the thigh by cutting the meat away from the bone, starting from the inside of the thigh and separating the muscles to expose the bone.
2. The lower legs can be boned in the same way, but tendons should also be removed by scraping the knife along each side of the tendon to separate it from the flesh.
3. Bone the breast by cutting down through the flesh on each side of the keel bone and along the wish bone; then cut off the few ribs attached at the sides.

B. Yield and Cost Comparison of Market Forms of Poultry

In comparing the yield and cost of various market forms of fresh chicken, it must be noted that some parts are considered more desirable than others. Thus, if the proportionate cost of the breasts obtained from a whole chicken is compared to the cost of breasts purchased by themselves, then the former will be the better buy, but the wings from the same bird will probably be more costly than if wings alone are purchased.

1. Enter the weight in lbs of the whole chicken or part of the chicken in column 1 and the total cost in column 3.
2. Calculate the grams of the chicken, column 2, for the whole carcass: Column 1 x 454 g/lb = column 2. Example: 3.53 lb x 454 g/lb = 1602 g.
3. Determine the weight in grams for the separate parts by actual weight and enter in column 2. Example: for thighs = 291 grams. It is not necessary to enter the amount in lbs except when the parts are purchased separately in the lower part of the table.
4. Calculate the cost of the parts by dividing the cost of the whole carcass (column 3) by the total weight of the chicken (column 2) and then multiplying by the weight of the part in grams. Example for thighs: $3.07 ÷ 1602g x 291 g = $0.56 the cost of the thighs. Enter the cost in column 3 for thighs. Repeat for the other parts.
5. Bone the thighs and remove the skin, fat, and connective tissue; record the weight of the lean meat in column 6 and of the refuse (bone, skin, fat) in column 4. The sum of columns 4 and 6 should equal the amount in column 2. Example: lean meat, column 6 = 164 g; refuse, column 4 = 127 g; 127 g + 164 g = 291 g.
6. Repeat step 4 for each of the parts and record the weight of the lean meat and refuse from each part.
7. Obtain the sum of the lean meat for all the parts and enter in column 6 for the whole carcass; do the same for the refuse.
8. Calculate the percent refuse: Divide the grams of refuse (column 4) by the total weight of the chicken or its part (column 2) and multiply by 100. Example: for thighs: 127 ÷ 291 = 0.44; 0.44 x 100 = 44%. Enter in column 5.
9. Calculate the cost of 100 g of lean meat by dividing the cost of the part (column 3) by the weight of lean meat (column 6) and multiplying by 100. Example: for thighs: $0.56 ÷ 164 g x 100 g = $0.34. Enter in column 7. Repeat for each of the parts and for the whole carcass.
10. In the same manner, obtain the yield and costs of chicken purchased as separate parts and record in the lower part of Table 22-1.

Table 22-1   Yield and Cost Comparisons of Market Forms of Poultry

| | 1 | 2 | 3 | 4 | 5 |
| | As Purchased | | | Lean Meat | |
Market Form	Total Weight (g)	Cost ($)	Cost per 100 g ($)	Weight (g)	Cost per 100 g ($)
Example:					
Whole carcass	1249	1.51	0.121		
Thighs	227	.274	0.121	128	0.214
Whole carcass					
Breast					
Back					
Legs					
Thighs					
Wings					
Cut-up, whole carcass					
Breasts					
Backs					
Legs					
Thighs					
Wings					

C. Yield and Cost Comparisons of Fresh and Processed Chicken

The fresh chicken must be cooked in order to compare it with the canned chicken.

1. Weight out 200 to 300 g lean meat of the fresh chicken used in section B; record the weight used in column 1 of Table 22-2. Example: 300 g
2. Record the cost of that amount of fresh chicken, using the cost of 100g of appropriate

lean meat from the whole carcass (Table 22-1, column 7): column 7 (Table 22-1) ÷ 100 x column 1 (Table 22-2) = column 2 (Table 22-2). Example: Using cost for thigh meat: $0.34 ÷ 100 x 300 = $1.02.

3. Place the meat (200 to 300 g) in a small saucepan with 1/2 c water; cover, simmer 15 to 20 minutes, and place in a strainer or colander to drain.

4. Record the weight of the drained cooked meat in column 3. Example: 195 g

5. Calculate the cost per 100 g of cooked meat: column 2 ÷ column 3 x 100 = column 4. Example: $1.02 ÷ 195 g x 100 g = $0.52.

6. For canned chicken, enter total weight of contents in column 1 and the cost of the can of chicken in column 2.

7. Drain the canned chicken in a colander or strainer and remove bones and skin. Obtain and record the weight of the drained, canned chicken meat in column 3; calculate the cost as shown in step 5 above and record finding in column 4.

8. Compare several brands and forms of canned chicken.

9. Discuss convenience, time, cost, flavor, and texture as factors in choosing and using the various forms of fresh and processed poultry products.

Table 22-2   Yield and Cost Comparison of Fresh and Processed Poultry

Market Form of Poultry	1 Weight (g)	2 Cost ($)	3 Drained Weight (g)	4 Cost per 100 g Lean Meat ($)
Example: Fresh chicken	300	1.02	195	0.52

PREPARATION AND EVALUATION OF SHELLFISH

A. Preparation of Shellfish

Fresh Shrimp

1. Drop fresh or frozen shrimp in the shell into boiling water to cover. As soon as the water returns to a boil, reduce the heat and simmer 3 to 4 minutes; drain immediately. Overcooking shrinks and toughens the shrimp.
2. Peel off the shells; the tails may be left on if the shrimp are to be batter dipped and fried.
3. Devein the shrimp using a sharp knife to scrape out the black vein that runs along the back of the shrimp.
4. Refrigerate or freeze the cooked shrimp until ready to use. (Shrimp may be shelled before cooking, if desired, but cooking shrimp and other seafoods in the shell may prevent solution losses of flavoring components. If shrimp are to be eaten without further seasoning or sauce, they should be cooked in stock or seasoned water for additional flavor.

Clams

1. Sand is a problem in preparing clams; to eliminate it, soak well-scrubbed, live clams in salt water, using about 1/3 c salt to 1 gallon of water. Add 1 c cornmeal per gallon to help remove intestinal wastes from the clams. Soak at least 3 hours or up to 12 hours in a cool location.
2. Wash clams in clear water and place them in the rack of a steamer or in a colander set over a pot of boiling water; steam the clams 5 to 10 minutes until the shells open; overcooking toughens the meat.
3. The clams can be opened and eaten from the shell or used in preparing a variety of dishes. The meat from hard-shelled clams is less tender than that from soft-shelled; therefore it is used in chowders and stews.
4. Washed clams in the shell can also be baked at 425°F (218.5°C) about 15 minutes. Crumple aluminum foil on a baking sheet and place the clams so that their juices will not leak out of the shell during baking.
5. Strain the broth from the clams through several thicknesses of cheesecloth to remove any residual sand.
6. Refrigerate clams until ready to use.

Oysters

1. Place washed oysters in a baking pan and heat at 400°F (204.5°C) 5 to 7 minutes; submerge them in ice water until cooled; drain.
2. The shells will open easily, and the oyster meat may be cut from the shell. Check each oyster to be sure it is free from pieces of shell and sand.
3. If the oysters are sandy, use 1/2 c water in a bowl for rinsing them, one at a time; the water can then be strained through cheesecloth and used for cooking.
4. Pat oysters dry with paper towels before frying them or adding them to sauces.
5. Refrigerate the oysters until ready to use.

Crab

1. Start from the bottom side of the crab; lift up and remove the cone-shaped section of the shell in the center.
2. At the point where the cone-shaped shell was removed, insert the right thumb; hold the top shell in the left hand and pull the two shells apart.
3. Scrape out the waste in the center of the body and wash clean under cool running water.
4. Remove the legs and claws, separate into sections, and crack the legs—a nut cracker is useful for this purpose. Dig the meat out of the shell with a pointed knife.
5. The body meat is edible and can be separated from the shell.
6. Refrigerate the meat until ready to use.

B. Comparisons of Various Market Forms of Shellfish

1. Record the weight of the product, as purchased, in column 1 of Table 22-3, and record the cost in column 2.
2. If the product is canned or bottled, drain and weigh it; record the drained weight in column 3. (Liquid should be reserved for use in cooking.)
3. If the product is fresh in the shell, shuck it, obtain the weight of the meat, and record in column 3.
4. Calculate the cost of 100 g, edible portion: column 2 ÷ column 3 x 100 = column 4.
5. Discuss convenience, time, cost, flavor, and texture as factors in choosing and using various market forms of fresh and processed seafood.

Table 22-3   Yield and Cost Comparison of Shellfish

	1	2	3	4
	As Purchased		Edible Portion—	Edible Portion—
Market Form of Shellfish	Weight (g)	Cost ($)	drained weight (g)	cost/100 g ($)

POULTRY COOKERY

A. Dry-Heat Method: Roasting

Roast Chicken

1. Choose a fresh or frozen fryer, roaster, or capon weighing 2-4 lb; thaw if fowl is to be stuffed. (See thawing timetable, BF, 409, Table 23.1.)

2. Remove any pinfeathers from skin and excess fat from body cavity.
3. Wash carcass (inside and out), giblets, and neck in running water; drain well.
4. Season inside of bird with salt and poultry seasoning mixture or with a mixture of 1/2 tsp thyme per tsp salt.
5. Fill with desired stuffing, allowing about 1/2 c stuffing per lb bird. Fold the neck skin over the stuffing in the neck cavity and fasten with skewers to the back of the bird. Skewer or sew together the edges of the lower opening to the body cavity.
6. Fold the wing tips back, behind and under the chicken; tie the legs together.
7. Place the bird, breast side up, on a rack in an open roasting pan. Do not add water or other liquid; do not cover the pan.
8. Preheat oven to 450°F (232°C), but lower the thermostat to 350°F (176.5°C) as soon as the chicken is placed in the oven.
9. Roast about 25 minutes per lb.

Cornbread Stuffing

2/3 c cornbread, cut into 1" cubes	1 tsp table fat
2/3 c wheat bread, cut into 1" cubes	1 large egg
1/4 tsp salt	1/2 c chicken stock
1 tsp poultry seasoning or 1/2 tsp each thyme, savory, and sage	1/4 c chopped onion
	1/4 c chopped celery

1. Melt the table fat in a frying pan and lightly sauté celery and onions.
2. Combine all ingredients, mixing until blended.

   Yield: 2 cups, enough for 2-4 lb bird. Leftover stuffing may be frozen for later use.

Savory Bread Stuffing

Prepare Cornbread Stuffing but omit cornbread and use 2 to 3 slices of fresh bread, or 2 c fresh bread cubes.

Rice Stuffing

1/3 c white or brown rice	1/3 c sliced mushrooms
1 c chicken or turkey stock	1/4 c sliced canned water chestnuts
1 tsp table fat	1/4 tsp poultry seasoning or 1/3 tsp each sage, savory, and thyme
2 Tbsp sliced celery	
1 Tbsp chopped onion	1/3 c wheat bread, cut into 1" squares

1. Place 2/3 c stock in a 2-qt sauce pan and heat to boiling; stir in the rice, cover, reduce heat to simmer, and cook until rice is tender (20 minutes for white rice, 40 minutes for brown rice).
2. Melt table fat in a frying pan; add celery, onion, and mushrooms; sauté lightly.
3. Combine cooked rice and sautéed vegetables with water chestnuts, poultry seasoning, bread cubes, egg, and 1/3 c stock; mix well.

   Yield: About 2 cups

Baked Rock Cornish Game Hen

1/2 c converted rice	1 Tbsp cornstarch
1/4 tsp salt	2 Tbsp Swiss cheese, grated
2 c chicken stock	1 Tbsp Parmesan cheese, grated
2 1-lb Rock Cornish game hens	dash of thyme
1/4 c chopped celery	

1. Heat 1-1/4 stock and 1/4 tsp salt to boiling in a 2-qt saucepan.
2. Stir the rice into the boiling stock, reduce heat, cover, and simmer about 20 minutes.
3. Cut the hens in half lengthwise, cutting through the backbone and along the keel bone of the breast; remove fat and organs from the body cavity and rinse the birds inside and out; drain.
4. Combine the celery and cooked rice in a 6 x 10" baking dish and spread the mixture evenly over the bottom.
5. Place the halved hens, cut side down, on top of the rice; the liver and heart may be tucked under the hens on top of the rice.
6. In the saucepan used for cooking the rice, combine 3/4 c stock and cornstarch, mixing until smooth.
7. Cook over moderately high heat, stirring constantly, until mixture boils.
8. Remove sauce from the heat and stir in the cheeses and thyme; pour sauce over hens.
9. Bake at 350°F (176.5°C) about 45 to 60 minutes or until hens are tender.

Yield: 2 servings

Chicken Mornay

1. Follow recipe for Rock Cornish Game Hen, using boned and skinned chicken breasts, about 8 oz each, instead of hens.

Microwave Oven:

1. Sauce can be prepared in the microwave oven as described in Unit 8.
2. Follow steps 1 through 5 above, using a glass baking dish.
3. Pour sauce over chicken breasts or hens; cover with a plastic wrap and puncture to vent.
4. Cook 3 minutes, rotating the dish every minute, then uncover and cook 2-3 minutes longer, again rotating the dish every minute.

B. Dry-heat Method: Broiling

Broiled Chicken

1. Use chicken fryers or Rock Cornish Game Hens cut in half lengthwise along the backbone and keel bone, or disjointed larger fryers.
2. Wash chickens under running water; drain; remove visible fat and excess skin if desired.
3. Place the pieces of chicken on the rack of the broiler pan, skin side down.
4. Sprinkle pieces lightly with seasoned salt; they may but need not be brushed with melted table fat.
5. Place the broiler pan about 5" below the heat source and broil the meat until browned.
6. Turn the pieces of chicken over. Add the liver and heart. Sprinkle again with seasoned salt.
7. Broil second side until browned.
8. Turn off the heat and leave the chicken in warm oven or broiler 10 to 20 minutes longer.

Microwave Oven:

1. Arrange some pieces of chicken in a glass baking dish so that the fleshy parts
   are at the outer circumference and the thin parts toward the center.
2. Brush with a mixture of 1 Tbsp catsup and 1 Tbsp barbecue or chili sauce.
3. Cook 3 minutes, then turn pieces over and arrange so that the lesser cooked
   areas of meat are near the outer edge. Again brush with catsup-barbecue
   sauce mixture and cook 3 minutes longer.

Chicken Teriyaki

2 chicken legs, including thighs, or	1 Tbsp sugar
2 whole chicken breasts	1/4 tsp crushed garlic
1/4 c soy sauce	1 tsp crushed ginger
1/4 c pineapple juice	

1. Wash and drain chicken pieces.
2. Trim off visible fat; remove skin if desired.
3. Combine all other ingredients and use as marinade for the chicken.
4. Marinate at least several hours in the refrigerator. (Pieces of chicken can be placed
   in a plastic bag and enough marinade added to coat the pieces. Squeeze the air out of the
   bag, twist the top and double it over, and secure with a rubber band.) Freeze for longer
   storage; thaw in the refrigerator overnight. Keep in the refrigerator for shorter storage
   (1 or 2 days).
5. Drain off the marinade when ready to cook. Leftover marinade may be frozen and reused.
6. Place pieces of chicken on the rack of the broiler pan, skin side down, and broil 5" below
   the heat source until browned.
7. Turn pieces of chicken over and broil until browned on the second side.
8. Turn off the heat and leave the chicken in the warm oven or broiler 10 to 20 minutes
   longer.

Microwave Oven:

1. Arrange and cook marinated chicken as described under Broiled Chicken.

Yield: 2 servings

C. Dry-Heat Method: Frying

Flour-Coated Fried Chicken

4 pieces of frying chicken	1/2 tsp salt
1/4 c flour	1/8 tsp pepper
oil	1/8 tsp thyme or savory

1. Wash and drain pieces of chicken.
2. Trim visible fat off the chicken; remove skin if desired.
3. Combine flour, salt, pepper, and herbs in a small brown paper bag.
4. Add the chicken pieces, one at a time, to the bag, close it, and shake to coat the chicken.
5. Heat frying pan with 2-3 Tbsp oil; do not allow the oil to smoke.
6. Place the pieces of chicken in the hot oil and cook over moderate heat until browned;
   turn and brown the second side.
7. Drain fried chicken on absorbent paper.

Yield: 2 servings

Crumb-Coated Fried Chicken

4 pieces of frying chicken	1 egg
1/4 c flour	1 Tbsp milk
1/2 tsp salt	1 Tbsp lemon juice
1/8 tsp pepper	1/8 tsp salt
dash of thyme or savory	2 c bread crumbs

1. Follow steps 1 through 4 for Flour-Coated Fried Chicken.
2. Combine egg, milk, lemon juice, and 1/8 tsp salt, mixing until blended.
3. Dip the floured pieces of chicken in the egg mixture and then roll them in crumbs.
4. Follow steps 5 through 7 for Flour-Coated Fried Chicken.

Yield: 2 servings

Oven-Fried Chicken

4 pieces of frying chicken	1/2 tsp salt
1/4 c flour	1/8 tsp pepper
1/8 tsp thyme or savory	1 Tbsp oil

1. Follow steps 1 through 4 for Flour-coated Fried Chicken.
2. Place oil in a 6 x 20" or 8"-square baking pan.
3. Preheat pan and oil in a 400°F (204.5°C) oven for 10 minutes.
4. Place chicken in the hot oil and turn to coat the pieces on all sides.
5. Bake the chicken with skin side down 30 minutes; turn the pieces over and bake 20 to 30 minutes longer. Cooking time depends on the size and thickness of the pieces.

Yield: 2 servings

Chicken Liver and Mushrooms

1/3 lb chicken livers	1 tsp table fat
1/4 lb fresh mushrooms	1/4 tsp salt
2 green onions	dash of pepper

1. Trim off fat and connective tissue from the livers and remove the green bile ducts.
2. Cut each liver into 2 or 3 pieces, about 1" cubes.
3. Wash mushrooms and trim off ends of stems. Slice from the stem end through the cap into 1/4" thick slices.
4. Trim, wash, and thinly slice the green onions, including the tops.
5. Melt the table fat in the frying pan; add the prepared liver and mushrooms. Cook over moderately high heat 3 to 4 minutes, stirring occasionally, until pieces of liver are slightly pink inside.
6. Sprinkle with salt, pepper, and the sliced green onions.

Yield: 2 servings

D. Moist-Heat Method: Stewing

Mature chicken must be cooked by moist heat to make it tender. It can be cooked in water, have vegetables added, broth thickened, and then served as a stew. Or the cooked meat may be removed from the bones for use in other dishes. Meat from mature chickens is less tender but more flavorful than that from young chickens similarly cooked. Mature chickens also have a higher fat content.

Pressure-Saucepan Stewed Chicken

1 lb or more of chicken pieces	1/2 tsp salt
1 c water	1 bay leaf

1. Wash the chicken and trim off visible fat; remove skin, if desired.
2. Place chicken, water, salt, and bay leaf in the pressure cooker.
3. Close the lid, heat over moderately high heat until steam has escaped the vent for 1 or 2 minutes, place the pressure control weight over the vent, and heat to 10 lb pressure.
4. Adjust the heat under the pot to maintain the pressure at 10 lb for 10 minutes for young (frying) chickens and 30 minutes for mature birds.
5. Reduce pressure under cold water; remove the pressure control weight and the lid.
6. Lift the pieces of chicken out of the liquid and set aside; discard bay leaf.
7. The fat in the stock should be removed by one of several methods:
    a. Chill the stock to solidify the fat so that it can be lifted off. It can be chilled in the freezer in a flat metal pan to speed the process.
    b. A baster can be used to separate the fat and stock.
    c. If the stock is poured into a narrow container, such as a jar, the fat can be skimmed off with a spoon without losing too much of the stock.
    d. If the stock is in a flat container and there is not too much fat, a paper towel can be laid on the surface of the stock to absorb the fat.

Saucepan Stewed Chicken

1 lb or more of chicken pieces	1/2 tsp salt
2 c water	1 bay leaf

1. Wash the chicken and trim off the visible fat; remove skin if desired.
2. Place chicken, water, salt, and bay leaf in a large saucepan; it should not be more than two-thirds full.
3. Bring chicken to a boil; then reduce the heat to maintain a slow simmer.
4. Simmer frying chickens about 20 to 30 minutes; mature hens will require 2 or more hours to become tender. Add more water if needed.
5. Follow steps 6 and 7 for Pressure-Saucepan Stewed Chicken.

Chicken Stew

1/2 lb carrots	1/4 tsp salt
1/2 lb potatoes	stewed chicken
1 onion	flour

1. Wash and peel potatoes and carrots; peel onion.
2. Cut the carrots into 1" chunks and the potatoes into 2" chunks; cut the onion into quarters.
3. Use stewed chicken prepared as directed above. Remove the chicken from the pot; remove the fat from the stock, using one of the methods suggested above under Pressure-Saucepan Stewed Chicken; discard the bayleaf.
4. Place the prepared vegetables in the stock; cook at 15 lb pressure for 3 minutes, or simmer in covered saucepan 20 to 30 minutes until tender.
5. Remove the vegetables and set aside to keep warm.
6. Thicken the stock with flour, using about 1 Tbsp flour to 1 c stock, mixing the flour in cold stock.
7. Return the meat (with or without bones) and vegetables to the gravy, and heat to boiling.

Yield: 2 servings

Oven-Braised Chicken
----

1 lb chicken pieces	pinch of marjoram
1/4 c flour	1 c water
1/2 tsp salt	flour
dash of pepper	NFDM
1 Tbsp oil	

1. Follow steps 1 through 6 for Flour-Coated Fried Chicken, using a minimum amount of oil for browning the chicken.
2. Place the pieces of browned chicken in a baking pan or casserole with a cover.
3. Add the water and marjoram, cover, and bake at 325°F (163°C) about 2 hours for mature birds. Younger birds can be cooked at 450°F (232°C) 20 to 30 minutes.
4. Remove fat from stock by one of the methods suggested for Pressure-Saucepan Stewed Chicken.
5. Prepare cream gravy by adding 1 Tbsp flour and 1/3 c NFDM for each cup of stock. Mix the flour and NFDM with a small amount of cool water, stir the mixture into the meat juices and cooking liquid, and bring to a boil, stirring constantly.

Yield: 2 servings

E. Combination Poultry Dishes

Chicken Curry

1-1/4 c chicken stock	1/2 tsp chicken-stock base
1-1/2 Tbsp cornstarch	1/4 c textured vegetable protein (optional)
1/2 tsp curry powder	1 c cooked chicken meat
1 Tbsp dehydrated onion	salt to taste
dash of pepper	

1. Combine stock, cornstarch, curry powder, chicken-stock base, onion, and pepper in a 2-qt saucepan. If textured vegetable protein is omitted, use only 1 c stock.
2. Cook over moderately high heat, stirring constantly, until the sauce starts to boil.
3. Stir in the textured vegetable protein and cooked chicken meat.
4. Reduce heat and simmer about 5 minutes.
5. Serve over hot steamed rice.

Microwave Oven:

The curry sauce can be cooked in the microwave oven by following the procedure outlined in Unit 8.

Yield: 2 servings

Almond Chicken
----

6 oz (2/3 c) chicken meat	1/2 of 8-oz can bamboo shoots
2/3 c diagonally sliced celery	1 Tbsp soy sauce
2/3 c sliced mushrooms	1/2 c chicken stock
2 Tbsp sliced green onions, including tops	1 Tbsp cornstarch
1 Tbsp oil	1/4 c whole, blanched almonds

1. Remove bones, skin, and fat from washed, drained, raw chicken; measure 2/3 c meat.
2. Slice the meat into 1/2" thick strips.
3. Heat the oil in a frying pan and add the meat, celery, mushrooms, and onion; sauté, using moderate heat and stirring occasionally, for about 5 minutes.
4. Add the soy sauce and drained bamboo shoots, cover, and steam about 5 minutes.
5. Mix the cornstarch into the stock and add to the meat and vegetables; heat to boiling; stir in the almonds.
6. Serve hot over rice or noodles.

Microwave Oven:

1. Follow steps 1 and 2 above.
2. Use oil to grease a 2-q glass casserole; add sliced chicken and soy sauce; stir to mix.
3. Arrange the meat in a single layer around the outer edges of the dish; cook at high power 2 minutes.
4. Add the sliced celery, mushrooms, bamboo shoots, and green onion, stir to mix; cover with a plastic wrap; puncture to vent, and cook 2 minutes.
5. Stir the cornstarch into the stock and then add to the meat-vegetable mixture and mix well; cook uncovered at high power 2-3 minutes or until the sauce is thickened.

Yield: 2 servings

Chicken à la King

2/3 c cooked chicken meat	1/8 tsp salt
1 tsp table fat	dash of pepper
1 Tbsp chopped onion	1-1/2 Tbsp flour
1/2 c sliced mushrooms	1/4 c NFDM
3/4 c chicken stock	2 tsp chopped pimiento

1. Use stewed chicken meat; remove bones, skin, and fat.
2. Melt table fat in frying pan; add onions, mushrooms, and chicken; sauté about 5 minutes.
3. Combine stock, salt, pepper, flour, and NFDM, mixing until smooth.
4. Add the flour mixture to the meat and vegetables and cook, stirring constantly, until the mixture starts to boil.
5. Turn off the heat and stir in pimiento.
6. Serve over hot, crisp toast or waffles.

Microwave Oven:

1. Follow step 1.
2. Melt table fat in a 1- or 2-q glass casserole in the microwave oven about 1/2 minute; add onions and mushrooms and cook 1 minute at high power.
3. Follow step 3 and add the mixture to vegetables with chicken; stir to mix and cook at high power 2 to 3 minutes, stirring to redistribute the heat at the end of every minute.
4. Follow steps 5 and 6.

Yield: 2 servings

Chicken Cacciatore

4 pieces frying chicken	1/2 c chopped green pepper
1/4 c flour	1 fresh tomato, skinned and quartered
1/2 tsp salt	2 Tbsp white wine
1/8 tsp pepper	pinch each of thyme and marjoram
1 Tbsp oil	1 Tbsp minced parsley
1 8-oz can tomato sauce	

1. Wash and drain pieces of chicken; remove visible fat; remove skin and bones if desired.
2. Combine flour, salt, and pepper in a small paper bag and drop the pieces of chicken into the bag, one at a time; shake to coat with flour.
3. Heat the oil in a frying pan, add the chicken, and brown on both sides.
4. Add the green pepper, tomato, tomato sauce, wine, thyme, and marjoram; cover and simmer about 20 minutes.
5. Correct seasoning, serve hot over spaghetti, garnish with minced parsley.

Yield: 2 servings

SEAFOOD COOKERY

A. Dry-Heat Method: Baking

Baked Whole Fish

2-3 lb dressed fish	1/2 tsp salt
1 Tbsp lemon juice	1/4 tsp thyme or basil
1 Tbsp table fat, melted	

1. Scrape scales off the outside of fish.
2. Wash and dry fish.
3. Combine melted table fat, lemon juice, salt, and thyme or basil; rub the inside of the body cavity and cut surfaces with the mixture.
4. Apply a light coating of pan spray or oil to the baking pan.
5. Place the fish in the pan and bake at 350°F (176.5°C) 20 minutes per lb or until flesh is opaque and flakes easily; it should be juicy, not dry, when properly cooked. For large pieces of fish, insert a meat thermometer into the thickest part of the flesh and cook to 140°F (60°C) maximum; at 150°F the fish becomes dry.

Yield: 4 to 6 servings (Allow 1/2 lb raw fish, with bones and skin, per serving)

Baked Fish Fillets

3/4 lb fish fillets	dash of pepper
2 tsp table fat, melted	1/2 tsp finely grated lemon rind
2 tsp lemon juice	2 Tbsp sliced almonds
1/4 tsp salt	1 Tbsp finely chopped chives
pinch of dill weed	

1. Apply pan spray or light coating of oil to baking pan.
2. Place flounder, sole, butterfish, or other fish fillets in a single layer in the pan.
3. Combine melted table fat, lemon juice and rind, salt, pepper, and crushed dill weed, and brush mixture onto the fillets.
4. Sprinkle the almonds over the fillets.
5. Bake at 350°F (176.5°C) about 25 minutes or until fish is opaque and flakes when tested with a fork.
6. Sprinkle with chives and serve.

Microwave Oven:

1. Lightly grease a glass baking dish or pie plate. Arrange fillets around the outer edges of the dish.
2. Follow steps 3 and 4; cook uncovered in the microwave oven 3 minutes; turn pieces over so that the lesser cooked parts are on the outer edges.
3. Cook 2 to 3 minutes longer until the fish is opaque. Sprinkle with chives.

Yield: 2 servings

Salmon Loaf

1 16-oz can salmon, drained, or other canned or leftover cooked fish	1 Tbsp lemon juice
	1 Tbsp finely chopped onion
3/4 c liquid from salmon + milk	1/4 tsp seafood seasoning salt or
1 large egg	1/8 tsp celery salt and a pinch each
1-1/2 c fresh bread crumbs	of basil, thyme, and rosemary, crushed

1. Mix all ingredients together and pour into a greased 9 x 5 x 3" loaf pan.
2. Bake at 350°F (176.5°) about 35 minutes.

Microwave Oven:

1. Mix all the ingredients together and transfer to a lighly oiled glass ring mold or arrange the mixture around the edges of a 1-q casserole.
2. Cook 6 minutes at high power, rotating one-quarter turn every minute.

Yield: 2 servings

B. Dry-Heat Method: Broiling

Broiled Fish Steaks or Fillets

3/4 lb fish steaks or fillets	1/8 tsp basil, crushed
2 tsp table fat, melted	dash of pepper
2 tsp lemon juice	1/2 tsp finely grated lemon peel
1/4 tsp salt	

1. Apply pan spray to rack and pan of broiling pan and lay fish on rack in a single layer.
2. Combine melted table fat, lemon juice and peel, salt, basil, and pepper, and brush mixture over the surface of the fish.

3. Place the broiler pan 2" below the heat source and broil until fish is browned and the meat is opaque and flakes easily. Do not try to turn the fish over as it tends to fall apart.

   Yield: 2 servings

Broiled Shrimp

3/4 lb medium or large shrimp in shell	1 Tbsp soy sauce
1/4 c orange juice	1/4 tsp onion powder
1/8 tsp crushed ginger	

1. Remove the shells from the uncooked shrimp.
2. Combine other ingredients, add the shrimp, and marinate for several hours or overnight in the refrigerator.
3. Drain the shrimp.
4. Apply pan spray or oil to rack and pan of broiler pan.
5. Lay the shrimp in a single layer on the rack and place 4" below the heat source. Broil 3 to 4 minutes on each side.

   Yield: 2 servings

Scallop Kabobs

1/2 lb shucked scallops or boneless chunks of fish	1/4 c tomato juice or vegetable juice cocktail
1 tsp chicken-stock base	1/8 tsp crushed rosemary

1. Heat tomato juice until steaming hot; add chicken-stock base and rosemary.
2. Add the scallops and marinate several hours or overnight in the refrigerator.
3. Thread the scallops on skewers and place on oiled rack of broiler pan.
4. Place the broiler pan about 3" below the heat source and broil scallops about 4 minutes on each side.

   Yield: 2 servings

C. Dry-Heat Method: Frying

Breaded Fillet of Sole

	1 egg
1/2 lb sole fillets	1 Tbsp milk
1/4 c flour	1/8 tsp salt
1/8 tsp salt	1/2 c bread crumbs
dash of pepper	2-3 Tbsp oil

1. Combine flour, salt, and pepper; coat pieces of sole.
2. Beat together egg, milk, and salt.
3. Dip the floured pieces of sole in the egg mixture and then in the bread crumbs.
4. Heat 1 Tbsp oil in the frying pan and add the breaded pieces of fish.
5. Brown on the first side, using moderate heat; turn pieces over to brown the second side, adding more oil if needed.
6. Serve with tartar sauce or lemon wedges.

   Yield: 2 servings

Pan-Fried Fish

2/3 lb fish fillets
salt and pepper
1/4 c buttermilk

1/2 c bread crumbs or corn meal
1-3 Tbsp oil or table fat

1. Sprinkle pieces of fish with salt and pepper.
2. Dip seasoned pieces of fish in buttermilk; then coat with bread crumbs of corn meal.
3. Heat 1 Tbsp oil in frying pan and add the fish; brown on both sides, using moderate heat; add more oil if needed.

Yield: 2 servings

Fish Cakes

3/4 c flaked cooked or canned fish,
   drained
1/2 c mashed potatoes or
   1/4 instant mashed potato flakes
   and 1/3 c nonfat milk

1/4 tsp seafood salt or 1/8 tsp celery
   salt and 1/8 tsp each powdered
   onion and thyme
1 large egg
1 Tbsp oil

1. Use canned or leftover cooked cod, tuna, salmon, mackerel, or similar fish.
2. Combine fish, mashed potato, egg, and seasoning, or place instant potato flakes in a bowl, heat the milk to scalding, and stir it rapidly into the potato flakes; then add the flaked fish, egg, and seasoning.
3. Heat the oil in the frying pan and drop the mixture by tablespoonfuls into the hot pan; brown on both sides, using moderate heat.

Yield: 2 servings

Fish Sticks

1. Follow the recipe for Breaded Fillet of Sole, but cut the fish fillets into strips about 1" wide and 2-3" long.
2. Other types of fish may be used, such as flounder, cod, butterfish.

Oven-Fried Fish

1. Follow recipe for Pan-fried Fish, using same ingredients.
2. Follow steps 1 and 2.
3. Melt 2 Tbsp table fat in baking pan and spread over bottom of pan.
4. Place the coated pieces of fish in the pan and turn over to coat with fat.
5. Bake at 500°F (260°C) about 10 minutes until pieces are browned and the fish flakes easily when tested with a fork.

Yield: 2 servings

D. Moist-Heat Method: Poaching
Basic Poached Fish

2/3 lb fish fillets
2 c water, stock, or milk
1 or 2 slices lemon

1/4 tsp salt
1 bay leaf
dash of pepper

1. Heat the liquid to boiling in an electric frying pan.
2. Place the fish fillets in the boiling liquid, add the seasonings, cover, reduce heat, and simmer about 3-5 minutes, until the fish flakes easily when tested with a fork.
3. Lift the fish from the liquid with a wide, slotted spatula or turner.
4. Serve with tartar sauce.

Microwave Oven:

1. Place 1 c of liquid in a glass casserole and add seasonings and fish.
2. Cook at high power 6 minutes, turning pieces over halfway through.

Yield: 2 servings

Chinese Poached Fish

1 Tbsp oil	1/4 c chicken stock
2/3 lb fish fillets	1/4 tsp salt
1/2 c sliced mushrooms	1 tsp dry sherry
1 Tbsp green onion, thinly sliced	1/4 tsp crushed garlic
1 Tbsp soy sauce	1/4 tsp crushed ginger

1. Heat the oil in a frying pan, place the fish in the hot pan in a single layer; quickly brown the bottom side over moderately high heat.
2. Turn off the heat, turn the fish over, and add the remaining ingredients.
3. Turn heat to high and quickly bring to a boil; cover, reduce heat, and simmer 3 minutes.

Yield: 2 servings

E. Combination Fish Dishes

Creole Shrimp

3/4 lb uncooked shrimp in shell or chunks of fish fillets	1/2 c sliced okra
	1 8-oz can tomatoes
1 tsp table fat	1/4 tsp salt
2 Tbsp chopped onion	dash of pepper
2 Tbsp chopped green pepper	1/2 tsp chili powder
1/2 c sliced mushrooms	

1. Wash shrimp, remove shells, and devein; set aside.
2. Melt the table fat in an electric frying pan and add the onions, green pepper, and mushrooms; sauté 5 minutes.
3. Add canned tomatoes and juice, okra, salt, pepper, and chili powder.
4. Heat mixture to boiling and add the shrimp; reduce heat and simmer about 5 minutes.
5. Correct seasoning; serve hot over steamed rice.

Yield: 2 servings

Savory Baked Fish

1 Tbsp table fat
2 Tbsp chopped onion
1/2 tsp crushed garlic
2/3 lb fish fillets
1 tomato, peeled, diced

1 Tbsp flour
2 Tbsp white wine
1/2 tsp salt
1/8 tsp basil, crushed
dash of pepper

1. Put table fat in a 10 x 6" baking pan and place in 400°F (204.5°C) oven until fat is melted.
2. Add the onion and garlic and mix to coat with fat; return to the oven for 5 minutes.
3. Remove the baking pan from the oven, lower the thermostat to 350°F (176.5°C), and place the fish fillets on top of the onions.
4. Combine the flour and wine and stir mixture into the tomatoes; stir in salt, basil, and pepper.
5. Spoon the tomato mixture over the fish fillets.
6. Bake 20 minutes.

Yield: 2 servings

Fish Au Gratin

1/2 lb scallops, butterfish, or
    sole fillets
2 Tbsp dry white wine
2 Tbsp water
1/4 tsp salt
1 2-oz can mushroom pieces

1/3 c NFDM
1-1/2 Tbsp flour
dash of pepper
dash of nutmeg
1/2 c grated cheddar or Monterey Jack
    cheese

1. Cut the scallops or boneless fish fillets into 1" cubes or chunks.
2. Combine seafood, wine, water, and salt in saucepan and heat to boiling; reduce heat, cover, and simmer 3 minutes.
3. Remove from heat; drain the liquid into a 1-cup liquid measure; keep poached fish warm.
4. Drain the liquid from the canned mushrooms into the cup with the poaching liquid and add water to make 1 cup.
5. Combine NFDM, flour, pepper, nutmeg, and liquid in a saucepan, mixing until smooth.
6. Heat the flour mixture to boiling, stirring constantly; remove from heat and stir in the grated cheese.
7. Add the fish and serve over toast.

Yield: 2 servings

Fish Stew

1 c fish or white stock
1 bay leaf
1/4 lb carrots
1/4 lb potatoes
1/4 c sliced leek

1 c canned tomatoes
1/2 lb boneless fish fillets
2 Tbsp dry white wine
1 Tbsp flour
salt and pepper to taste

1. Place stock and bay leaf in a 3- to 4-qt saucepan; cover and bring to a boil.
2. Peel carrots, cut into 1" lengths, and add to pot.
3. Peel potatoes, cut into 1-1/2" chunks, and add to pot.
4. Slice the leeks and add to pot; add tomatoes; reduce heat to simmer.
5. Check fish fillets and remove all bones; cut into 1-2" chunks and add to pot.
6. Combine flour and wine to form a smooth paste; stir into the stew.
7. Simmer about 5 minutes until the vegetables are tender and the fish flakes easily when tested with a fork.
8. Season to taste with salt and pepper; remove and discard the bay leaf.

Yield: 2 servings

UNIT 23   VEGETABLE PROTEINS COOKERY

Suggested reading: Basic Foods, Chapter 24

Objectives

- To cook various types of legumes at atmospheric pressure and in a pressure saucepan
- To use legumes in preparing a variety of dishes
- To compare the cost of cooked dried and canned legumes

COOKING LEGUMES

Table 23-1 shows the amount of water to use per cup of legume for each type of bean when beans are cooked in a closed system, the pressure saucepan. Additional water is needed at atmospheric pressure in order to replace water lost by evaporation.

Older beans (last year's crop) and beans cooked in very hard water take longer to cook. If water is very hard, distilled water may be used for soaking and cooking the beans.

Table 23-1   Preparation and Yield of Legumes

Legume	Water per Cup of Legume (c)	Cooking Time (minutes)		Atmospheric Pressure Soaked (min)	Yield of Cooked Legume per Cup of Dried Legume (c)
		15 lb Pressure			
		Soaked (min)	Not Soaked (min)		
Beans					
Kidney or red	3	10	30	120	2-3/4
Large lima	3	10	30	120	2-1/2
Small lima	3	8	25	60	2
Navy	2	10	30	90	2-1/2
Great Northern or Yelloweye	2	7	20	65	2-3/4
Soy	2-1/2	10	35	120	2-3/4
Peas					
Chickpeas (garbanzo)	3	10	30	120	2-3/4
Cowpeas (blackeyed)	3	3	10	30	2-1/2
Split peas	2	3	10	30	2-2/3
Lentils	2	2	8	15	2-2/3

A. Cleaning and Soaking Legumes

1. Sort the beans or peas; remove damaged legumes, pebbles, and lumps of dirt.
2. Measure out desired amount of legume.
3. Place the legumes in a strainer or colander and rinse them with warm water to remove surface dust.
4. Place the legumes in the cooking pan and add the amount of water recommended in Table 23-1; add 1 tsp salt per cup of legume. (Salt hastens hydration of the legumes.)
5. Place the pan of legumes on the surface unit and, using high heat, bring them to a boil; reduce heat and simmer 2 minutes. Remove pan from heat.
6. Allow legumes to soak 1 hour or overnight. The longer they are soaked, the shorter the cooking time.

B. Saucepan Cooking Method

1. Add 1 tsp oil to the soaked beans to reduce foaming; cook the legumes in the soaking liquid for greatest nutrient retention.
2. Cover and simmer until tender; add water if needed. Times shown in Table 23-1 are approximate; check at intervals.
3. If the legumes boil over during cooking, use a larger pot and tilt the cover to allow steam to escape.
4. Beans are done when they are soft throughout. Test by pressing bean between thumb and forefinger, or eat one. If beans are to be cooked with seasonings for a long time or if they are to be frozen, discontinue cooking before they become completely soft. Freezing softens cooked legumes.

C. Pressure-Saucepan Cooking Method

1. Add 1 tsp oil to the soaked legumes and liquid in the pressure saucepan. The pressure saucepan should not be more than one-third full of beans and liquid in order to allow room for expansion and boiling up.
2. Place cover on saucepan and heat, allowing steam to escape the vent for at least 1 minute.
3. Place pressure control weight on vent and bring the pressure up to 15 lb.
4. Adjust heat under the pan to maintain the pressure at 15 lb for the time specified in Table 23-1.
5. At the end of the specified time, place the pressure saucepan in the sink and run cold water over it to reduce the pressure quickly.
6. Remove the pressure control weight and the cover.

D. Cooking Unsoaked Legumes

1. Follow steps 1 through 5 for Cleaning and Soaking Legumes.
2. Then follow the steps in either B or C for cooking the beans.
3. Longer cooking time and more water will be required to complete the cooking.

E. Use and Storage of Cooked Legumes

1. Cooked legumes may be stored in the refrigerator up to one week.
2. To freeze legumes for longer storage, place them in sturdy plastic bags, freezer containers, or jars; allow head room for expansion, and freeze. Freezer shelf-life is about 6 months.
3. Desired seasonings can be added to refrigerated or thawed frozen beans; heating will help to blend flavors.

COOKED LEGUMES IN PREPARED DISHES

Most of the following recipes specify the use of cooked legumes. Indicated in parentheses is the amount of dried legume providing the specified amount of cooked legume. In many recipes it is possible to use legumes interchangeably; for example, soy beans can be used to make chili beans.

Hominy Bean Casserole

2 slices bacon
2 Tbsp chopped onion
2 Tbsp chopped green pepper
3/4 c canned hominy, drained
3/4 c cooked red beans, drained
    (1/3 c dried beans)
1 c canned tomatoes

1 tsp chili powder
1/4 tsp cumin
1/3 c liquid from beans or hominy
salt and pepper to taste
1-1/2 c corn chips, barbecue flavor
2/3 c grated cheddar cheese

1. Cut the bacon into small pieces and sauté until crisp and brown; drain the bacon on paper towels and discard the fat.
2. Add onion and green pepper to the frying pan and sauté.
3. Add hominy, beans, tomatoes, chili powder, cumin, and liquid to the onions and green pepper; mix; cover; and simmer about 5 minutes.
4. Season to taste with salt and pepper.
5. Crumble about 3/4 c corn chips in the bottom of a greased 1-1/2-qt casserole, add 1/2 bean mixture and 1/2 cheese.
6. Crumble the rest of the corn chips into the casserole, add remaining bean mixture, and top with remaining cheese.
7. Sprinkle the fried bacon over the cheese.
8. Bake at 350°F (176.5°) about 30 minutes.

Yield: Three servings

Baked Beans

3 slices bacon
1/2 c chopped onion
2 c cooked navy beans
    (7/8 c dried beans)
2 Tbsp molasses

1 tsp prepared mustard
1/2 c catsup
2 Tbsp dry sherry (optional)
salt and pepper to taste

1. Slice the bacon into very thin slices and sauté until well browned; drain the meat on paper towels and discard the fat.
2. Add onions to the frying pan and sauté.
3. Add beans, molasses, mustard, catsup, wine, and browned salt pork to the onions; mix.
4. Transfer mixture to a greased 1-qt casserole.
5. Bake covered at 350°F (176.5°C) 45 minutes.

Yield: Three servings

Refried Beans (Frijoles)

2 c cooked red beans   1 c grated cheddar cheese
    (3/4 c dried beans)   salt and pepper to taste
1/4 c table fat

1. Mash the beans in an electric mixer, if desired, and season to taste with salt and pepper; hot beans are easier to mash than cold.
2. Melt and heat the table fat in a frying pan; add beans.
3. Cook beans over low heat, stirring occasionally, about 10 minutes.
4. Just before serving, stir in cheese.

Yield: Three servings

Lima Bean Curry

1 5-oz jar dried beef   1/2 tsp curry powder
1 tsp table fat   3/4 c grated cheddar cheese
1/3 c chopped onion   3/4 c canned cream of mushroom soup,
2 c cooked lima beans   undiluted
    (1 c dried small limas)

1. Place the dried beef in a strainer and rinse it under running water to remove excess salt; chop into 1/2" pieces.
2. Melt the table fat in a 2-qt saucepan; add the onion and sauté.
3. Add lima beans, meat, curry powder, cheese, and soup; mix.
4. Pour the mixture into an oiled casserole and bake at 350°F (176.5°C) for about 35 minutes.

Yield: Three servings

Blackeyed Pea Casserole

2 frankfurters (1/4 lb)   1 tsp dehydrated onion flakes
2 c cooked blackeyed peas   1/8 tsp thyme
    (3/4 c dried peas)   salt and pepper to taste
1 8-oz can tomato sauce   1/4 c grated cheddar cheese
1/2 2-oz can mushroom stems, pieces

1. Slice frankfurters crosswise into 1/8" thick slices; sauté in electric frying pan until browned.
2. Remove frankfurters and drain on paper towels.
3. Use paper towels to blot up fat in the pan.
4. Add the cooked peas, tomato sauce, mushrooms with liquid, onion flakes, and thyme.
5. Heat until steaming hot; season to taste with salt and pepper.
6. Transfer the mixture to a 1-qt casserole; sprinkle the cheese over the top.
7. Bake at 350°F (176.5°C) about 30 minutes.

Yield: Four servings

Hopping John

4 slices bacon	1 c liquid from peas
1/2 c chopped onion	3/4 c cooked rice
1-1/2 c cooked blackeyed peas	1 tsp beef-stock base
(2/3 c dried peas)	salt and pepper to taste

1. Cut the bacon into narrow strips and sauté until crisp and brown.
2. Remove the bacon and drain on paper towels; discard fat.
3. Sauté onion in the same pan.
4. Stir in the rest of the ingredients and pour all into a greased 1-1/2-qt casserole.
5. Cover and bake at 350°F (176.5°C) about 35 minutes.

Yield: Three servings

Lentil Stew

2/3 c uncooked lentils	1 large carrot
1-1/3 c water	1/3 c chopped onion
1/2 tsp salt	1/4 c chopped celery
1/3 lb ground beef	1 large potato
1/8 tsp salt	2/3 c beef stock
dash of pepper	1 bay leaf

1. Wash the lentils and combine them with the water and 1/2 tsp salt in a saucepan; bring to a boil, boil 2 minutes. Turn off heat and allow to soak about 15 minutes.
2. Combine beef, 1/8 tsp salt, and pepper; shape into balls about 1" in diameter.
3. Brown the meat balls in an electric frying pan; remove the browned meat from the pan and drain on paper towels; discard the fat.
4. Peel and dice the potato and carrot.
5. Sauté the celery, onion, and diced carrot in the frying pan.
6. Add the potatoes, beef stock, lentils, and bay leaf. Cover and simmer about 6 minutes.
7. Add the meat balls and simmer until vegetables are tender; lentils should be slightly crunchy, like nuts.
8. Correct seasoning; discard bay leaf.

Yield: Three servings

Soybean Loaf

1 egg	1 Tbsp dehydrated onion flakes
1/3 c catsup	2 c cooked soybeans drained
2 Tbsp soy sauce	(3/4 c dried beans)
1 Tbsp brown sugar	1 tsp beef-stock base
1/2 c cooking liquid from beans	1 c grated cheese

1. Place the ingredients in the blender in the order listed and process until well blended.
2. Transfer the mixture to a greased 9 x 5" loaf pan; stir the grated cheese into the mixture and smooth the top.
3. Bake at 350°F (176.5°C) about 40 minutes.

Yield: Three to four servings

COST COMPARISON OF COOKED DRIED AND CANNED LEGUMES

A. Cook 1/2 to 1 lb of dried legumes, drain, measure the volume, and calculate the cost per cup of cooked beans. Enter data in Table 23-2. Or, instead of cooking the beans, use data from Table 23-1 and from Basic Foods, Table 24.3, p. 427 to calculate yield and cost of the cooked legumes. Enter data in Table 23-2.
B. Drain the liquid from a can of the same type of legume, measure the volume, and calculate the cost per cup of canned beans. Enter the data in Table 23-2.
C. Compare yields, cost, convenience, and quality of the two products.

Table 23-2   Yield and Cost Comparison of Dried
and Canned Legumes

Type of Legume	Market Unit			Cost per Cup ($)
	Size	Cost ($)	Drained Volume (c)	

USE OF TEXTURED VEGETABLE PROTEIN AS A MEAT EXTENDER

Textured vegetable protein (TVP) is used in these recipes to extend the meat and is not necessary for flavor or consistency. To omit textured vegetable protein, reduce the volume of liquid in the recipe by half the volume of TVP that is removed. To add, use a ratio of 1 cup TVP to 1/2 cup liquid for its hydration; 1/2 cup protein per lb ground meat will not affect the flavor adversely.

Swedish Meat Balls
_____

1/2 lb lean ground beef
2 Tbsp textured vegetable protein
2 Tbsp milk
2/3 c fresh bread crumbs
1/2 tsp salt
1/8 tsp pepper
1 c brown stock
1 tsp tomato paste
1/8 tsp nutmeg

1/8 tsp thyme, crushed
1/8 tsp basil, crushed
2 Tbsp minced onion
1 egg
1 Tbsp oil
1/2 tsp crushed garlic
1-1/2 Tbsp flour
2/3 c sour half-and-half

1. Combine textured vegetable protein with milk and set aside.
2. In the large bowl of the mixer combine bread crumbs, salt, pepper, nutmeg, thyme, and basil; mix.
3. Add the ground beef, protein-milk mixture, onion, and egg, mixing well.
4. Shape the meat mixture into balls 1" in diameter.
5. Heat the oil in an electric frying pan, add the meat balls, and cook with moderate heat, browning several sides.
6. Remove meat balls and drain on paper towels. Discard remaining fat, and blot the pan with a paper towel to absorb the fat.
7. With the heat turned off, combine garlic, stock, tomato paste, and flour in the frying pan, mixing until smooth.
8. Cook with moderate heat, stirring constantly, until the gravy starts to boil; season to taste.
9. Return meat balls to gravy and simmer on low heat about 5 minutes.
10. Stir the sour half-and-half into the simmering meat balls just before serving; do not boil after adding the cultured milk.
11. Serve over hot steamed noodles.

Yield: 3 servings

Spaghetti

1/2 lb ground beef	1/4 tsp oregano, crushed
1/4 c chopped onion	1/2 tsp basil, crushed
1/2 tsp crushed garlic	1 2-oz can mushroom pieces
1/2 tsp salt	3 oz spaghetti
1/8 tsp pepper	1-1/2 c water
1/4 c textured vegetable protein	1/4 tsp salt
1 16-oz can tomato sauce	Parmesan or Romano cheese, grated
1/4 c tomato paste	

1. Crumble meat into an electric frying pan and cook over high heat, stirring and turning occasionally, until browned.
2. Turn off the heat; drain off and discard the fat rendered from the meat.
3. Blot the meat with paper towels to remove as much fat as possible.
4. Add onion, garlic, 1/2 tsp salt, pepper, textured vegetable protein, tomato sauce, tomato paste, oregano, basil, and mushrooms to the meat and mix well.
5. Cover and simmer the meat mixture over very low heat while the spaghetti is cooking.
6. Place the water and 1/4 tsp salt in a 2- or 3-qt saucepan and bring to a boil.
7. Gradually ease the spaghetti into the boiling water until it is completely submerged; stir, cover, and simmer about 15 minutes, or until the spaghetti is tender and the water is mostly absorbed.
8. Add the spaghetti, including remaining cooking liquid, to the meat mixture; spoon the meat sauce over the spaghetti; cover and steam 5 to 10 minutes to allow flavors to blend.
9. Serve topped with grated Parmesan or Romano cheese.

Yield: 3 servings

Spanish Rice
―――――――

1/2 lb ground beef	1 16-oz can tomato sauce
1/4 c chopped onion	1/4 c tomato paste
1/4 c chopped green pepper	1/2 tsp basil, crushed
1/2 tsp crushed garlic	1/4 tsp rosemary, crushed
1/4 c chopped celery	1/2 c converted rice
1/4 tsp salt	1-1/4 c water
1/8 tsp pepper	1/4 tsp salt
1/4 c textured vegetable protein	minced parsley

1. Follow steps 1 through 3 for Spaghetti.
2. Add onion, green pepper, garlic, celery, 1/2 tsp salt, pepper, textured vegetable protein, tomato sauce and paste, basil, and rosemary to the meat and mix well. Cover and simmer on low heat about 5 minutes.
3. Heat the water and salt to boiling; stir in the rice, cover, reduce heat to simmer, and steam about 20 minutes or until tender and most or all of the water is absorbed.
4. Pour the cooked rice and any remaining cooking liquid into the meat mixture and mix well; cover, cook over very low heat 5 to 10 minutes to allow flavors to blend.
5. Serve hot garnished with minced parsley.

   Yield: 3 servings

Tacos
―――――

1/2 lb ground beef	1 8-oz can tomato sauce
1/4 c chopped onion	6 to 8 corn tortillas
1/2 tsp crushed garlic	oil
1/4 tsp salt	4 oz cheddar cheese, grated
1/8 tsp pepper	1 large tomato, unpeeled
1/4 c textured vegetable protein	3 green onions with tops, sliced
1/4 tsp cumin	2 c shredded head lettuce
1/2 tsp chili powder	

1. Follow steps 1 through 3 for Spaghetti.
2. Add chopped onion, garlic, salt, pepper, textured vegetable protein, cumin, chili powder, and tomato sauce to the meat; mix, cover, and simmer over very low heat about 5 minutes.
3. Transfer the meat mixture to a small saucepan; wash and dry the electric frying pan.
4. Chop the tomato into 1/4" cubes.
5. Heat about 2 tsp oil in the frying pan on highest heat. Place one tortilla at a time in the hot frying pan, heat it about 30 seconds, turn it over, and place a heaping tablespoon of the hot meat mixture on top.
6. Fold the tortilla in half and push to one side of the pan to cook while starting another. Cook the folded, filled tortillas on both sides until crisp. Place the cooked tortillas on a hot plate in a warm oven until all are cooked.
7. Place cheese, onions, tomatoes, and lettuce each in separate dishes to be served with the cooked tacos.
8. Serve with taco sauce, chili sauce, or catsup dribbled over the filling of the tacos and eat like a sandwich.

   Yield: 3 servings

Microwave Oven: (Tacos*)

1. Crumble meat in a glass casserole and cook at high power uncovered 2 minutes.
2. Pour off drippings, stir, and cook 2 minutes at high power.
3. Pour off drippings, stir, and add tomato sauce, TVP, onion, garlic, cumin, chili powder, salt, and pepper and mix well.
4. Cover with a plastic wrap and cook 4 to 6 minutes, stirring every 2 minutes.
5. Place a paper towel in a pie plate and place one tortilla on top of the towel; cook at high power 1 minute.
6. Place 1 or 2 tsps of meat mixture in the center of the heated taco, fold in half and cook 1/2 minute; turn and cook 1/2 minute on other side.
7. Follow steps 7 and 8 above.

   *When tortillas are cooked in the microwave oven by this method, no added fat is used, so they are lower in calories; however, they lack the crispness that is characteristic of tacos when they are cooked in fat in the frying pan.

Enchiladas

1/2 lb ground beef	1/2 tsp chili powder	6 oz cheddar cheese, grated
1/4 c chopped onion	1/4 tsp cumin	oil
1/2 tsp crushed garlic	1/4 c textured vegetable	1/2 c black olives, pitted,
1/2 tsp salt	protein	sliced
1/8 tsp pepper	1 16-oz can tomato sauce	
	6 corn tortillas	

1. Follow steps 1 through 3 for Spaghetti.
2. Add onion, garlic, salt, pepper, chili powder, cumin, textured vegetable protein, and 1/2 c tomato sauce to the meat and mix.
3. Cover and cook the meat mixture over very low heat for about 5 minutes; transfer to a saucepan and keep hot.
4. Wash and dry the electric frying pan; add about 2 tsp oil and heat to moderately high heat.
5. Pour 1/2 c of tomato sauce into a glass 8 x 8" baking dish, and spread it evenly over the bottom.
6. Place one tortilla at a time in the hot frying pan and heat until limp, cooking on both sides; do not allow to get crisp.
7. Place the heated tortilla on a hot plate, add a heaping tablespoon of the hot meat mixture, and spread it over the tortilla.
8. Sprinkle 1 Tbsp cheese over the meat and roll the tortilla up like a jelly roll.
9. Place the filled tortillas in the baking dish.
10. Combine the remaining meat mixture and tomato sauce and pour over the filled tortillas.
11. Sprinkle remaining cheese over the top.
12. Bake at 375°F (190.5°C) about 30 minutes or until bubbly.
13. Garnish with olives and serve.

Yield: 3 servings

Microwave Oven:

1. Follow steps 1 through 5 under the microwave method for tacos to prepare the filling for enchiladas.
2. Follow steps 7 through 11 under Enchiladas for filling tortillas.
3. Heat in the microwave oven 4 to 6 minutes to heat through and melt cheese; garnish with olives and serve.

USE OF TOFU AS A MEAT EXTENDER

Fresh soybean curd cakes, one form of which is called Tofu, are sold immersed in water. The cakes are 2-1/2 x 2-1/2 x 1" and 1-1/2 of these cakes yield about 1 cup of 1/2" cubes. Cut the cakes into cubes and let them stand a few minutes, then drain off the liquid before adding to the meat mixture.

Ground Beef with Bean Curd (Tofu)

1/3 lb ground beef
1/2 c sliced mushrooms (1-1/2 oz)
1/4 tsp crushed garlic
1 c soybean curd (Tofu), cut into 1/2" cubes

2 tsp soy sauce
1/2 tsp sugar
1 tsp cornstarch
1/4 c beef stock
2 Tbsp sliced green onions, including tops

1. Crumble and brown the ground beef in an electric frying pan.
2. Turn off the heat and blot the meat and pan with paper towel to remove the fat.
3. Add the mushrooms, garlic, bean curd, soy sauce, and sugar; cover and simmer about 10 minutes.
4. Stir the cornstarch into beef stock and add to meat mixture; heat to boiling; correct the seasoning.
5. Stir the onions into meat just before serving.

    Yield: 2 servings

Pork with Tofu

1/3 lb lean pork
1/3 c chicken stock
1 Tbsp cornstarch
2 Tbsp soy sauce
1 cup Tofu, cut into 1/2" cubes

1/8 lb bean sprouts
1/8 lb fresh mushrooms, sliced
1/8 lb snow peas
1/2 c diagonally sliced celery
1 green onion, sliced

1. Trim pork free of fat and connective tissue; cut into 1/2" cubes.
2. Place pork cubes in a lightly oiled 2-q casserole; cook in the microwave oven at high power 2 minutes, stir and cook 2 minutes more.
3. Add the cubed Tofu to the meat.
4. Combine the stock, soy sauce, and cornstarch; mix until smooth and add to the meat and Tofu.
5. Wash snow peas, break off flower and stem ends and remove strings; slice diagonally into 1/4" slices.
6. Add the sliced snow peas, celery, mushrooms, onions, and bean sprouts to the casserole and toss lightly.
7. Cook uncovered 3 minutes, stir and cook 3-4 minutes more.
8. Serve over hot rice.

    Yield: Two servings

UNIT 24   SOUPS AND CASSEROLES

Suggested reading: Basic Foods, Chapter 25

Objectives

- To prepare different stocks
- To prepare a variety of soups
- To prepare and evaluate a variety of casseroles

PREPARATION OF STOCK

A. Brown Stock

1. Use one or more of the following for preparing the stock: beef and/or lamb shanks, short ribs, soup bones with some meat attached; oxtails; connective tissue, fat, and bones trimmed from meat.
2. Crack or saw bones to expose the marrow.
3. Either render some fat from the meat or use oil in a pan to brown the meat and bones. A richer brown will produce a better flavor.
4. Add water to cover the meat and bones; add about 1/4 tsp salt per qt of water, cover, and simmer for several hours or until volume is reduced to half. Or process in a pressure cooker 30 to 60 minutes.
5. Place a colander in another pot and pour in the stock to separate the bones and other ingredients. Pour stock through a fine sieve to remove coarse particles that passed through the colander. Remove meat from the bones for use in soup or other dishes. Chill the stock to solidify the fat, which can then be lifted off.
6. The stock can be clarified as follows:
    a. Whip an egg white until frothy and add a crushed egg shell.
    b. Heat 1 qt fat-free stock to boiling and stir in the egg white and shell; heat until the broth returns to a boil.
    c. Remove the stock from the heat and let stand about 5 minutes; then pour it through a sieve lined with several layers of moistened cheesecloth; discard egg white and shell.
    d. If the stock is still not clear, repeat the process.
7. Stock, clarified or not, can be stored in the refrigerator 4 or 5 days or in the freezer for longer periods. Fill freezer containers or jars about 3/4 full to allow for expansion during freezing, or fill ice-cube trays with stock, transfer the frozen cubes to plastic bags, expel the air, and close tightly. Be sure to label with the type of stock.

B. White Stock

1. Use one or more of the following: chicken backs, necks, wings, skin, fat, and bones left over when chicken is trimmed or boned; veal shanks, ribs, and soup bones.
2. Follow the steps outlined for Brown Stock, omitting step 3; the meat for white stock is not browned.

C. Fish Stock

1. Use one or more of the following: fish bones, heads, tails, fins, skin, trimmings; shells removed from uncooked shrimp or prawns.
2. Cover with water and simmer no longer than 30 minutes, uncovered.
3. Strain and clarify, if desired, as described for Brown Stock.

PREPARATION OF SOUPS

A. Clear Soups

The flavor of these clear soups depends primarily on the flavor of the stock used to make them. If the flavor of the stock is weak, it may be enhanced by the addition of chicken- or beef-stock base. These are not the same as bouillon cubes, which produce a different flavor effect. Both the stock base and the bouillon cubes are high in salt; therefore, if they are used, add the salt later, to taste, to prevent excessive saltiness.

French Onion Soup
_____

1 Tbsp table fat	2 1"-thick slices French bread
2/3 c cliced onion	1 Tbsp table fat, melted
1-1/2 c beef stock	1 Tbsp Parmesan cheese
salt and pepper to taste	

1. Melt 1 Tbsp table fat in 2-qt saucepan; add onions and sauté until golden brown.
2. Add stock and simmer uncovered about 10 minutes.
3. Season to taste with salt and pepper.
4. Place slices of French bread on a baking sheet and toast in a 325°F (163°C) oven until they are dried and golden brown.
5. Brush the toasted slices of French bread with table fat and sprinkle with cheese.
6. Serve the hot soup in heated bowls with the toasted French bread, cheese side up, on top.

Yield: Two servings

Curried Tomato Bouillon
_____

3/4 c beef stock	1/4 tsp onion powder
3/4 c tomato juice	salt and pepper to taste
1/4 tsp curry powder	2 Tbsp sliced green onions, including tops

1. Combine stock, tomato juice, curry powder, and onion powder; simmer 5 minutes.
2. Season to taste with salt and pepper.
3. Serve in hot bowls and sprinkle onions on top.

Yield: Two servings

Egg Flower Soup
_____

2 c chicken stock	salt to taste
1/4 c thin somen noodles or	1 egg
other very narrow noodle	1/4 c fresh or frozen green peas

1. Bring the stock to a boil and add the peas; simmer 5 minutes; add the noodles and cook

about 2 minutes.

2. Beat the egg and stir into the hot soup; salt to taste.

Yield: Two servings

Won Ton Soup

2 c chicken stock	8-10 filled won tons (see Unit 2)
1/8 tsp curry powder	salt to taste
1 tsp soy sauce	sliced green onion or minced parsley

1. Heat the stock, curry powder, and soy sauce to boiling; add the won ton, simmer until won ton wrappers are opaque and cooked.
2. Season with salt; stir in onion or parsley just before serving.

Yield: Two servings

Bean Curd Soup

1 oz lean beef round	1-1/2 c beef stock
1 Tbsp table fat	1/2 c bean curd (Tofu) cut into 1/2" cubes
1 Tbsp soy sauce	
1 Tbsp sliced onion	sprigs of watercress
1/4 c mushrooms sliced vertically	

1. Trim fat and connective tissue from beef; cut into 1/8"-thick strips.
2. Melt table fat in a 1 qt saucepan; add and sauté beef strips until lightly browned; stir in soy sauce.
3. Add onions and mushrooms to meat; cover and steam about 3 minutes.
4. Add beef stock and bring to boil; turn off heat but leave the pan on surface unit.
5. Drain bean curd and add cubes to ingredients in saucepan.
6. Serve garnished with sprigs of watercress.

Yield: Two servings

B. Cream Soups

Cream of Tomato Soup

3/4 c milk	1/2 c tomato juice
1-1/2 Tbsp flour	1 small tomato, peeled, chopped
1/4 tsp salt	pinch of basil, crushed
1 tsp table fat	2 slices of lemon or sprig of parsley
1 Tbsp finely chopped onion	

1. Combine milk, flour, and salt in 1-qt saucepan and mix until smooth.
2. Cook over moderately high heat, stirring constantly with a spring stirrer, until the mixture starts to boil; set aside.
3. In another 1-qt saucepan melt table fat and add onion; cook over moderate heat, stirring occasionally, until translucent.
4. Add tomato juice, chopped tomato, and basil to the onions and heat until mixture starts to boil.
5. Just before serving, heat the two mixtures until steaming hot; then combine them and season to taste.

5. Garnish with thin slices of lemon or sprigs of parsley.

    Yield: Two servings

Cream of Carrot Soup

1/4 lb carrots	1 Tbsp flour
1 tsp table fat	1/2 tsp salt
1/4 c chopped onion	dash of nutmeg
3/4 c chicken stock	dash of pepper
3/4 c milk	2 sprigs parsley

1. Wash, peel, and coarsely grate the carrots.
2. Melt the table fat in a 1-qt saucepan; add and sauté the onion.
3. Add the chicken stock and grated carrot to onion and simmer until tender; pour mixture into the blender and allow to cool.
4. Place milk, flour, salt, nutmeg, and pepper in the same pan and mix until smooth.
5. Cook over moderately high heat, stirring constantly with a spring stirrer, until mixture starts to boil; turn off heat.
6. Blend the carrots until smooth and add to the hot white sauce; correct seasoning and serve garnished with sprigs of parsley.

    Yield: Two servings

Cream of Green Pea Soup

	3/4 c milk
1 tsp table fat	1 Tbsp flour
1 Tbsp chopped onion	1/4 tsp salt
1/2 c brown stock	pinch of basil, crushed
3/4 c fresh or frozen green peas	1 Tbsp sliced green onion

1. Melt the table fat in a 1-qt saucepan and add and sauté the onion.
2. Add the brown stock and peas and simmer until tender; pour the peas and liquid into the blender and allow to cool.
3. Combine milk, flour, salt, and basil in the same saucepan, mixing until smooth.
4. Cook over moderately high heat, stirring constantly with a spring stirrer, until mixture starts to boil; turn off heat.
5. Blend the peas until smooth and add to the hot white sauce; correct seasoning; garnish bowls of soup with slices of green onion.

    Yield: Two servings

Cream of Potato Soup

1/2 lb (1 medium) white potato	1 Tbsp flour
1 tsp table fat	1/4 tsp salt
1 Tbsp chopped onion	dash of pepper
1/2 c white stock	pinch of marjoram, crushed
3/4 c milk	chopped chives

1. Wash, peel, and chop the potato.
2. Melt the table fat in a 1-qt saucepan; add and sauté the onion.
3. Add stock and chopped potato to the onion and simmer until tender.
4. Pour potatoes and onions with the liquid into the blender; allow to cool.
5. Place milk, flour, salt, pepper, and marjoram in the same suacepan and mix until smooth.

6. Cook over moderately high heat, stirring constantly with a spring stirrer, until the mixture starts to boil; turn off heat.
7. Blend the potatoes until smooth and add to the hot white sauce; correct seasoning. Garnish the bowls of soup with chopped chives sprinkled over the top.

   Yield: Two servings

Shrimp Bisque

1 tsp table fat	dash of white pepper
1 Tbsp finely chopped onion	dash of celery salt
1 c milk	dash of nutmeg
1/2 c fish or white stock	1 c fresh or frozen cleaned shrimp or
1 Tbsp flour	1 7-oz can shrimp, drained
1/4 tsp salt	

1. Melt the table fat in a 1-qt saucepan; add and sauté the onions; remove from heat.
2. Add milk, stock, flour, salt, pepper, celery salt, and nutmeg to onions; mix until smooth.
3. Cook over moderately high heat, stirring constantly with a spring stirrer, until the mixture starts to boil.
4. Add the shrimp and heat just to boiling; turn off the heat and leave the soup on the warm burner for a few minutes before serving.

   Yield: Two servings

Oyster Bisque

1 egg	dash of pepper
1-1/4 c milk	pinch of thyme
1 Tbsp flour	pinch of basil
1/4 tsp salt	1 10-oz jar oysters and liquid
1/2 tsp onion powder	

1. Beat egg in a 1-qt saucepan; add milk, flour, salt, onion powder, pepper, thyme, and basil; mix until smooth.
2. Cook over moderately high heat, stirring constantly with a spring stirrer, until the mixture starts to boil; turn off heat and stir in the oysters and liquid; correct seasoning.

   Yield: Two servings

C. Thick Soups or Chowders

Vegetable-Beef Soup

3/4 c brown stock	pinch of basil
1 bay leaf	1/2 Tbsp finely chopped onion
2 Tbsp peeled, diced carrot	1/4 c chopped canned tomato
2 Tbsp peeled, diced potato	1/4 c chopped cooked beef
1 Tbsp fresh or frozen green peas	1/2 c juice from canned tomatoes
1 Tbsp chopped celery	salt and pepper to taste

1. Combine stock, bay leaf, and carrots and bring to a boil; cover and simmer about 3 minutes.

2. Add potatoes and peas, and simmer about 5 minutes.
3. Add remaining ingredients and simmer about 10 minutes; discard bay leaf.
4. Season to taste with salt and pepper.

Yield: Two servings

Scotch Broth

1 lamb shank	1 Tbsp chopped celery
2 c water	1 Tbsp chopped onion
1/4 tsp salt	pinch of thyme
1/4 c pearl barley	1 Tbsp flour
2 Tbsp peeled, diced carrots	1/4 c cold water
2 Tbsp peeled, diced turnip	salt and pepper to taste

1. Trim the lamb shank free of visible fat; place it in a pressure saucepan with the water and salt.
2. Close the lid and heat until steam escapes the vent for 1 minute; then place the pressure control weight on vent and bring pressure up to 15 lb; adjust heat under the pot to maintain 15 lb pressure for 30 minutes. Place the pan in the sink and run cold water over it; remove the pressure control weight and lid.
3. Remove the lamb shank to a plate; cool, remove the meat from bone; dice or chop meat and set aside.
4. If time permits, chill the stock and remove the fat; otherwise, skim off the fat with a baster, spoon, or a layer of paper towel placed on the surface.
5. Add the barley to the fat-free stock in the pressure saucepan and repeat step 2, processing the barley 10 minutes.
6. Add carrots, turnips, celery, onion, thyme, and meat. Replace the cover but not the pressure control weight; simmer until vegetables are tender, about 10-15 minutes.
7. Combine flour with water and stir into the soup; cook until soup returns to a boil; correct seasoning and serve.

Yield: Two servings

Minestrone

1-1/2 c brown stock	4 1/4"-thick slices zucchini, halved
1 Tbsp salad macaroni, dry	2 Tbsp chopped canned tomato
1 Tbsp diced carrot	1/2 c cooked red beans
1 Tbsp frozen or fresh green beans	1/2 c juice from canned tomato
1 Tbsp diced potato	pinch of basil, crushed
1 Tbsp chopped onion	pinch of oregano, crushed
1 Tbsp chopped celery	dash of garlic powder
1 Tbsp sliced leek	salt and pepper to taste

1. Place stock in a 2-qt saucepan and bring to a boil; stir in the macaroni and diced carrots; simmer 5 minutes, covered.
2. Divide the cooked red beans in half; mash half and set aside.
3. Add remaining ingredients and bring to a boil; cover; reduce heat to simmer and simmer about 20 minutes; then stir in the mashed beans. Correct seasoning.

Yield: Two servings

Chicken Gumbo

1 Tbsp table fat	1/2 tsp Worcestershire sauce
2 Tbsp converted rice	1/4 tsp chili powder
2 Tbsp chopped onion	pinch of basil, crushed
1 c chicken stock	dash of ground cloves
1 bay leaf	dash of pepper
1/4 c sliced okra	2 tsp flour
1/4 c cooked chicken, cut up	1/2 c juice from canned tomatoes
1/4 c chopped canned or fresh tomatoes	2 Tbsp cleaned shrimp
2 Tbsp chopped green pepper	salt to taste

1. Melt the table fat in a 2-qt saucepan; add rice and onion, and sauté until lightly browned.
2. Add stock and bay leaf; reduce heat to maintain a simmer, cover, and simmer about 15 minutes.
3. Add okra, chicken, tomatoes, green pepper, Worcestershire sauce, chili powder, basil, cloves, and pepper; cover and simmer 5 minutes.
4. Mix the flour into the juice from the tomatoes to form a smooth paste and stir it into the other ingredients; return to simmer.
5. Stir in the shrimp and simmer about 3 minutes; add more chicken stock if evaporation has been excessive. Discard bay leaf.
6. Correct seasoning.

Yield: Two to three servings

Bouillabaisse

1 Tbsp table fat	1/8 tsp saffron
2 Tbsp sliced leek, including top	salt and pepper to taste
2 Tbsp sliced onion	1/2 c juice from canned tomatoes
1/2 tsp garlic, crushed	1/4 lb assorted fish: cod, flounder,
1/4 c white wine	haddock, bass, red snapper
1/4 c chopped canned or fresh tomato	1/8 lb cleaned shellfish: crab, shrimp,
1 c chicken or fish stock	clams, lobster
1/4 c fresh or frozen green peas	salt and pepper to taste
1/2 bay leaf	

1. Melt the table fat in a 2-qt saucepan; add and sauté the leek, onion, and garlic.
2. Add wine, tomato, stock, green peas, bay leaf, and saffron; cover, bring to a boil, reduce heat, and simmer about 5 minutes.
3. Remove bones and skin from the fish and cut into 2" chunks; add to the other ingredients and simmer about 3 minutes.
4. Add cleaned, shucked shellfish and simmer another 3 minutes.
5. Remove bay leaf; season to taste with salt and pepper.

Yield: Two servings

New England Fish Chowder

1 slice bacon	2 tsp flour
2 Tbsp chopped onion	1/4 c instant NFDM
1/3 lb (1 medium) potato	dash of nutmeg
1 c + 1/2 c chicken or fish stock	salt and pepper to taste
1/4 lb fish fillets or shellfish: cod, haddock, bass, flounder, clam	

1. Cut the slice of bacon into thin strips and sauté in 2-qt saucepan until crips and brown; drain on paper towel.
2. Add onion and sauté until translucent.
3. Wash and peel the potato; dice into 1/2" cubes.
4. Add the potato and 1 c stock to onion; cover, bring to a boil, reduce the heat and simmer about 10 minutes.
5. Remove the skin and bones from the fish fillets, shuck and clean the clams; cut the fish into 1" chunks, and dice the clams.
6. Mix the flour and NFDM with 1/2 c stock, stir into the potatoes, and bring to a boil; stir in the prepared fish and bring to a boil.
7. Add nutmeg and season to taste with salt and pepper.
8. Pour into hot soup bowls; garnish with crisp bacon pieces.

Yield: Two servings

Soybean Soup
_____

1/2 c cooked soybeans	1/4 tsp crushed garlic
1 tsp flour	1 Tbsp soy sauce
1/2 c + 1 c brown stock	1 bay leaf
3 oz pork sausage	dash of hot pepper sauce
1/4 c peeled, diced carrot	pinch of thyme
2 Tbsp chopped onion	salt and pepper to taste
2 Tbsp chopped celery	1 Tbsp chopped chives or minced parsley

1. Combine soybeans, flour, and 1/2 c stock in the blender; process until smooth.
2. Crumble and sauté sausage in a 2-qt saucepan until well browned; drain off and discard the fat.
3. Add carrot, onion, celery, garlic, and soy sauce to the meat in the saucepan; mix, cover, and cook on low heat about 5 minutes, stirring occasionally.
4. Add 1 c brown stock, bay leaf, hot pepper sauce, and thyme to the meat and vegetables; cover, heat to boiling, reduce heat, and simmer about 15 minutes.
5. Discard bay leaf; add the soybean mixture to the saucepan and heat to boiling, stirring occasionally.
6. Season to taste with salt and papper; garnish with chives or parsley.

Yield: Two servings

Split Pea Soup
_____

	2 Tbsp chopped onion
1/3 c split peas, dry	1 Tbsp sliced celery
1-1/2 c brown stock	2 Tbsp coarsely grated carrot
ham shank and meat	salt and pepper to taste

1. Combine peas, stock, and ham bone in the pressure cooker, close the lid, and heat until steam escapes for 1 minute.
2. Place the pressure control weight in place, bring the pressure up to 15 lb, and maintain that pressure for 15 minutes.
3. Place the pressure saucepan in the sink and run cold water over it to reduce the pressure; remove pressure control weight and lid.
4. Remove the bone and separate the meat from it.
5. If possible, chill the peas to separate the fat from the stock; otherwise, blot the surface with paper towels.

6. Add onion, celery, carrot, and meat from the shank; simmer until the vegetables are tender; add more brown stock, if needed, to obtain the desired consistency.
7. Season to taste with salt and pepper.

    Yield: Two servings

USE OF THE MICROWAVE OVEN IN PREPARATION OF SOUPS AND CASSEROLES

1. Soups and casseroles often use either stock or sauces. These can be heated or thickened in the microwave oven. It is best to use a deep, narrow container; glass measures are ideal. Allow about 3 minutes per cup of liquid to reach the boiling point. See Unit 8 for specific instructions.
2. Rice and pasta for casseroles and soup can be cooked in the microwave oven but require about the same time as when cooked on the surface unit; many people prefer to cook these on the surface unit.
3. Dried beans and peas cook most quickly in a pressure cooker.
4. The whole casserole can be cooked quite successfully in the microwave oven. Allow about 7 minutes per pound of food being cooked. (Weigh the empty casserole, fill it, then weigh again to determine the weight of the contents by the difference.)
5. The best results are obtained if the contents are stirred once or twice during cooking, since large dishes of food do not cook very well in the middle in the microwave oven.
6. If the casserole cannot be stirred (enchilada pie, for instance), tape a 3" wide strip of aluminum foil around the top of the casserole and fold it over so that it extends over the food about 1-2". Cook half of the time using high power, then remove the foil and finish the cooking using high power.
7. Regardless of the method used—stirring or using foil—rotate the casserole a one-quarter turn every 2 minutes during the cooking to obtain more even heating.
8. Probably the greatest efficiency is obtained if conventional cooking methods are combined with the use of the microwave oven, rather than using one or the other method of cooking exclusively.

CASSEROLES

A. Chicken Casseroles

Almond Chicken

2 c chicken stock
1/3 c converted rice
1 Tbsp cornstarch
1 Tbsp table fat
2 Tbsp sliced celery
2 Tbsp sliced almonds
1/4 c sliced fresh or canned (drained) mushrooms

1/4 c sliced fresh or frozen green beans
2 Tbsp sliced water chestnuts, fresh or canned
1 Tbsp soy sauce
1/2 c cooked chicken meat, bones and and skin removed
salt to taste

1. Heat 1 c chicken stock to boiling in a 1-qt saucepan, stir in rice, reduce heat, and simmer 15 minutes.
2. In another 1-qt saucepan combine 1 c stock and cornstarch; mix until smooth and heat to boiling, stirring constantly.
3. Melt the table fat in a frying pan; add and sauté the celery and almonds; add and sauté the mushrooms and green beans.
4. Combine rice and remaining liquid, if any, the sauce, the sautéed vegetables and almonds, and the water chestnuts, chicken, and soy sauce; correct seasoning.
5. Pour the mixture into a 1-qt casserole and bake at 400°F (204.5°C) 20 minutes.

Yield: Two servings

Chicken Paprika

1-1/2 c chicken stock	pinch of oregano
1/4 tsp salt	1-2 Tbsp oil
1 tsp oil	1/4 c sliced onion
3 oz (about 1-1/2) uncooked noodles	1/4 tsp crushed garlic
4 pieces frying chicken: legs, thighs,	1/4 c sliced fresh or canned mushrooms
breasts	1/2 c chopped canned tomato
1/4 c flour	2 tsp flour
1-2 tsp paprika	1/2 c juice from canned tomato
1/4 tsp salt	1 Tbsp dry sherry

1. Combine stock, salt, and oil in a 1-qt saucepan and bring to a boil; stir in the noodles, reduce heat, cover, and simmer 5 minutes.
2. Pour the noodles and remaining cooking liquid into a 2-qt casserole.
3. Bone the pieces of chicken and remove the skin and fat.
4. Combine flour, salt, paprika, and oregano in a paper bag; add the pieces of chicken, one at a time, and shake to coat with flour.
5. Heat 1-2 Tbsp oil in a frying pan and add the chicken; brown both sides; then place them on top of the noodles in the casserole.
6. Add onion, garlic, and mushrooms to the frying pan and sauté; add the canned tomato.
7. Combine juice from the canned tomato, flour, and sherry; mix until smooth and add to the vegetables in the frying pan; heat to boiling.
8. Pour the vegetable mixture over the chicken and bake at 400°F (204.5°C) about 25 minutes.

Yield: Two servings

To reduce calories, omit flour and oil. Sprinkle salt and paprika on the pieces of chicken; then place them in the casserole on top of the partially cooked noodles. Combine the oregano with the onion, garlic, mushrooms, and canned tomatoes; add the flour-tomato juice-wine mixture and heat the mixture to boiling before adding to the casserole. Bake about 45 minutes.

Low-Calorie Chicken Tetrazzini
_____

1-1/2 c water	1/8 tsp celery salt
1/4 tsp salt	dash of pepper
3 oz vermicelli	dash of nutmeg
1-2 tsp table fat	1/2 c instant NFDM
2 oz fresh or canned mushrooms	3/4 c cooked chicken meat, bones and
1/2 tsp lemon juice	skin removed, in large pieces
1-1/4 c chicken stock	2 Tbsp Parmesan cheese, grated
1 Tbsp flour	paprika
1/4 tsp onion powder	

1. Bring water and salt to a boil in a 2-qt saucepan; add the vermicelli so that water does not stop boiling; stir to separate the pieces; cover, reduce heat, and simmer 5 minutes. Pour the vermicelli and any leftover cooking liquid into a 1-1/2-qt casserole.
2. Melt the table fat in a small frying pan, add the sliced mushrooms, sprinkle the mushrooms with lemon juice, and sauté them until soft but not brown; stir them into the vermicelli.
3. Combine stock, flour, onion powder, celery salt, pepper, nutmeg, and NFDM, mixing until smooth.
4. Cook over moderate heat, stirring constantly with a spring stirrer, until mixture starts to boil; correct seasoning.
5. Pour 2/3 the sauce over the vermicelli and toss to mix.
6. Add the chicken meat to the remaining sauce and toss; pour the chicken and sauce on top of the vermicelli in the casserole; sprinkle with cheese and paprika.
7. Bake at 400°F (204.5°C) about 20 minutes until heated through.

Yield: Two servings

B. Ground Beef Casseroles

Enchilada Pie
_____

1/2 lb ground beef	1/2 c black olives, pitted, sliced
1/4 c chopped onion	1/4 c textured vegetable protein
1/2 tsp crushed garlic	1 16-oz can tomato sauce
1/4 tsp salt	4 corn tortillas
1/8 tsp pepper	6 oz cheddar cheese, grated
1/4 tsp cumin	

1. Follow the recipe for Enchiladas under Ground Meat Dishes in Unit 21, steps 1 through 3. It is not necessary to transfer the meat to another container.
2. Grease a casserole that is the same diameter as the tortillas.
3. Lay a tortilla in the bottom of the casserole and spread 1/4 the meat mixture over it; then sprinkle with 1/4 the grated cheese and 1/4 the sliced olives.
4. Repeat step 3 until all of the ingredients are used, ending with cheese and olives.
5. Bake at 375°F (190.5°C) about 30 minutes until heated through.

Yield: Three servings

Tamale Pie

1/2 lb ground beef	1/2 c canned whole-kernel corn, drained
1/4 c chopped onion	1/2 c yellow corn meal
1/2 tsp crushed garlic	1/2 c milk
1/4 tsp salt	1/2 tsp salt
1/8 tsp pepper	1 egg
1/2 tsp chili powder	8 ripe olives, pitted
1/4 tsp cumin	1 oz cheddar cheese, grated
1 16-oz can tomato sauce	

1. Follow the recipe for Enchiladas under Ground Meat Dishes in Unit 21, steps 1 through 3. It is not necessary to transfer the meat to another container.
2. Stir the corn into the meat mixture and then pour into a 1-1/2-qt casserole.
3. Combine corn meal, milk, salt, and egg into a smooth batter and pour into the meat mixture.
4. Press the whole olives into the mixture in the casserole.
5. Sprinkle grated cheese over the top of the mixture.
6. Bake at 350°F (176.5°C) 45 minutes or until the corn meal mush is cooked.

Yield: Three servings

Lasagna

1-2/3 c water	1/8 tsp pepper
1/4 tsp salt	1/2 tsp basil
6 lasagna noodles, uncooked, about 10 x 2" (4 oz)	1 16-oz + 1 8-oz can tomato sauce
	1/4 c textured vegetable protein
1/3 lb ground beef	1/2 c ricotta (or small-curd cottage) cheese
1/4 c chopped onion	
1/2 tsp crushed garlic	2 oz Mozzarella cheese, grated
1/4 tsp salt	1/4 c Parmesan cheese, grated

1. Combine water and salt in an electric frying pan or other 12" pan, cover, and bring to a boil.
2. Lay the lasagna noodles flat in the boiling water, cover, and simmer about 15 minutes.
3. To prepare the meat sauce, follow the recipe for Spaghetti in the section on Ground Meat Dishes, Unit 21, steps 1 through 3.
4. Add onion, garlic, salt, pepper, basil, tomato sauce, and textured vegetable protein to the cooked meat; mix well.
5. Spread 1/3 meat mixture in the bottom of a 10 x 6" baking dish and distribute the ricotta cheese over the meat.
6. Place a single layer of noodles over the meat and cheese, spread 1/3 meat mixture over the noodles, and sprinkle the Mozzarella cheese over the meat.
7. Place another single layer of noodles over the meat. Combine the cooking liquid from the noodles with the meat mixture and spread it over the noodles; top with Parmesan cheese.
8. Bake at 400°F (204.5°C) 30 minutes.

Yield: Three to four servings

C. Seafood Casseroles

Tuna Rice Curry
_____

1 c water	1-2 tsp table fat
1/4 tsp salt	1/3 c celery, sliced diagonally
1/3 c converted rice	1/4 c chopped onions
3/4 c milk	1 7-oz can tuna, including liquid
1 Tbsp flour	1/4 c sliced water chestnuts
1 Tbsp soy sauce	1/4 c salted peanuts
1 tsp curry powder	

1. Heat water and salt to boiling in a 1-qt saucepan, stir in the rice, cover, and simmer about 15 minutes.
2. Combine milk, flour, soy sauce, and curry powder, mixing until smooth; cook over moderately high heat, stirring constantly, until mixture starts to boil.
3. Melt the table fat in a small frying pan; add and sauté the celery and onions.
4. Combine rice, curry sauce, sautéed celery and onions, tuna and liquid, water chestnuts, and peanuts; mix well.
5. Pour the mixture into a 1-1/2 qt casserole.
6. Bake at 375°F (190.5°C) about 20 minutes.

Yield: Two servings

Shrimp Custard Casserole
_____

2 slices bread	1 c milk
1 4-1/2-oz can shrimp, drained	1/4 tsp salt
1/2 c grated Monterey Jack cheese	dash of pepper
2 large eggs	paprika

1. Trim the crusts from the slices of bread and cut the slices into 1/2" cubes; place the cubes of bread in the bottom of a greased 1-1/2-qt casserole.
2. Sprinkle shrimp and 1/4 c cheese over the bread.
3. Beat together the eggs, milk, salt, and pepper; pour the custard mixture over the ingredients in the casserole, top with the remaining grated cheese, and sprinkle with paprika.
4. Place the casserole in a pan and surround with boiling water.
5. Bake at 400°F (204.5°C) 20 to 30 minutes or until set.

Yield: Two servings

Seafood Noodles Au Gratin
_____

1-1/2 c water	salt and pepper to taste
1/4 tsp salt	3/4 c cooked seafood pieces: shrimp,
3 oz uncooked noodles	crab, tuna, salmon, clams, cod
1 c milk	1/3 c grated cheddar cheese
1 Tbsp flour	

1. Combine water and salt in a 1-qt saucepan and heat to boiling; stir in the noodles, cover, and simmer about 5 minutes.
2. Combine milk, flour, salt, and pepper in another 1-qt saucepan, mixing until smooth. Heat over moderately high heat, stirring constantly, until mixture starts to boil; stir in seafood and remove from heat. Correct seasoning.
3. Combine noodles and seafood mixture and pour into a greased 1-1/2-qt casserole; sprinkle grated cheese on top.
4. Bake at 400°F (204.5°C) about 20 minutes.

Yield: Two servings

Creole Seafood au Gratin

1-1/2 c water	1/4 c chopped green pepper
1/4 tsp salt	1/4 tsp basil
3 oz uncooked macaroni	pinch of thyme
1 Tbsp table fat	salt and pepper to taste
1/4 c chopped onion	3/4 c cooked seafood pieces: shrimp,
1-1/2 c canned tomatoes with juice	crab, tuna, salmon, clams, cod
1/3 c fresh or frozen green peas	1/3 c grated Romano cheese

1. Combine water and salt in a 1-qt saucepan and bring to a boil; stir in the macaroni, cover, and simmer about 15 minutes.
2. Melt the table fat in a frying pan; add and sauté onions and green pepper.
3. Add tomatoes, peas, basil, thyme, salt, and pepper; simmer about 5 minutes.
4. Combine the tomato mixture, seafood, and cooked macaroni, and pour into a 1-1/2-qt casserole; sprinkle cheese on top.
5. Bake at 400°F (204.5°C) about 20 minutes.

Yield: Two servings

D. Miscellaneous Casseroles

Scalloped Potatoes and Ham

1/2 lb (2-3 small) potatoes	dash of pepper
1-2 tsp table fat	3/4 c milk
1/4 c chopped onion	3/4 c cheddar cheese grated
2 Tbsp celery	3/4 c coarsely chopped cooked meat:
1 Tbsp flour	ham, canned luncheon meat, canned
1/4 tsp salt	corn beef, or chipped beef

1. Scrub potatoes well, place in a 2-qt saucepan, cover with water, and boil until tender, about 25 minutes.
2. Cool, peel, and slice the potatoes.
3. Melt table fat in a 1-qt saucepan; add and sauté the celery and onion; remove from heat; stir in flour, salt, pepper, and milk.
4. Cook over moderately high heat, stirring constantly, until the mixture starts to boil; remove from heat and stir in 1/2 cup cheese and the meat.
5. In a greased 1-1/2-qt casserole alternate layers of sliced potato and the cheese-meat sauce, ending with the sauce.
6. Sprinkle 1/4 cup cheese over the top.
7. Bake at 375°F (190.5°C) 35 minutes.

Yield: Two servings

Macaroni and Cheese

1-1/2 c water
1/2 tsp salt
2/3 c uncooked elbow macaroni (3 oz)
3/4 c milk
1 Tbsp flour
salt and pepper to taste

1/2 c cheddar cheese, grated
3/4 c coarsely chopped cooked meat:
    ham, canned luncheon meat, frank-
    furters, canned corned beef, chipped
    beef
1 egg
1 Tbsp Parmesan cheese, grated

1. Combine water and salt in a 3-qt saucepan, bring to a boil, stir in the macaroni, reduce heat, cover, and simmer about 15 minutes. If macaroni tends to boil over, add 1 tsp oil and tilt lid a crack.
2. In a 1-qt saucepan combine milk, flour, salt, and pepper, mixing until smooth.
3. Cook over moderately high heat, stirring constantly, until the mixture starts to boil; remove from heat and stir in cheddar cheese and meat.
4. Beat the egg and stir it into the cheese mixture; stir in the cooked macaroni along with any remaining cooking liquid.
5. Pour the mixture into a greased 1-1/2-qt casserole and sprinkle Parmesan cheese over the top.
6. Bake at 375°F (190.5°C) 35 minutes.

Yield: Two servings

Jambalaya

1 c chicken stock
1/3 c converted rice
1-2 tsp table fat
1/4 c chopped onion
1/4 c chopped green pepper
1/4 tsp crushed garlic
1/4 tsp salt

1/2 tsp Worcestershire sauce
dash of thyme
dash of pepper
1 8-oz can tomato sauce
3/4 c coarsely chopped cooked meat:
    chicken, sausage, ham, shrimp,
    crab, clams, oysters

1. Heat stock in a 1-qt saucepan to boiling, stir in the rice, reduce heat, cover, and simmer about 15 minutes.
2. Melt table fat in a 1-qt saucepan, add and sauté onion, green pepper, and garlic, and then add salt, Worcestershire sauce, thyme, pepper, tomato sauce, and meat.
3. Stir in the rice, including remaining cooking liquid, and pour into a 1-1/2-qt casserole.
4. Bake at 375°F (190.5°C) 25 minutes.

Yield: Two servings

Gateau Florentine

Crepes

1 c milk
2 eggs
1/4 tsp salt

1 Tbsp melted table fat
1/2 c + 2 Tbsp flour

1. Combine milk, eggs, salt, melted table fat, and flour in the blender; process 10 seconds; scrape down sides of container with a rubber scraper; process 40 seconds.
2. If time permits, refrigerate the batter for at least 2 hours.
3. Follow instructions for cooking crepes given in Unit 10, steps 3 through 8; set aside the cooked crepes.

Mornay Sauce

1 c chicken stock
1 Tbsp flour
1/4 c NFDM
dash of pepper

1/4 c grated Swiss cheese
2 Tbsp grated Parmesan cheese
salt to taste

1. In a 1-qt saucepan, combine the stock, flour, NFDM, and pepper, mixing until smooth.
2. Cook over moderately high heat, stirring constantly, until mixture starts to boil; remove from heat, stir in the cheeses, season to taste, and set aside.

Mushroom Filling

1/4 lb mushrooms
1 Tbsp table fat
1 Tbsp minced green onion
1 8-oz pkg Neufchatel cheese

1 egg
1/4 c grated Swiss cheese
1/4 c Mornay sauce
salt and pepper to taste

1. Wash mushrooms and trim off dark ends of stems; slice from end of stem through the cap.
2. Melt the table fat in a frying pan; add and sauté the mushrooms and onion about 5 minutes, stirring occasionally.
3. Combine the softened Neufchatel cheese and egg, beating until smooth; stir in the Swiss cheese, Mornay Sauce, and sautéed mushrooms; mix and correct seasoning.

Spinach Filling

1 10-oz pkg frozen chopped spinach
1 tsp table fat
1 Tbsp minced green onion

1/4 tsp salt
1/2 c Mornay sauce

1. Thaw the spinach and squeeze it dry by pressing it firmly in a strainer.
2. Melt the table fat in a 1-qt saucepan; add and sauté the onion for 1 minute; then add the spinach and cook over moderately high heat for 3 minutes, stirring frequently.
3. Stir in the salt and Mornay Sauce.

Assembling the Casserole

1. Grease a 2-qt round casserole, about the diameter of the crepes.
2. Place a crepe in the bottom and spread with 1/3 the Spinach Filling.
3. Top with another crepe and spread with 1/3 the Mushroom Filling.
4. Repeat steps two times, using up all the fillings.
5. Place a crepe on top and cover with remaining Mornay Sauce.
6. Bake at 350°F (176.5°C) 25 to 30 minutes.
7. Cut into wedges to serve; garnish with sprigs of parsley.

Yield: Four to six servings

E. Comparison of Casseroles from Package Mixes or Recipes

1. Choose package mixes for which comparable recipes are available, like spaghetti, lasagna, macaroni and cheese, tuna-noodle casserole, and rice pilaf. Note that some of these mixes require the addition of an important ingredient, such as ground beef or canned tuna.

   - Enter the costs of the package and the cost of any added ingredients in Table 24-1 and determine the total cost.
   - Prepare the package mix according to directions.
   - Measure the volume in cups of the finished dish and enter in the "Yield" column of Table 24-1.
   - Calculate the cost per cup of the product by dividing the total cost by the number of cups yielded.

Table 24-1   Cost and Yield of Casseroles from Package Mixes

Type of Mix; Brand	Cost of pkg ($)	Additions to the Mix			Total Cost[1] ($)	Yield (c)	Cost per One-cup Serving ($)
		Ingredient	Amount	Cost ($)			

[1]Total cost is the cost of the package plus the cost of all added ingredients.

2. Prepare the recipe that matches the packaged mix.
   - List the ingredients used in the recipe in Table 24-2 and determine cost.
   - Measure the yield in cups of the finished casserole and enter it in the table.
   - Calculate the total cost and the cost per 1-cup cerving.

Table 24-2   Cost and Yield of Casseroles from Recipes

Type of Casserole	Ingredients	Amount	Cost ($)	Total Cost ($)	Yield (c)	Cost per One-cup Serving ($)

3.   Compare the two products for

- Cost per 1-cup serving
- Flavor and eating quality
- Time required for preparation
- Comparable amounts of animal protein: meat, cheese, egg

UNIT 25   SANDWICHES

Suggested reading: Basic Foods, pages 447–452

Objective

- To prepare a variety of cold and hot sandwiches

COLD SANDWICHES

A. Preparation of Sandwiches

1. Choose one or more of the following for the filling:
   a. Sliced cold meat: beef, ham, turkey, tongue
   b. Sliced sandwich meat: salami, bologna, pastrami, pimiento loaf
   c. Cheese
   d. Prepared filling mixture
2. Choose suitable bread, bun, or roll; crusts may be removed if desired.
3. Choose spread:
   a. Salad dressing (65 cal/Tbsp), imitation mayonnaise (50 cal/Tbsp), mayonnaise (100 cal/Tbsp)
   b. Table fat (100 cal/Tbsp)
   c. Relishes: hot dog, hamburger, India (16 cal/Tbsp)
   d. Prepared mustard (5 cal/Tbsp)
4. Choose and prepare appropriate garnishes: lettuce, watercress, slices of tomato, pickle, green pepper, onion, or cucumber
5. Assemble the sandwich:
   a. Remove slices of bread from the package in pairs so that their shapes will fit together neatly.
   b. Spread the sides facing up with the desired spread.
   c. Place the filling on one of the pieces of bread and top with the garnish(es) and the second slice of bread, spread side down.
   d. Cut the sandwich in halves or quarters, either perpendicularly or diagonally.
   e. If sandwich is not to be eaten immediately, cover with plastic wrap. Keep refrigerated or frozen. (Do not use mayonnaise on sandwiches to be frozen.)

B. Filling Mixtures

Tuna Salad (or other seafoods)
_____

1 7-oz can tuna	2 Tbsp India relish
1/3 c finely chopped celery	2 Tbsp imitation or real mayonnaise
1 Tbsp minced green onion, including tops	1 tsp lemon juice

1. Drain the tuna well and flake.
2. Add remaining ingredients and mix well.
   Yield: 1-1/3 cups

Chicken (or Turkey) Salad

1 c chopped or ground cooked
    chicken or turkey
1 Tbsp chopped pimiento
1/4 c chopped celery

1 Tbsp chopped olives
2 Tbsp imitation or real mayonnaise
dash of curry powder

1. Combine all ingredients and mix well.

Yield: 1-1/3 cups

Ground Roast Beef (or other cooked meat)

1 c cooked roast beef, chopped
1/4 c hamburger relish

2 Tbsp imitation or real mayonnaise
1 Tbsp minced green onion, including tops

1. Place 1/2 cup meat in the blender, cover, and process until finely divided; transfer to a bowl and process remaining meat.
2. Combine other ingredients with the meat, mixing well.

Yield: 1-1/3 cups

Egg Salad

2 hard-cooked eggs
2 Tbsp hot-dog relish

1 Tbsp imitation or real mayonnaise
a few drops Worcestershire sauce

1. Chop the eggs; add remaining ingredients.

Yield: 1/2 cup

Grated Cheese

4 oz cheese: Swiss, cheddar, Jack
2 Tbsp chopped olives

2 Tbsp imitation or real mayonnaise

1. Grate the cheese and mix with other ingredients.

Yield: 1 cup

C. Special Sandwiches

Club Sandwich

1. Use three slices of bread (matched) or slice uncut hot dog or hamburger bun into three slices.
2. Spread the middle slice of bread on both sides with desired spread. Spread the side of the outside slices adjacent to the center slice with the same or a different spread (i.e., imitation mayonnaise and pickle relish or mustard).
3. Choose two or more types of fillings: sliced meats or cheese, sandwich filling mixtures. Chicken, bacon, lettuce, and tomato are usual.
4. Place the fillings on the slices of bread and put them together to form a double-decker sandwich.
5. Cut in half diagonally.

Submarine Sandwich

1. Cut a loaf of French bread, or French rolls, in half lengthwise; the small French rolls are appropriate as a single serving; the large loaves can be cut into 4-6 servings.
2. Spread the cut sides with the desired spread.
3. Distribute several kinds of sliced meats and cheeses, lettuce, tomatoes, and pickle slices over the bottom half; top with the other half.

HOT SANDWICHES

Grilled Cheese Sandwich

2 slices bread   1 oz sliced cheddar cheese
1 Tbsp table fat

1. Spread the table fat on the outside of the bread slices.
2. Place one slice, buttered side down, in a frying pan.
3. Place cheese on the bread in the frying pan; top with the second slice of bread, buttered side up.
4. Cover the pan; cook over moderate heat until the bottom of the sandwich is lightly browned (3 to 5 minutes).
5. Turn the sandwich over with a pancake turner while holding the top slice in place with fingers; brown the second side.
6. Cut in half diagonally to serve.

Hot Meat Sandwich

2 oz sliced meat: roast beef, turkey,   2 slices bread
    chicken, ham, pastrami   1/3 c hot gravy[1]

1. Toast the bread slices and lay side by side on serving plate.
2. Place thin slices of heated, cooked meat on the bread and pour hot gravy over them.
3. Garnish with parsley and/or sliced tomato on lettuce.

[1]Use turkey gravy with turkey, beef gravy with beef. Ham may be served on raisin or spice bread and accompanied by a hot fruit sauce, like Orange Sauce (Unit 8, Table 8-3).

Sloppy Joe

1/4 lb ground beef   1 8-oz can tomato sauce
2 Tbsp chopped onion   pinch of thyme
1/8 tsp salt   1 hamburger or hot-dog bun
dash of pepper   2 Tsp Parmesan cheese

1. Follow steps 1 through 3 for Spaghetti under Ground Meat Dishes, Unit 21.
2. Stir in onion, salt, pepper, thyme, and tomato sauce; simmer for 5 minutes.
3. Toast the split bun and place it on a serving plate.
4. Pour the hot meat mixture over the bun halves and sprinkle with Parmesan cheese.

Monte Carlo Sandwich

2 slices bread	1 egg
2 slices Swiss cheese	1 Tbsp milk
1 oz sliced turkey	1/8 tsp salt
1 oz sliced ham	1 Tbsp table fat

1. Place a slice of Swiss cheese on one of the slices of bread.
2. Place the slices of turkey and ham on the slice of cheese and top with the second slice of cheese and the second slice of bread.
3. In a small flat dish beat together the egg, milk, and salt.
4. Melt the table fat in a frying pan.
5. Cut the sandwich in half diagonally and dip each half in the egg mixture, turning to coat both sides.
6. Place the egg-coated sandwich halves in the frying pan; cover, and cook on low to moderate heat until the bottoms are browned; turn and brown the second side.

Pizza Sandwich

Follow the instructions given for Pizza in Unit 16 for sauce, cheeses, fillings, garnishes, assembling and baking, but use split French rolls, bread, or English muffins instead of the yeast dough. They need be baked only long enough to heat the ingredients and melt the cheese. Chili sauce or catsup may be used for the sauce, if desired.

Reuben Sandwich

2 slices rye or pumpernickel bread	1 oz Swiss cheese, sliced
1 Tbsp table fat	2 Tbsp canned sauerkraut, drained
2 oz corned beef, sliced	

1. Spread the outside of the bread with table fat.
2. Place one of the slices, buttered side down, in the frying pan.
3. Place the corned beef, Swiss cheese, and sauerkraut on the bread and top with the second slice of bread, buttered side up.
4. Follow steps 4 through 6 for Grilled Cheese Sandwich.

UNIT 26   HORS D'OEUVRES AND CANAPÉS

Suggested reading: <u>Basic Foods</u>, pages 452-461

Objective

- To prepare a variety of hors d'oeuvres and canapés

DIPS AND DIPPERS

A. Dips

Onion Dip
_____

    1 pt sour half-and-half
    1 pkg (1-1/2 oz) dry onion soup mix

1. Combine ingredients in bowl of electric mixer and beat until smooth.

    <u>Yield</u>: 2 cups

Guacamole
_____

    1 ripe avocado, peeled   1 green onion including tops
    1 small ripe tomato, peeled   1 Tbsp lemon juice
    1/4 tsp celery salt

1. Cut avocado and tomato into chunks.
2. Remove root and outer dried layer from green onion and cut into 1" lengths.
3. Place prepared vegetables in the blender; add celery salt and lemon juice. Process until smooth, scraping down sides of container as necessary.

    <u>Yield</u>: 1-1/4 cups

Roquefort Dip
_____

    1 c small-curd low-fat cottage cheese   1 tsp lemon juice
    3 oz Roquefort cheese   1/2 tsp Worcestershire sauce
    1 Tbsp milk   1/2 tsp onion powder

1. Combine all ingredients in a blender and process until smooth.

    <u>Yield</u>: 1-1/3 cups

Seafood Dip

1 3-oz pkg Neufchatel or cream cheese
1/2 c drained seafood: clams, shrimp,
   crab, lobster, tuna
yogurt or buttermilk

1/4 tsp seasoned salt
pinch of basil, crushed
1 Tbsp lemon juice

1. Combine cheese, seafood, seasoned salt, basil, and lemon juice in a blender and process until smooth.
2. Add yogurt or buttermilk as needed to obtain desired consistency.

Yield: 1 cup

Curry Dip

2 hard-cooked eggs
1/2 c imitation or real mayonnaise

1-1/2 tsp curry powder
1/8 tsp salt

1. Press shelled eggs through a sieve.
2. Combine the sieved eggs with remaining ingredients.

Yield: 3/4 cup

Chili Dip

1 3-oz pkg Neufchatel or cream cheese
1/3 c chili sauce
1-1/2 tsp lemon juice

1 tsp Worcestershire sauce
1/4 tsp seasoned salt
1/2 tsp prepared mustard

1. Combine all ingredients in bowl of electric mixer; beat until smooth.

Yield: 2/3 cup

Pineapple Cheese Dip

2/3 c crushed pineapple, drained
1 c small-curd low-fat cottage cheese
pineapple juice

pinch of salt
1 Tbsp sugar, or to taste

1. Combine pineapple, cheese, salt, and sugar in the blender and process until smooth; add pineapple juice as needed to obtain the proper consistency.

Yield: 1-2/3 cups

Savory Cheese Dip

4 oz sharp cheddar cheese, grated
1/3 c yogurt or buttermilk

1/4 tsp crushed garlic
2 tsp caraway seeds

1. Combine all ingredients in bowl of electric mixer and beat until smooth.

Yield: 1-1/4 cups

Pimiento Ham Dip
———————————

1 4-1/2-oz can deviled ham   1 green onion, including top
1 2-oz jar pimientos, drained   1/4 c yogurt
1/2 tsp Worcestershire sauce

1. Combine all ingredients in a blender and process until smooth.

   Yield: 3/4 cup

B. Dippers

1. Breads: bread sticks, chunks of French bread or rolls served with food picks
2. Crackers: snack crackers, various flavors
3. Chips: potato, corn, tortilla: plain, barbecue, or cheese
4. Protein foods: chunks of hard cheese, cooked roast meats, shrimp, wieners; served with food picks
5. Vegetables: carrot and celery sticks, 1-2" long, cucumber and zucchini squash slices, cauliflower and broccoli flowerets
6. Fruits: berries, grapes, chunks of apple, pineapple, melon, banana, pears, served with food picks
   (Dip apples, pears, and bananas in pineapple or orange juice to prevent enzymatic browning.)

TIDBITS AND FINGER FOODS

Marinated Mushrooms
———————————

1/4 lb fresh "button" mushrooms or   1/2 c French or Italian salad dressing
    drained canned mushrooms   (Unit 5)

1. Wash the mushrooms well and trim off the dried ends of stems.
2. Place the mushrooms and the dressing in a saucepan and bring to a boil.
3. Remove from heat and allow the mushrooms to marinate in the dressing several hours or overnight in the refrigerator.
4. Serve with food picks.

Marinated Broccoli and Cauliflower
———————————

1 lb fresh broccoli or cauliflower
1/2 c French or Italian dressing

1. Wash the broccoli or cauliflower and break it into bite-size flowerets, leaving 1/2-1" stem on each piece for a handle.
2. Place the flowerets and the dressing in a saucepan and bring to a boil.
3. Remove from the heat and marinate for several hours or overnight in the refrigerator.

Ham Rollups
———————————

1 5-oz jar flavored cheese spread   stuffed green olives
4 oz boiled ham slices

1. Soften cheese by allowing it to reach room temperature.
2. Trim fat from ham slices and cut into 4" squares.
3. Spread a layer of softened cheese over the ham.
4. Lay stuffed olives along one edge of the slice of ham and roll the ham spread with cheese around the olives; secure with food picks.
5. Chill the rolls for several hours; then slice into 1/2" lengths and insert a food pick into each piece.

Sweet-Sour Cocktail Wieners

2 cans Vienna sausage	2 Tbsp catsup
1/4 c pineapple juice	2 Tbsp brown sugar
1/4 tsp crushed ginger	1 Tbsp vinegar

1. Drain sausages and cut in half crosswise.
2. Combine all the ingredients in a saucepan and heat to boiling.
3. Remove from heat and allow to marinate for several hours or overnight in the refrigerator.
4. Serve with food picks.

Petits Choux (Miniature Puffs)

1/2 c water	2 large eggs
1/4 c table fat	meat filling: chicken, turkey, ham,
1/2 c all-purpose flour	crab, tuna

1. Prepare the miniature puffs according to directions for Cream Puffs (Unit 10); drop the batter onto the baking pan in mounds of about 2 tsp each. A pastry bag and a No. 20 or 30 tip may be used.
2. Sandwich filling mixtures given in Unit 25 can be used for filling the puffs.
3. Refrigerate until served.

   Yield: About 20 puffs

Radish Roses

1. Choose and wash symmetrical radishes; leaves may be left on if desired and if fresh; cut off roots.
2. Cut a thin slice from each of the four sides. Behind each of these white spots, make a slash from the root end toward the stem, but not quite to the end, to form the petals of the rose (Fig. 26-1).
3. Place radishes in a bowl of ice and water to open the petals.

Carrot Curls and Ribbons

1. Wash and peel carrots; then use a floating-blade peeler to slice thin strips of carrot.
2. Wrap carrot strips around the forefinger, remove, and secure with food pick passed through the curl; or weave a strip of carrot back and forth on a food pick to form ribbon (Fig. 26-2).
3. Chill carrot curls and ribbons in a bowl of ice and water.

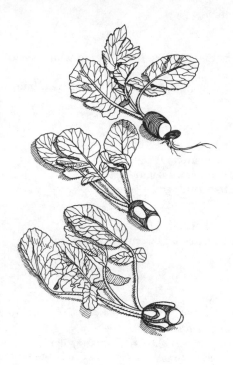

Fig. 26-1: Preparation of radish rose

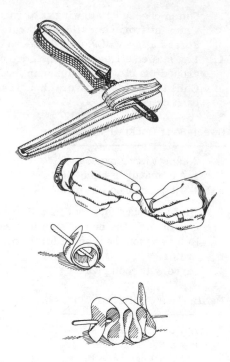

Fig. 26-2: Preparation of carrot curl and ribbon

Celery Curls

1. Cut wide pieces of celery into 2 to 3" lengths.
2. Slash each end of the piece of celery almost to the middle to form strips about 1/4" thick (Fig. 26-3).
3. Place the slashed celery in a bowl of ice and water.

Vegetable Canapés

1. Slice peeled carrots, peeled daikon (white radish), unpeeled cucumber, or zucchini either crosswise or diagonally to form slices at least 1" in diameter and 1/3" thick to use as bases for canapés.
2. Top with a small mound of seasoned cheese or meat mixture. Use any of the Sandwich Fillings in Unit 25 or the spreads for Canapés given in this unit.
3. Garnish with olive or radish slices, parsley, or watercress.

Fig. 26-3: Preparation of celery curl

KABOBS

Thread two or more chunks of food on food picks or short bamboo skewers. Anchor the skewers of food in a head of cabbage or cauliflower, a large grapefruit, a ball of cheese, like Edam, or fresh pineapple or melon. Suggestions for kabobs include:

- A pickled onion or beet, a slice of chunk of pickle, a cherry tomato, or an olive with a chunk of meat or cheese
- Chunks of fruit, such as apple, pear, pineapple, melons, berries, pitted cherries, avocado, orange sections, banana, or seeded grapes skewered with chicken, ham, turkey, or other meats or cheese
- Chunks of such raw vegetables as celery, carrot, cucumber, green pepper, or zucchini with seafoods, cheese, or other meats

CANAPÉS

A. Bread Bases

1. Trim the crusts from 1/2"-thick slices of bread and flatten the slices with a rolling pin. (It is more economical to have the bakery slice the loaf lengthwise; BF, 454, Fig. 26.4.)
2. Cut out the desired shapes from flattened slices and toast on one side on a lightly greased griddle.
3. One-half hour before serving, spread with filling.

Note: Other canapé bases are crackers, pie pastry, or shortbread cookies.

B. Canapé Fillings

Chicken Spread

1 c cooked chicken pieces, without bones or skin	1/2 tsp curry powder
1/4 c celery pieces	2 Tbsp mayonnaise
	salt to taste

1. Place chicken and celery in blender and process until finely chopped.
2. Transfer the chicken and celery to a bowl and add the curry powder and mayonnaise; mix well; correct seasoning.

Yield: 1-1/2 cups

Ham Spread

1 c cooked lean ham pieces	2 Tbsp mayonnaise
1/4 c sweet pickle relish	

1. Place the ham pieces in the blender and process until finely chopped.
2. Transfer ham to a bowl, add the pickle relish and mayonnaise; mix well.

Yield: 1-1/3 cups

Roast Beef Spread
_____

    1 c lean roast beef chunks   2 Tbsp mayonnaise
    1/4 c hamburger relish

1.   Follow instructions for Ham Spread.

    Yield: 1-1/2 cups

Sardine Spread
_____

    1 3-oz can sardines, drained   1 Tbsp mayonnaise
    2 Tbsp lemon juice   1 3-oz pkg Neufchatel or cream cheese
    1/2 tsp onion powder

1.   Combine all ingredients in bowl of electric mixer and beat until smooth.

    Yield: 3/4 cup

Broiled Cheese Spread
_____

    2 slices bacon   1/2 tsp Worcestershire sauce
    4 oz Swiss cheese, grated   3 Tbsp mayonnaise
    1/4 tsp onion powder

1.   Cut bacon into small pieces and sauté until crisp and well browned; drain on paper towels; discard fat.
2.   Add bacon pieces to remaining ingredients; mix well.
3.   Spread on untoasted side of bread base and broil until bubbly; serve hot.

    Yield: 1 cup

Roquefort Spread
_____

    3 oz Roquefort cheese   1 tsp chopped chives
    3 oz Neufchatel or cream cheese   1 Tbsp milk

1.   Combine all ingredients in bowl of electric mixer and beat until smooth.

    Yield: 3/4 cup

Savory Cream Cheese Spread
_____

    3 oz Neufchatel or cream cheese   1/4 tsp garlic powder
    1 tsp onion powder   2 Tbsp mayonnaise

1.   Combine all ingredients in bowl of electric mixer and beat until smooth.

    Yield: 1/2 cup

C. Garnishes for Canapés

Basic Foods, Table 26.2, p. 453, lists a large variety of garnishes suitable for canapés. Slices, strips, or shreds of raw vegetables, eggs, cheese, cocktail wieners, pickles, olives, pimiento, cocktail onions, canned mushrooms, and a number of fruits add color and design to canapés.

D. Preparing the Canapé

1. Choose base, spread, and garnish that will blend together in flavors as well as in appearance.

2. Apply the spread to the canapé base in one of the following ways:

    a. Place a mound of the spread in the center of the base and press the garnish into the center.

    b. Place smooth spread, such as Roquefort or Savory Cream Cheese in a pastry bag with No. 44 or 46 tip for layering the filling on the canapé base. Use the shell tip (No. 98) to make a border around the outer edges of the canapé, if desired. Use other tubes to decorate the canapés with leaves or flowers, using colored cream-cheese spread, just as in decorating a cake.

    c. A combination of (a) and (b) can be used: a mound of chicken, ham, or sardine filling can be placed in the center of the base; then the cream-cheese filling can be piped in a border around the outer edge.

UNIT 27   CANDIES

Suggested reading: <u>Basic Foods</u>, pages 463-472

Objective

- To prepare a variety of cooked and uncooked candies

COOKED CANDIES

A. Crystalline Candies

General Instructions
_____

1. Test candy thermometer in actively boiling water and determine any correction needed:
    a. Place 2 cups water in a 1-qt saucepan, bring to a boil, and boil actively for 3 minutes before reading the temperature.
    b. Hold the thermometer so that the bulb is 1/2" from the bottom of the pan; read it with the top of the mercury at eye level.
    c. If the observed temperature is <u>below</u> the standard, add the difference between the observed and standard temperatures to the end point temperature given in the recipe (Table 27-1).
    d. If the observed temperature is <u>above</u> the standard, subtract the difference between the observed and standard temperatures from the end point temperature given in the recipe (Table 27-1).
2. Combine sugar and liquid in saucepan, bring to a boil, cover, and simmer 2 to 3 minutes to allow the steam formed to wash down the undissolved crystals on the sides of the pan; then cook uncovered to evaporate the liquid and obtain the desired consistency.
3. To prevent premature crystallization, remove crystals as they form on the sides of the pan above the level of the syrup with the tines of a fork wrapped in damp cheesecloth. Alternatively, the pan can be covered for 1 or 2 minutes during evaporation, but this lengthens cooking time.
4. When the syrup is about 5° below the end point temperature, remove the pan from the heat and test a few drops of the syrup in ice water. Pour 1/4 tsp syrup into about 1 Tbsp ice water in a cup. Roll the syrup around under the water with the finger tip and check its consistency. If too soft, return the syrup to the heat and check the consistency again when the syrup temperature is 2°higher. If the ball in the water is too firm, stir 1 Tbsp water into the syrup, bring to a boil, and repeat the cold water test. Use fresh cold water for each test. The syrup must be boiling and the thermometer held correctly for measuring the temperature, but always remove the pan from the heat when testing for consistency.
5. While the syrup is cooling, prior to being beaten, do not disturb or agitate it as this would start premature crystallization. Hasten cooling by placing pan of syrup in pan of cold water. Once beating is started, continue without stopping until crystallization starts; then quickly transfer candy to the plate or pan in which it will be molded.

Table 27.1   Procedure for Correcting Thermometers

Boiling Point of Water			End Point Temperature	
Standard	Observed	Difference	In Recipe	Corrected
100°C	98°C	2°C	113°C	115°C
100°C	101°C	1°C	113°C	112°C
212°F	210°F	2°F	236°F	238°F
212°F	213°F	1°F	236°F	235°F

Fondant

1/2 c water	pinch of salt
3/4 c sugar	1/16 tsp cream of tartar

1. Combine ingredients in a 1-qt saucepan, mixing until the sugar is wet; heat to boil, cover, and boil 1 minute.
2. Remove cover and boil without stirring until temperature reaches 235°F (112.5°C); remove crystals from sides of pan during the evaporation process.
3. Test for consistency in cold water; discontinue cooking at soft-ball stage (BF, 467, Table 27.2).
4. Leave the thermometer submerged in the syrup; let syrup cool to 122°F (50°C) undisturbed. Remove thermometer and beat syrup with wooden spoon or table fork until it becomes too stiff to beat; then knead it with the hands (like dough) on a marble slab or greased plate until almost firm.
5. Shape into a layer about 1/2" thick, on waxed paper, pushing the edges up with the sides of the hands. Cool and cut into squares.
6. The still pliable fondant can also be molded into shapes.
7. Color and flavor may be added to the fondant at start of beating.

Cream Fondant

1/2 c milk or cream	pinch of salt
3/4 c sugar	1/16 tsp cream of tartar

1. Follow instructions for Fondant.

Chocolate Coated Fondant

1 cup (6 oz) semi-sweet chocolate pieces   Fondant

1. Heat chocolate drops in top of double boiler until melted; remove from heat.
2. Shape fondant into small (1/2" diameter) balls and roll in the melted chocolate, using two forks.
3. Place dipped fondant candies on waxed paper to cool.
4. A blanched whole almond, half walnut, or other nut may be surrounded with fondant and dipped in chocolate, or shredded coconut or chopped nuts mixed with the fondant

before shaping it into balls. The dipped fondants may also be rolled in chopped nuts or grated coconut and then placed on waxed paper to cool.

Fudge 2 8

1 square (1 oz) baker's chocolate or 3 Tbsp cocoa	1/8 tsp salt
	2 Tbsp table fat *Sweet butter*
1/2 c milk	1/2 tsp vanilla
1 Tbsp corn syrup	1/2 c chopped nuts
1 c sugar	

1. Cut chocolate into pieces and place in a 1-qt saucepan; melt over low heat, stirring with a wooden paddle or spoon.
2. Add milk, corn syrup, sugar, and salt to the chocolate and mix until smooth. If cocoa is used, add it to mixture.
3. Cook over moderate heat until the sugar is dissolved and mixture starts to boil; cover and boil for 1 minute.
4. Remove cover and cook over moderately high heat to 235°F (112.5^{O}C); test consistency in ice water and discontinue cooking at soft-ball stage. Remove crystals from side of pan during cooking. Stir occasionally during cooking until temperature reaches 230°F (110°C); then stir continuously.
5. Add the table fat to the fudge and leave thermometer in the fudge while cooling to 122°F (50°C). To hasten cooling, set pan of fudge in a pan of cold water. Allow to cool undisturbed.
6. Beat the fudge with wooden spoon or table fork until it gets too stiff to beat, then add vanilla and nuts, and knead on waxed paper until firm.
7. Pat the fudge into a layer about 1/2" thick on waxed paper or a greased plate; cool, cut into squares.

Microwave Oven:

1. Place chocolate, corn syrup, and table fat in a 2-q glass casserole and cook at high power about 2 minutes to melt the chocolate.
2. Stir in the sugar, salt, and milk. Cover with a plastic wrap and cook at high power 5 minutes.
3. Stir and cook uncovered at high power 5 minutes. Test consistency in ice water and continue cooking 1/2 to 1 minute intervals until soft ball stage is obtained.
4. Cool to 122°F (50°C). The casserole can be placed in cold water after it has cooled 10 minutes. Avoid extremes of temperature with glass.
5. Follow steps 6 and 7 above.

Panocha 2 x

1/2 c milk	2 Tbsp table fat
1 c dark brown sugar, packed	1/2 tsp vanilla
1/8 tsp salt	1/2 c chopped nuts

1. Combine milk and sugar in a 1-qt saucepan and mix until smooth.
2. Follow steps 3 through 7 for Fudge.

Divinity Fudge *2 σ*

1/4 c water	1 large egg white
1/4 c light corn syrup	1/2 tsp vanilla
1 c sugar	1/2 c chopped nuts
1/16 tsp salt	

1. Combine water, corn syrup, sugar, and salt in a 1-qt saucepan and mix until smooth.
2. Cook over moderately high heat until the mixture starts to boil, cover, and cook 1 minute.
3. Remove cover and boil actively to 255°F (124°C); remove crystals from side of the pan.
4. Test the consistency in ice water and discontinue cooking at hard-ball stage.
5. As the end point approaches, combine the egg white and vanilla in the small bowl of the electric mixer and beat to stiff-peak stage.
6. When the syrup reaches the hard-ball stage, slowly pour into the stiffly beaten egg white, continuing to beat; pour the last of the syrup into the egg white mixture rapidly, but do not scrape the syrup from the pan. *exception*
7. Beat until the mixture will almost hold a peak; it should still be glossy; stir in the chopped nuts.
8. Pour or pat the divinity fudge into a greased 8" square pan; cool, cut into squares.

B. Noncrystalline Candies

Caramel *2 ⊕ 1*

1 c evaporated milk, undiluted	1/4 tsp salt
1/4 c table fat	1 tsp vanilla
1 c sugar	1 c chopped nuts
1 c corn syrup	

1. Combine milk and table fat in a saucepan and heat, stirring, until the table fat is melted; set aside to keep warm.
2. Combine the sugar, corn syrup, and salt in a heavy 2-qt saucepan and cook over moderate heat until syrup reaches the firm-ball stage and temperature is 244°F (118°C). When temperature reaches 230°F (110°C), stir constantly with a wooden paddle and scrape the bottom of the pan (mixture scorches easily after reaching this temperature).
3. When the firm-ball stage is reached, slowly add the milk-table fat mixture while continuing to cook and stir the syrup so that the boiling does not stop.
4. Cook over moderate to low heat, stirring constantly until temperature is again 244°F and the candy has reached the firm-ball stage.
5. Remove the candy from the heat, stir in the vanilla and nuts, and pour the mixture into a greased 8" square pan; scraping the pan to obtain complete transfer of the candy. (This is permissible since this is a noncrystalline candy.)
6. Allow to cool for 3 hours or longer; remove from the pan and cut into 1" squares.

soft → firm → hard ball stage?

Orange Taffy

1/2 c orange juice   2 Tbsp water
1-1/4 c sugar

1. Combine the orange juice, sugar, and water in a heavy 2-qt saucepan and bring to a boil.
2. Cook over high heat to about 230°F (110°C); reduce heat to moderate and cook to 265°F (130°C), stirring constantly to prevent scorching.
3. Test the consistency in ice water and discontinue cooking when candy reaches hard-ball stage.
4. Pour the syrup onto a greased plate, scraping out the pan, and allow to cool. (The outer portions can be turned into the center with a metal spatula to help equalize the temperature and speed cooling.)
5. When cool enough to handle, grease fingers with shortening (remove rings) and pull taffy, twisting and folding until the taffy becomes opaque and firm.
6. Stretch the taffy into a long strip and twist it on a sheet of wax paper. Cut into 1" lengths with kitchen shears.

Peanut Brittle

1/4 c water   1 c peanuts
1/2 c light corn syrup   1 Tbsp table fat
1 c sugar   1 tsp vanilla
1/8 tsp salt   1/2 tsp baking soda

1. Combine the water, corn syrup, sugar, and salt in a 2-q saucepan and bring to a boil.
2. Cook over high heat, stirring constantly after the temperature reaches 230°F (110°C).
3. At 260°F (126.5°C) stir in the peanuts and the table fat; continue cooking, stirring constantly, until the temperature reaches 293°F (145°C).
4. Remove from the heat and, working quickly, stir in the vanilla and baking soda; immediately transfer to a greased platter, scraping the syrup from the pot with a rubber scraper that has also been greased. (The syrup will foam when the baking soda is added.)
5. Allow the brittle to cool, then crack into pieces.

Microwave Oven:

1. Omit the water in the above recipe. Combine the corn syrup, sugar, and salt in a 2-q glass casserole and mix well. Cook on high power uncovered 5 minutes.
2. Stir in the peanuts and table fat; cook at high power uncovered 6 minutes, stirring at the end of 2 and 4 minutes.
3. At the end of 6 minutes the syrup should be lightly browned (caramelized). Follow steps 4 and 5 above.

UNCOOKED CANDIES

Cream Cheese Fondant

3 oz Neufchatel or cream cheese   flavoring
2-1/2 c confectioners' sugar   coloring (optional)

1. Cream together the softened cheese and the sifted sugar. Add desired flavoring and color.
2. Work in 1/2 c chopped nuts, if desired, to use for stuffing pitted dates or prunes.

Apricot Coconut Balls

3/4 c dried apricots   1/3 c sweetened condensed milk
1 c shredded coconut   sifted confectioners' sugar

1. Grind or finely chop the dried, uncooked apricots.
2. Combine coconut and milk with apricots and mix well.
3. Shape the mixture into 1" diameter balls and roll in confectioners' sugar.
4. Let stand until firm.

Peanut Butter Fruit Bars

1 c pitted dates   1 c peanut butter
1/2 c seedless raisins   1/4 c sweetened condensed milk
1/2 c pitted prunes

1. Grind the fruits in a food chopper.
2. Add peanut butter and milk to fruits and mix well.
3. Press the mixture into the bottom of a greased 8" square pan.
4. Chill well and cut into 1 x 2" pieces.

UNIT 28   FROZEN DESSERTS

Suggested reading: <u>Basic Foods</u>, Chapter 28

Objective

- To prepare a variety of agitated and still frozen desserts

AGITATED FROZEN DESSERTS

A. Preparation and Assembly of the Freezer and Freezing Mixture

1. Consult BF, 485, Fig. 28.2, for parts and assembly of freezer.
2. Wash freezer can, dasher, and lid in hot soapy water; rinse, dry, and store in a food-storage freezer to chill.
3. Prepare the frozen dessert mixture according to directions given below.
4. Place the dasher in the chilled can and pour in the dessert mixture, filling can no more than 2/3 full.
5. Place the lid on the can and return to food-storage freezer to chill while preparing the freezing mixture.
6. Crush the ice and choose measuring utensils for ice and rock salt; use 1-qt pan for ice and a nested measuring cup for salt.
7. Place the wooden bucket in a tub or sink to catch the brine that will seep out the drain hole during freezing.
8. Place the can of chilled dessert mixture in the bucket; adjust the gear frame and hand crank or motor unit on top of can and bucket.
9. Turn the crank a few times to be sure that it is operating correctly.
10. Distribute 1 qt ice in the bucket around the can of dessert mix and sprinkle rock salt over the ice. Use 1/4 cup rock salt per 1 qt ice for ice milk and ice cream; use 1/3 cup rock salt per 1 qt ice for ices and sherbets. Alternate ice and rock salt, in the same proportions, until bucket is filled to top of can.

B. Freezing and Hardening the Dessert Mixture

1. Crank freezer slowly, about 1 revolution of crank every 2 seconds, for 2 or 3 minutes or until cranking becomes difficult. This permits maximum incorporation of air, especially in mixtures containing whipping cream.
2. Crank the freezer more rapidly, about 2 revolutions per second, until it becomes too hard to turn. Rapid and continuous churning is required at this stage for small crystal formation. If necessary, add ice and salt to keep level at top of can.
3. Tilt the freezer and drain off most of the brine; then scoop out the ice and salt until the level is midway down the can.
4. Remove the motor unit or the gear and crank; wipe off the top of the lid with a clean cloth. Avoid dripping brine into dessert mixture.
5. Remove lid and dasher; scrape mixture on the dasher back into the can and pack contents into can; cover with plastic wrap, foil, or waxed paper.

6.   Replace the lid and plug the hole with a clean cork or cloth.
7.   Place additional salt and ice around the can in bucket. Use 1/2 cup rock salt for each
     2–4 cups crushed ice. Use higher proportion of salt to ice for fast hardening and for
     ices and sherbets.
8.   Cover freezer with folded blanket or newspaper for insulation and allow to stand for 30
     to 60 minutes. Alternatively, the dessert mixture can be transferred to well-chilled
     plastic containers in step 6, covered, and placed in the coldest part of the freezer.

C.   Frozen Dessert Mixtures

Ingredients for a variety of frozen desserts are given in Table 28-1. The volume of mixture
should fill the 1-qt freezer can about 2/3 full. Amounts can be doubled or quadrupled for
2-qt or 4-qt cans.

Orange Ice
_____

1.   Combine 1/2 cup water, sugar, and salt in a 1-qt saucepan and heat, stirring only until
     sugar is dissolved.
2.   Combine syrup, remaining water, and frozen concentrate in freezer can. Add orange
     rind and chill.
3.   Freeze using 1/3 cup rock salt per 1 qt ice.

Orange Sherbet I
_____

1.   Combine 1/2 cup milk, sugar, and salt in a 1-qt saucepan and heat, stirring, only until
     the sugar is dissolved.
2.   Add remaining ingredients and pour the mixture into the freezer can.
3.   Freeze using 1/3 cup rock salt per 1 qt ice.

Orange Sherbet II
_____

1.   Combine 1/2 cup milk, sugar, salt, and gelatin in a 1-qt saucepan and heat, stirring,
     until mixture is steaming hot.
2.   Add the remaining ingredients and pour the mixture into the freezer can.
3.   Freeze using 1/3 cup rock salt per 1 qt ice.

Vanilla Ice Milk
_____

1.   Combine 1/2 cup milk, sugar, salt, and gelatin in a 1-qt saucepan and heat, stirring,
     until mixture is steaming hot and gelatin dissolved.
2.   Remove the pan from the heat and add the remaining ingredients.
3.   Pour the mixture into the freezer can; chill.
4.   Freeze using 1/4 cup rock salt per 1 qt ice.

Vanilla Custard Ice Milk
_____

1.   Combine 1/2 cup milk, sugar, salt, and egg in a 1-qt saucepan and heat, stirring con-
     stantly with a spring stirrer, until mixture is steaming hot and coats a silver spoon.
2.   Follow steps 2 through 4 for Vanilla Ice Milk.

Table 28-1   Ingredients to Yield 1 qt Agitated Frozen Dessert

Frozen Dessert	Liquids Type	(c)	Sugar (c)	Salt (tsp)	Vanilla (tsp)	Other Ingredients
Orange Ice	water frozen orange-juice concentrate[1]	2 1/2	3/4	1/16	—	1/2 tsp finely grated orange rind
Orange Sherbet I	whole milk frozen orange-juice concentrate[1]	2 1/2	1/2	1/16	—	1/2 tsp finely grated orange rind
Orange Sherbet II	whole milk frozen orange-juice concentrate[1]	2 1/2	1/2	1/16	—	1/2 tsp finely grated orange rind 1 tsp unflavored gelatin
Vanilla Ice Milk	whole milk	2-1/2	1/2	pinch	1-1/2	1 tsp unflavored gelatin
Vanilla Custard Ice Milk	whole milk	2-1/2	1/2	pinch	1-1/2	1 large egg
Vanilla Custard Ice Cream	half-and-half	2-1/2	1/2	pinch	1-1/2	1 large egg
Rich Vanilla Ice Cream	whole milk whipping cream	1-1/2 1	1/2	pinch	1-1/2	—
Chocolate Ice Cream	whole milk half-and-half	1 1-1/4	1/2	pinch	1	1/3 c cocoa powder 1/4 c light corn syrup 1 large egg
Strawberry Ice Cream	whole milk whipping cream	1/2 3/4	1/2	pinch	—	1 large egg 1 10-oz pkg frozen strawberries, partially thawed
Coconut Ice Cream	sweetened condensed milk whole milk half-and-half	3/4 1/2 1-1/4	—	pinch	1	1/2 tsp almond extract 3/4 c angel-flake coconut

[1] Fresh, frozen, or canned drained fruit, like raspberries, strawberries, apricots, peaches, or nectarines, may be puréed and used in place of orange-juice concentrate. Pieces of fruits may also be added.

Vanilla Custard Ice Cream

1. Combine 1/2 c half-and-half, sugar, salt, and egg in a 1-qt saucepan and heat, stirring constantly with a spring stirrer, until mixture is steaming hot and coats a silver spoon.
2. Follow steps 2 through 4 for Vanilla Ice Milk.

Rich Vanilla Ice Cream

1. Combine 1/2 c milk, sugar, and salt in a 1-qt saucepan and heat, stirring, only until sugar is dissolved.
2. Follow steps 2 through 4 for Vanilla Ice Milk.

Chocolate Ice Cream

1. Combine sugar and cocoa powder in a 1-qt saucepan and mix until smooth and free of lumps; stir in 1/2 c milk, egg, corn syrup, and salt.
2. Cook, stirring constantly with a spring stirrer, until mixture is steaming hot.
3. Follow steps 2 through 4 for Vanilla Ice Milk.

Strawberry Ice Cream

1. Combine milk, sugar, salt, and egg in a 1-qt saucepan and heat, stirring constantly with a spring stirrer, until mixture is steaming hot and coats the spoon.
2. Add the strawberries and follow steps 2 through 4 for Vanilla Ice Milk.

Coconut Ice Cream

1. Mix together all ingredients; follow steps 3 and 4 for Vanilla Ice Milk.

STILL FROZEN DESSERTS

Chocolate Mousse

1/2 c whole milk	1/2 tsp vanilla
1 tsp unflavored gelatin	6 large marshmallows, quartered, or
2 1-oz squares unsweetened chocolate	1/3 c miniature marshmallows
1/2 c sugar	1-1/4 c evaporated whole milk
pinch of salt	1/4 c chopped walnuts

1. Chill the undiluted evaporated whole milk in an ice-cube tray until partially frozen.
2. Combine whole milk, gelatin, sugar, salt, and finely chopped chocolate in a 1-qt saucepan; heat, stirring, until the chocolate is melted; then cool and add vanilla.
3. Whip the evaporated milk to soft peaks; fold it into the cooled chocolate mixture with the marshmallows and nuts.
4. Pour mixture into a freezer tray and freeze in the coldest part of the freezer with control set at lowest setting.

Yield: 1 qt

Ambrosia Mousse

1/2 orange, peeled, seeded, quartered	1/4 tsp almond extract
several slices of colored orange peel	2 large bananas
1/4 c sugar	1 c (1/2 pt) whipping cream
1/8 tsp salt	1/3 c coconut

1. Combine orange, orange peel slices, sugar, and salt in the blender and process until smooth.
2. Add pieces of banana gradually; process until smooth. Add almond extract.
3. Whip the cream to stiff peaks and fold in fruit mixture and coconut.
4. Pour the mixture into a chilled freezer tray and freeze in the coldest part of the freezer with control set at lowest setting.

Yield: 1 qt

Maple Nut Mousse

2/3 c sweetened condensed milk	1/2 tsp vanilla
1/3 c water	1 c evaporated whole milk, undiluted
2 tsp maple flavoring	1/4 c chopped walnuts

1. Chill evaporated milk in a freezer tray until partially frozen.
2. Combine condensed milk, water, vanilla, and maple flavoring, and chill.
3. Whip the evaporated milk to soft peaks and fold into condensed-milk mixture.
4. Pour mixture into a freezer tray and freeze until it is thick.
5. Turn mixture into a chilled bowl of electric mixer and beat until fluffy but not melted; fold in chopped nuts.
6. Return to freezer tray, cover with plastic wrap or waxed paper, and freeze until firm.

Yield: 3 cups

Toasted Almond Parfait

1/2 c water	1 c (1/2 pt) whipping cream
1/3 c sugar	1/2 tsp vanilla
pinch of salt	1/4 c sliced almonds
2 egg whites	1/4 tsp table fat

1. Melt the table fat in a pie pan and add the almonds; bake at 300°F (149°C) for 15 to 20 minutes; set aside.
2. Combine water, sugar, and salt in a 1-qt saucepan and bring to a boil; cover and boil 1 minute; uncover and boil to 230°F (110°C).
3. When the temperature is almost at end point, place egg whites in small bowl of electric mixer and beat to stiff peaks.
4. Slowly pour the hot syrup over egg whites, beating constantly; continue beating until mixture is cool.
5. In another bowl beat the whipping cream to stiff peaks.
6. Fold cream, vanilla, and almonds into the egg mixture and pour into a freezer tray.
7. Freeze in the coldest part of the food storage freezer with control set at lowest setting. Do not stir.

Yield: About 1 qt

Avocado Sherbet

---

2 c buttermilk or yogurt
1/2 lemon, seeded, with peel, quartered
1/2 c sugar

1/2 c corn syrup
1 ripe avocado, peeled, pitted

1. Combine buttermilk, lemon, sugar, and corn syrup in blender and process until smooth.
2. Pour mixture into a freezer tray and freeze until mushy.
3. Place a few spoonfuls of the frozen mixture in the blender and add the avocado; process until smooth.
4. Fold the avocado purée into the partially frozen mixture and return to the freezer tray.
5. Freeze until firm.

Yield: About 1 qt

UNIT 29 / BEVERAGES

Suggested reading: Basic Foods, Chapter 31

Objective

- To prepare a variety of beverages: fruit and vegetable drinks; milk, egg, and chocolate drinks; tea and coffee

FRUIT AND VEGETABLE BEVERAGES

A. Fruit Punches and Drinks

Pink Lemonade

1 c water	1/2 c Hawaiian Punch concentrate
1 c sugar	6 c ice and water
1 c lemon juice	

1. Combine sugar and 1 cup water in a 1-qt saucepan and heat, stirring, only until the sugar is dissolved.
2. Remove from heat and combine with remaining ingredients.

   Yield: 2 qts

Golden Glow Fruit Punch

1 c orange juice (fresh or diluted frozen)	1 c pineapple juice
1 c apricot nectar	1 c lemon-lime soda or ginger ale

1. Combine juices and chill.
2. Just before serving, add the carbonated beverage.

   Yield: 1 qt

Cran-Apple Juice Cocktail

1-1/2 c cranberry juice	1-2 Tbsp honey
1-1/2 c apple juice	1 c lemon-lime soda or ginger ale

1. Combine juices and honey, sweetening to taste; chill.
2. Just before serving, add the carbonated beverage.

   Yield: 1 qt

Orange-Berry Nectar

1 6-oz can frozen orange-juice
    concentrate
1 10-oz pkg frozen strawberries

3 c water and ice

1. Place berries and juice in blender; process until smooth.
2. Add water and ice; blend to mix.
3. If desired, strain before serving.

Yield: 1-1/4 qt

Fruit Julep

1 c water
1/2 c sugar
1/4 c lemon juice
3/4 c pineapple juice

1 c orange juice
2 c cranberry juice
mint leaves

1. Combine water and sugar in a 1-qt saucepan and heat, stirring, only until sugar is dissolved.
2. Combine with other ingredients; chill.
3. Serve garnished with sprigs of mint.

Yield: 1-1/4 qt

Hawaiian Medley

1 c Hawaiian Punch concentrate
6 oz frozen lemonade
6 oz frozen grape juice

6 oz frozen orange juice
2-1/2 qt ice and water
1 qt ginger ale

1. Thaw frozen juices and combine all ingredients except ginger ale; chill.
2. Add the ginger ale just before serving.

Yield: 1 gallon

Banana Fruit Shake

1/2 banana
3/4 c fruit juice: orange, pineapple, apricot nectar, lemonade

1. Place juice and banana, cut into chunks, in blender; process until smooth.
2. Serve at once.

Yield: One serving

Hot Spiced Grape Punch

4 c Concord grape juice
1 tsp whole cloves

3 sticks cinnamon
3 slices orange, including rind

1. Combine all ingredients in a 2-qt saucepan and simmer about 5 minutes.
2. Strain and serve hot.

Yield: 1 qt

Hot Citrus Apple Punch
_____

1 qt apple juice	3 sticks cinnamon
1 orange, sliced, seeded, with peel	2 tsp whole cloves
1 lemon, sliced, seeded, with peel	6 c orange juice, fresh or frozen diluted

1. Press the cloves into the rinds of the orange and lemon slices.
2. Combine apple juice, fruit slices, and cinnamon sticks in a 3-qt saucepan; simmer about 5 minutes.
3. Add the orange juice and heat to serving temperature; do not boil.
4. Serve hot; garnish each cup of punch with a slice of orange or lemon.

Yield: 2-1/2 qt

B. Vegetable Juice Cocktails

Tomato Juice Special
_____

2 c tomato juice	1 Tbsp lemon juice
1 tsp Worcestershire sauce	1/4 tsp celery salt
1/4 tsp onion powder	

1. Combine all ingredients and mix well in a shaker or blender. Chill.

Yield: 1 pt

Tomato Bouillon
_____

1 c tomato juice	1/2 c water
1/2 c canned bouillon	1/4 tsp seasoned salt

1. Combine all ingredients and mix well. Chill.

Yield: 1 pt

Clam-Tomato Cocktail
_____

1 c tomato juice	1/4 tsp celery salt
1 c clam juice	1 Tbsp lemon juice
1/4 tsp onion powder	salt to taste
1 tsp Worcestershire sauce	

1. Combine all ingredients; correct seasoning. Chill.

Yield: 1 pt

Vegetable Juice Cocktail
_____

1 c tomato juice	1 c vegetable juice cocktail

1. Combine juices; serve hot or cold with a slice of lemon as garnish.

Yield: 1 pt

FRUIT-MILK DRINKS

Orange-Banana Whiz

1 c cold milk	1/4 c sugar
2 oranges, peeled, seeded, cut into	pinch of salt
chunks	4 ice cubes
1 large banana, sliced	

1. Place 1/2 cup milk, orange chunks, and banana slices in the blender; cover, and process about 1 minute.
2. Add remaining milk and ice cubes; process 30 seconds.
3. Serve immediately.

   Yield: 1 qt

Orange Chiller

4 c cold water	6 oz frozen orange-juice concentrate
1-2/3 c NFDM	1 Tbsp sugar (or to taste)

1. Place 2 cups water in blender; add NFDM, orange-juice concentrate, and sugar; blend until smooth.
2. Add remaining water, mix; chill.

   Yield: 1-1/2 qt

Buttermilk Refresher

2 c buttermilk	1 slice of orange rind, colored part only
1 orange, peeled, seeded, cut in quarters	1 Tbsp honey (or to taste)
2 Tbsp lemon juice	pinch of salt

1. Place the orange quarters, rind, and lemon juice in the blender and process until smooth.
2. Add remaining ingredients; process. Chill.

   Yield: 3 cups

Avocado Smoothie

1 c orange juice	1 c milk
1 Tbsp lemon juice	1 Tbsp honey
1 avocado, peeled, quartered	pinch of salt

1. Place all ingredients in blender and process until smooth. Chill.

   Yield: 3 cups

Apricot Royal

1 c canned apricot halves, drained	1/4 c syrup from canned aprocots
1 c yogurt	1/2 tsp almond extract

1. Combine all ingredients in blender and process until smooth. Chill.

    Yield: 2 cups

MILK, EGG, AND CHOCOLATE BEVERAGES

A. Eggnogs

Basic Egg Nog

> 2 c milk, cold   1/2 tsp vanilla
> 2 eggs   grated nutmeg
> 2 Tbsp sugar

1. Combine milk, eggs, sugar, and vanilla in blender; process 1 minute.
2. Serve in mugs or glasses; sprinkle top with grated nutmeg.

    Yield: 2 cups

Banana Nog

> 1 banana, peeled, sliced   1 c milk, cold
> 1/4 c pineapple juice   1 egg
> 1 Tbsp sugar

1. Combine banana slices and pineapple juice in the blender and process until smooth.
2. Add egg and milk; process 1 minute.

    Yield: 2 cups

Hot Chocolate Nog

> 2 eggs   1 square (1 oz) unsweetened chocolate
> 1/4 c sugar   1/2 tsp vanilla
> 1-1/2 c milk

1. Combine eggs and sugar in the blender and process until smooth.
2. Chop the chocolate and combine with milk in a 1-qt saucepan. Heat, stirring, until mixture is scalding hot and chocolate is melted.
3. Gradually pour the hot milk into the egg-sugar mixture while blender is operating at low speed; add the vanilla. Serve hot.

    Yield: 2 cups

B. Milkshakes

Vanilla Milkshake

> 1 c milk   2 scoops vanilla ice cream
> 1/2 tsp vanilla

1. Combine milk and vanilla in blender; add ice cream and blend a few seconds. The

longer it is blended, the thinner the milkshake will be.

Yield: One serving

Banana Nut Shake

1 c milk
1/2 banana, peeled, sliced

1/2 tsp vanilla
2 scoops banana nut ice cream

1. Combine milk, banana, and vanilla in the blender; process a few seconds.
2. Add the ice cream and process a few seconds. Serve immediately.

Yield: One serving

Other Fruit Milkshakes

Different kinds of fruit and ice cream may be substituted for the banana in this recipe. Some of the variations include strawberry, pineapple, orange, or blueberry.

Peanut Butter Milkshake

1 c milk
1/2 tsp vanilla
2 tsp sugar

2 Tbsp peanut butter
2 scoops vanilla ice cream

1. Combine the milk, vanilla, sugar, and peanut butter in the blender and process until smooth.
2. Add the ice cream and process a few seconds.

Yield: One serving

C. Chocolate Drinks

Cocoa or Chocolate Milk

1/4 c cocoa powder, unsweetened or
   1-1/2 squares (1-1/2 oz) chocolate,
   unsweetened
1/4 c sugar
1/8 tsp salt

3/4 c water
3-1/2 c milk, cold or hot
1 tsp vanilla
marshmallows

1. Combine cocoa powder, sugar, and salt in a 1-qt saucepan and mix until smooth. If squares are used, chop and combine with sugar, salt, and water.
2. Stir the water into the cocoa mixture and mix; heat, stirring constantly, until the mixture starts to boil.
3. Reduce heat and simmer about 3 minutes.
4. Add the vanilla; then add mixture to cold or hot milk.
5. For hot cocoa, place a marshmallow in each cup or mug.

Yield: 1 qt

TEA AND COFFEE

A. Tea

Brewing Tea

1 Tbsp tea leaves: green, oolong, black, or jasmine	1 qt freshly boiling water, naturally soft or distilled

1. Preheat a glass or ceramic tea pot by filling it with boiling water.
2. Heat 1 qt of water to boiling; empty the water from the tea pot and place the tea leaves in the pot.
3. Pour the boiling water over the tea leaves and steep for 3 to 5 minutes.
4. Strain the leaves from the infusion.

Note: The tea leaves may be placed in a tea ball, in which case the tea ball is removed and straining is not necessary; or tea bags may be used and removed when brewing is completed.

Lemon Iced Tea Base

6 tea bags or 3 Tbsp tea leaves	1-3/4 c sugar
1 c freshly boiling water	2 c lemon juice
1 Tbsp grated lemon peel	

1. Heat water to boiling and pour over the tea and lemon peel.
2. Steep 4 minutes; strain out the tea leaves and lemon peel.
3. Stir in the sugar until dissolved; add the lemon juice.
4. Pour into a glass or plastic container and store in the refrigerator.
5. To use, combine 1/4 cup mixture with 1/2 to 3/4 cup cold water and ice cubes.

Yield: Twelve servings

B. Coffee

General Instructions

1. Always be sure that coffee maker is clean.
2. Prepare no less than two-thirds of the capacity of the coffee maker.
3. Use the correct grind of coffee for the coffee maker.
4. Use 1 level Tbsp coffee per cup (6 oz) water.
5. As soon as the coffee is brewed, remove coffee grounds from the coffee maker.
6. Keep brewed coffee hot until ready to serve, preferably less than a half hour.

Drip Coffee

1. Place filter basket over the lower reservoir of the pot and measure drip-grind coffee into it.
2. Place upper reservoir in place.
3. Measure water and bring it to a boil; pour it into the upper reservoir; cover the reservoir.
4. As the water drips into the lower reservoir, place the pot over low heat to keep the coffee warm.

5.   When all of the water has dripped into the lower reservoir, remove the upper reservoir and the basket of grounds; cover the lower reservoir and keep hot.

Percolated Coffee

1.   Measure cold water into the percolator; place the pump and basket in the pot.
2.   Measure regular-grind coffee into the basket; cover the basket and the pot.
3.   Heat over moderate heat until the coffee starts to percolate.
4.   Reduce heat to maintain a gentle stream of water over the grounds; allow to percolate about 8 minutes.
5.   Remove the pot from the heat and allow it to stand a minute, then remove the basket and pump.
6.   Cover and keep hot.

Electric Percolator Coffee

1.   Follow steps 1 and 2 for Percolated Coffee, using an electric-percolator grind if available.
2.   Plug in the pot and allow it to percolate until the cycle is finished.
3.   Follow steps 5 and 6 for Percolated Coffee.

Vacuum Coffee

1.   Measure cold water into the lower reservoir of the coffee maker.
2.   Assemble the filter in the top reservoir and place the reservoir securely into the lower section to form a seal.
3.   Measure drip-grind coffee into the bottom of the upper reservoir.
4.   Heat the water in the bottom reservoir; when almost all the water has risen into the top reservoir, stir the water and grounds in the top reservoir and turn off the heat.
5.   When the coffee infusion has returned to the lower reservoir, remove the top, cover the lower reservoir and keep hot.

Filter Coffee

1.   Place the upper reservoir of the coffee maker over the lower reservoir and place the filter paper in the bottom of the upper reservoir.
2.   Measure drip-grind coffee into the filter paper.
3.   Measure the water and bring it to a boil.
4.   Pour the boiling water over the ground coffee and allow to filter into the bottom reservoir.
5.   Remove the upper reservoir. Cover the pot and keep hot.

Automatic Drip-Filter Coffee

1.   Place filter paper in the basket and measure the grind of coffee recommended by the manufacturer into the basket; place the basket in position.
2.   Be sure the unit is turned on; then measure the cold water and pour into the reservoir.
3.   Discard the grounds when the infusion has finished.

UNIT 30   MEAL PLANNING AND PREPARATION

Suggested Reading: Basic Foods, Chapter 30

Objectives

- To plan meals that are nutritious, attractive, and tasty
- To supervise and/or assist in the preparation of one or more meals

MEAL PLANNING

A. Preparation of Menu

1. Plan, for one or more days, meals based on the typical patterns suggested in BF,
    552, Table 32.1.
2. Check foods used in each meal for color, texture, flavor, and shape variation and com-
    patibility.
3. Check meals for seasonal availability of suggested food items and for ease of prepation.

B. Evaluation of Suggested Meals

1. Fill out Table 30-1 for the day's menu to check if foods from all the food groups are
    used. (For the Basic Seven Food Groups, see BF, 23, Table 1.6.)
2. Fill out Table 30-2 to determine the nutrient composition of one day's food.
    a. List amounts of food both by volume and by weight in grams.
    b. For mixed dishes for which a nutrient analysis is not available, list and record the
        nutrient composition of the ingredients in the dish.
    c. Be sure to include all ingredients used in cooking and seasoning the foods.
    d. Obtain totals of nutrients for day's menu.
    e. Record the Recommended Dietary Allowances for an adult; circle applicable sex.
        (See BF, 610, Table 10.)
    f. Subtract the difference between the daily total for each nutrient and the RDA for that
        nutrient; if the total exceeds the RDA, precede the amount with a "+"; if the total is
        less than the RDA, precede the amount with a "-".
3. Write a paragraph evaluating the choice of foods in the menu according to the standards
    given in Tables 30-1 and 30-2. Account for any discrepancies and suggest substitute
    foods that might make the menu more nutritionally adequate.
4. Evaluate the esthetic quality of the meal: colors, textures, flavors, and so forth.

MEAL PREPARATION

A. Responsibilities of the Meal Manager

1. Use Table 30-3 for itemizing the ingredients required for each food or dish used in the
    menu.
2. Use Table 30-4 for the market order and for calculating costs.

    a. Combine ingredients used more than once in the meal and list them only once on the market order.

    b. Coordinate the amounts of foods and ingredients listed in Tables 30-2, 30-3, and 30-4 so that there are no discrepancies.

    c. Determine the amount of the market unit necessary to obtain the required amount of prepared food, consulting one or more of the following:

- Labels on food container for yield when prepared
- U.S. Department of Agriculture Home Economics Research Report No. 37, Family Food Buying (1969)
- U.S. Department of Agriculture Handbook No. 8, Composition of Food, Table 2: Nutrients in the edible portion of 1 lb of food as purchased
- BF, 388, Table 22.2 for amounts of meat to yield 20 g of protein when cooked
- BF, 594-607, Table 9, for food yields and measures

3. Use Table 30-5 to list the time required for preparing each food in the meal and for performing such other duties as table setting and clean-up.

4. Prepare a work schedule using Table 30-6.
    a. Assign jobs equitably to each member of the group, including yourself.
    b. Allow time in the manager's schedule for supervising activities.
    c. Coordinate time alloted for each task with the times in Table 30-5.

5. Prepare job descriptions for each member of the group and coordinate these with the work schedule.
    a. Use the format shown in BF, 580-581, Table 32.11.
    b. If possible, type information on 5 x 9" file cards.
    c. Supply recipes on separate cards.

6. Plan the type of service desired for the meal.
    a. Draw cover diagrams for the beginning of each course.
    b. Make a list of linens, flatware, dinnerware, beverageware, serving dishes, and serving utensils required for the meal.
    c. Decide on placement of serving dishes, serving utensils, and accessory dishes on the table and when they will be placed and removed.
    d. Plan centerpiece or other table decoration.
    e. Make a list of any special equipment needed for preparation of the meal.

7. Supervise the preparation of the meal.
    a. Assign group members to their work areas.
    b. See that each group member has the necessary supplies and equipment.
    c. Observe group members to be sure that their jobs are being carried out satisfactorily and on time; offer suggestions and help when needed.
    d. Reassign jobs if necessary to complete the meal as scheduled.
    e. Carry out tasks assigned to yourself.

8. Evaluations should be assessments of performance and suggestions for improvement.
    a. Evaluate yourself using form in Table 30-7.
    b. Evaluate each member of the group using form in Table 30-8.

B. Responsibilities of Group Members

1. Read job descriptions prior to starting the meal and question the meal manager ahead of time on points that are not clear.
2. Perform duties listed in the job description; cooperate in reassignment.
3. Evaluate the meal manager using form in Table 30-7.
4. Evaluate your own activities using form in Table 30-8.

Table 30-1 Checklist for Foods from Basic Seven Food Groups

| Foods in Menu | Number of Servings | | | | | | |
| | Fruits-Vegetables | | | | | | |
	Vitamin A	Ascorbic Acid	Other	Milk	Meat or Substitute	Bread or Cereal	Fat
Recommended Daily Servings: Adult	1 or more	1 or more	2 or more	2 or more	2 or more	4 or more	1 or more

Student Name _____   Date _____

Table 30-2 Nutrient Composition of One Day's Food

Student Name _____

Date _____

Foods in Menu	Volume Measure	Weight (g)	Calories	Protein (g)	Fat (g)	Calcium (mg)	Iron (mg)	Vitamin A (IU)	Thiamin (mg)	Riboflavin (mg)	Niacin (mg)	Ascorbic Acid (mg)
Totals												
Recommended Dietary Allowances: Adult, M or F (circle)												
Over or under RDA												

Table 30-3   Ingredients for Preparation of Menu

Foods in Menu	Ingredients	Amounts

Student Name _____   Date _____

Table 30–4   Market Order and Cost Calculations for Menu Ingredients

Ingredients	Market Unit				One Cup			Recipe		
	Weight		Volume	Cost $	g	Cost $	Volume	Weight g	Cost $	
	oz	g								

Table 30–5 Time Estimates for Food Preparation

Food to Be Prepared or Other Duties	Steps in Preparation	Time (min)

Student Name _____ Date _____

Table 30-6   Work Schedule for Group Preparation of Meal

Time Start–End	Assigned Jobs	Person Responsible

Student Name_____   Date _____

Table 30-7 Evaluation of Meal Manager

Score: Excellent — 4   Very good — 3   Fair — 2   Poor — 1

Score	Rating Factors	Suggestions for Improvement
	I. Choice of foods in menu	
___	A. Compatible flavors _____	
___	B. Variety in texture _____	
___	C. Attractive color _____	
___	D. Variety in preparation methods _____	
	II. Organization and planning of meal	
___	A. Equitable job assignments _____	
___	B. Clearly written recipes _____	
___	C. Explicit job descriptions _____	
	III. Service of meal	
___	A. Attractive table setting _____	
___	B. Service suitable for the meal _____	
	IV. Preparation of food (specify food) _____	
___	A. Properly cooked _____	
___	B. Properly seasoned _____	
___	C. Economical use of food _____	
___	D. Efficiency in work habits _____	
___	V. Adequate supervision of the meal _____	
	VI. Food service	
___	A. Food ready on time _____	
___	B. Correct service and removal of dishes _____	
___	C. Quiet, efficient service of meal _____	
	VII. Table manners	
___	A. Correct use of flatware _____	
___	B. General good manners _____	
	VIII. Clean-up	
___	A. Responsibilities efficiently and properly completed _____	
	_____	
	_____	
	_____	

Table 30-8 Evaluation of Group Members

Score: Excellent — 4   Very Good — 3   Fair — 2   Poor — 1

_____

     I. Preparation of food (specify food) _____

____   A. Properly cooked _____

____   B. Properly seasoned _____

____   C. Economical use of food _____

____   D. Efficiency in work habits _____

____   II. Cooperative and helpful in carrying out assignments

        _____

    III. Food service

____   A. Food ready on time _____

____   B. Correct service and removal of dishes _____

____   C. Quiet, efficient service of food _____

    IV. Table manners

____   A. Correct use of flatware _____

____   B. General good manners _____

     V. Clean-up

____   A. Responsibilities efficiently and properly completed _____

        _____

        _____

        _____

APPENDIX I

ABBREVIATIONS

tsp	teaspoon
Tbsp	tablespoon
oz	avoirdupois ounce
fl oz	fluid ounce
c	cup
pt	pint
qt	quart
gal	gallon
ml	millilitre
l	litre
mg	milligram
g	gram
Kg	kilogram
lb	pound
°C	degree Celsius
°F	degree Fahrenheit
cal	calorie
Kcal	kilocalorie
NFDM	nonfat dry milk
PUFA	polyunsaturated fatty acid
RDA	Recommended Dietary Allowance

APPENDIX II

SEASONING MIXTURES

<u>Apple Pie Spice</u>   Combine 2 Tbsp ground cinnamon, 2 tsp ground nutmeg, and 2 tsp ground allspice. Store in a closed container. One tsp will contain 3/5 tsp cinnamon and 1 tsp each of nutmeg and allspice.

<u>Pumpkin Pie Spice</u>   Combine 4 tsp ground cinnamon, 1 tsp ground nutmeg, 1 tsp ground cloves, 1 tsp ground allspice, and 1 tsp powdered ginger. Store in a closed container. One tsp of mixture will contain 1/2 tsp cinnamon and 1/8 tsp each of the other spices.

<u>Cinnamon Sugar</u>   Combine 1 cup white granulated sugar and 2 Tbsp ground cinnamon. Store in a shaker cup.

<u>Crushed Garlic</u>   Remove husks from the cloves of several garlic bulbs and wash peeled cloves. Place cloves in the blender with 1/3 cup vegetable oil. Process until smooth. Transfer the blended garlic to a small covered jar and store in the refrigerator or freezer; it will keep indefinitely. Use 1/2 tsp crushed garlic as a substitute for a small clove of garlic.

<u>Crushed Ginger</u>   Peel about 1/3 lb fresh ginger; wash. Slice the ginger roots crosswise about 1/8" thick. Place ginger in the blender with 3/4 cup dry white wine and process until smooth. Transfer blended ginger to a closed jar and store in the refrigerator or freezer. Use in the same amount as dry powdered ginger in meat marinades, salad dressings, and sweet-and-sour sauces.

<u>Seasoned Flour</u>   Combine 1 cup flour, 2 tsp salt, and 1/2 tsp finely ground pepper. Store in a covered jar or freezer container. Sift after each use to remove scraps of meat or lumps of flour and meat juice.

<u>Poultry Seasoning</u>   Combine 2 Tbsp salt, 1 Tbsp sage, 2 tsp thyme, 1 tsp marjoram, and 2 tsp onion powder. Crush all the ingredients into a fine powder with a mortar and pestle. Store in a closed container. Sprinkle or rub on poultry before cooking; use in poultry stuffings.

APPENDIX III

INGREDIENTS: DESCRIPTION AND SOURCES

Bean Sprouts   The flavor and texture of fresh bean sprouts are far superior to canned. The fresh sprouts can be purchased in Oriental food stores and in the produce departments of many large metropolitan markets.

Nutritional Yeast   This powdered yeast, used to enrich baked products and cereals, is an excellent source of protein and B vitamins. Since it is a rich source of the amino acid lysine, it is ideal for supplementing wheat and corn. Brewer's yeast is a by-product of the beer industry; it has a milder flavor than torula yeast, which is a by-product of the wood pulp-paper industry. Neither yeast produces carbon dioxide for leavening; use as a replacement for about 5—10% of the flour; start with the lower level in order to become accustomed to the flavor. Both are available in health food stores.

NFDM Nonfat Dry Milk   NFDM refers to the instant nonfat milk powder, in the dry form without reconstituting. If substituting the regular, or non-instant, high-density nonfat milk powder, reduce the amount used: 1/4 c regular nonfat dry milk is equivalent to the 1/3 c instant NFDM.

Parchment Paper   This paper is excellent for lining baking pans to facilitate removal of products and to reduce clean-up. Bakery supply houses carry it.

SAS Baking Powder   SAS (sodium-aluminum-sulfate-phosphate) is double-acting baking powder, like Calumet.

Seafood Seasoning   This mixture of celery and onion salts, monosodium glutamate, dill, and other herbs and spices is available in delicatessens and fish markets.

Soy Sauce   Different brands of soy sauce vary in flavor and saltiness. Sauce is available in 1/2 gal cans.

Textured Vegetable Protein (TVP)   TVP is available in natural and caramel-colored granules. Most health food stores and some metropolitan supermarkets carry it.

Tofu   Tofu is a type of soybean curd sold in Oriental markets and in the produce section of some large metropolitan markets. It comes in a plastic container immersed in liquid in a block about 3 x 3 x 5".

Tortillas   Tortillas can often be found in large metropolitan markets in the refrigerated food section or in markets that specialize in sale of Mexican foods. Frozen corn tortillas are not satisfactory for tacos as they tear easily, but they can be used for enchiladas and enchilada pie casserole.

Whole-Wheat Pastry Flour   This finely ground whole-wheat flour, made from soft wheat, becomes bitter if allowed to turn rancid. Purchase it from markets or health-food stores where it is kept refrigerated.

Won Ton Skins (or Wrappers)   These 3"-square pieces of thin dough are sold in cellophane packages of about 60 pieces in Oriental food stores and in the produce sections of some large metropolitan markets.

INDEX

ambrosia, 22; gel, 136
apple(s): baked, 23; brown betty,
    80; compote, 23; crisp, 24;
    glazed, 23; strudel, 120
applesauce, 22; cinnamon, 22;
    jellied cinnamon, 135
apricot cheese mold, 138; coconut
    balls, 282
asparagus oriental, 40
aspic: beef, and tomato relish, 137;
    cranberry, 135; tomato, 56
avocado shrimp mold, 138

bagels, 129
bananas in orange-apricot sauce, 25
batter-fried foods (tempura), 10-11
beans: baked, 245; chili, 222;
    green, with almonds, 40a; re-
    fried (frijoles), 246
beef: ground, with bean curd (tofu),
    248d; kabobs, 212; stew, 217;
    Stroganoff, 218; teriyaki, 213;
    tongue, 216
beet greens vinaigrette, 37
beets: Harvard, with canned beets,
    30; Harvard, with fresh beets, 29
biscuit mix, homemade, 99
biscuits, 96-99
bisque: oyster, 253; shrimp, 253
blancmange (vanilla pudding), 78
blintzes, 148
bok choy (Chinese chard), 35
bons bons, walnut, 195
bouillabaisse, 255
bouillon: curried tomato, 250,
    tomato, 291
breads, yeast, methods of preparing,
    122-131; raisin, 130; variations,
    123-124
breads, fruit-nut, 203-205
broth, Scotch, 254
brownies, 199; wheat germ butter-
    scotch, 200
Brussel sprouts with chestnuts, 36
buns, hot cross, 131

cabbage: Chinese, 35; red,
    Pennsylvania Dutch, 38

cakes: angel, 172-173; chiffon, 175-177;
    fillings for, 190-191; frosting and
    decorating, 191-192; shortened, 181-
    183; whole egg and yolk sponge, 173-175
canapés, 275; fillings for, 275-276;
    vegetable canapés, 274
caramel, 281
carrots, steamed, 31
casseroles: blackeyed pea, 246; hominy
    bean, 245; shrimp custard, 261
cereals, cooking methods, 62
chapatis, 87
chard, Swiss, with Swiss cheese, 35
cheese cake: baked, 148; unbaked, 148
chicken: à la King, 235; almond, 234;
    broiled, 233; cacciatore, 236; casserole,
    almond, 257; fried, 231; gumbo, 255;
    Mornay, 230; mousse, 55; oven braised,
    234; oven-fried, 232; paprika, 258;
    pressure-saucepan stewed, 233; stuffings
    for, 229; Teriyaki, 230; Tetrazzini,
    low-calorie, 259
chiles rellenos con queso, 67
chips, butterscotch nut, 197
chop suey, 220
chops, pan-broiled, 213
chowder, New England fish, 255
cocktail tidbits, 272-274
cocoa or chocolate milk, 294
coffee, 295-296
coffee cake, applesauce, 96; quick, 96
cole slaw, 57
collard greens with green chiles, 38
cookies: almond tea, 196; cherry coconut,
    197; chocolate chip, 194; chocolate
    refrigerator, 198; cinnamon sugar, 197;
    cottage cheese, 194; cream cheese, 199;
    gingerbread, 196; oatmeal drop, 193;
    sesame seed, 194; spritz, 198
cornish hen, rock, baked, 230
cottage cheese, 144; and fruit, 60
cranberry-orange relish mold, 54
cream: apricot Bavarian, 166; cocoa
    whipped, 191; strawberry Bavarian,
    167; chocolate Spanish, 168
cream cheese pompoms, 195
cream puffs, 88
crepes, 89; suzette, 89

crisps, peanut butter, 195
croquettes, salmon, 12
croutons, 51–52
curry: chicken, 234; lamb, 220; lima bean, 246; sauce, 74; tuna rice, 261
custard(s): baked, 155–156; condensed milk, 145; double chocolate, 139; lemon chiffon, 168; soft (stirred), 154–155

date-nut bars, 199
dippers, 272
dips, 270–272
divinity fudge, 281
doughnuts: cake, 12; yeast-raised, 133
dumplings, 98

egg(s): miscellaneous recipes, 157–159; nogs, 293; preparation of, 150–151
enchiladas, 248c; pie, 259

fish: au gratin, 241; baked, savory, 241; baked whole, 236; cakes, 240; fillets, baked, 236; oven-fried, 240; pan-fried, 239; poached, 239, 240; steaks or fillets, broiled, 237; stew, 241; sticks, 239
foams: egg white, 161–162; gelatin, 165–166; gelatin-egg, 168; gelatin-milk, 166–167; milk, 162–165
fondant, 278; cream, 279; cream cheese, 282
fondue: baked cheese, 146; Swiss, 146
French toast, 157
fritters, corn, 12
frosting(s): broiled, 187; cream cheese, 189; creamy decorative, 189; maple, 190; seven-minute, 189; uncooked (butter cream), 187–189
fruit(s): cup, 22; dried, rehydration of, 25; fresh, preparation of, 19–21; julep, 290; jumble, 53; medley, hot, with canned fruit, 24; hot, with fresh fruit, 24; -milk drinks, 292; nectar, jellied, 56; punches and drinks, 289–291; purées, preparation and use of, 25a; spicy, 25a
fudge, 280

gateau Florentine, 263–264
gelatin mixtures, preparation of, 134
glazes, 186–187
guacamole, 270

hamburgers, seasoned, 214
Hawaiian medley, 290
hopping John, 247

ice, orange, 284
ice creams, 286
ice milks, 284
icings, flat, 186–187; ornamental, 189

jambalaya, 263
jelly, lemon whey, 136
jelly roll, 175

kabobs: cocktail, 275; scallop, 238
kale with egg sauce, 37
kolachy, 201

lasagna, 260
legumes: cooked, in prepared dishes, 245–247; cooking methods, 243–245
lemon whip, 165
lentil stew, 247
liver: beef and onion, pan-fried, 214; chicken, and mushrooms, 234; creole, 220

macaroni and cheese, 263
macaroons, 170; salted peanut, 194
mayonnaise, 43; imitation, 45
meat balls, Swedish, 248
meat(s): cookery, 210–211; ground, dishes, 220; loaf, 221
meringues, 171
microwave cookery of vegetables, 39–40
milkshakes, 293–294
minestrone, 254
mousse, dessert, 286–288
muffins, 93–95; English, 129
mustard greens, 36

noodle dishes, 69
nut chews, 200

okra, sautéed, 39
omelets: egg, 152-153; puffy, 169
onions, creamed, 31
orange-pineapple whirl, 137
orange tea cakes, 198

pancakes, 89-91; homemade mix, 92
panocha, 280
parfait, toasted almond, 287
parmigiana, veal or beef, 215
parsnips Parmesan, 30
pastas, cooking methods, 65
pastry: Danish, 132; methods of
    preparing, 107
peanut brittle, 282
peanut butter fruit bars, 282
peanut krinkles, 199
peas: and mushrooms, 40; black-
    eyed curried, 40a
pies: chiffon, 113-116; cream, 113-116;
    custard, 111-112; fruit, 116-118;
    meringue, 113-116; shells, 110
pineapple: angel whip, 167; boat, 53
pizza, 125
popovers, 88
pork, sweet-and-sour, 219
pot roast, 216
potato(es): baked, 33; baked, stuffed,
    33; chips, 10; French-fried, 9; mashed,
    34; pancakes, German, 34; pan-fried, 8;
    scalloped, and ham, 262
poultry, preparation of, 223-225
pudding(s): caramelized condensed milk,
    145; cottage cheese, 147; dessert,
    78-80; rice, 68; Yorkshire, 88
puff pastry, basic recipe, 118
puris, 87

quiche Lorraine, 146

ragout, veal, 217
rarebit: tomato, 146; Welsh, 145
rice and barley dishes, 66-68; Spanish
    rice, 248b
ring, peasant, 131
roll(s): cinnamon (quick dough), 99;
    cinnamon (yeast dough), 130; pecan,
    99; yeast dinner, 127-128
rosettes (timbales), 12
roulade, 170; beef, 213
rutabagas, mashed, 32

salad(s): cranberry soufflé, 166; dressings,
    43-48; fruit, 52-54; gelatin, 54-56;
    green, 52; main dish, 58-61; preparation
    of basic ingredients, 49-52; vegetable,
    56-58
salmon loaf, 237
sandwich(es): cold, filling mixtures,
    266-267; club, 267; hot, 268-269;
    submarine, 268
sauce(s): Béarnaise, 47; dessert or sweet,
    75-77; Hollandaise, 44; meat and
    vegetable, 72-74; tartar, 47; white, 72
scones, 98
seafood: au gratin, Creole, 262; noodles
    au gratin, 261
shellfish, preparation of, 227-228
sherbet: avocado, 288; orange I and II, 284
shish kabob, lamb, 212
shortbread, 98
shrimp: broiled, 238; Creole, 240
sloppy Joe, 268
sole, breaded fillet of, 238
soufflé(s): lemon, 80; egg, 169-170
soups, 250-257
soybean loaf, 247
spaghetti, 248a
spinach: salad mold, 137; sesame, 38
squash: acorn, baked, 39; yellow,
    fiesta, 40
starch, methods to thicken mixtures
    with, 70
steak: chicken-fried, 214; Swiss, 218;
    tenderized beef round, 211
stock, preparation of, 249
stollen, 132
strawberry whirl, 135
sweet dough, basic, 130
sweet potatoes: candied with pineapple,
    32; easy glazed, 33

tacos, 248b
taffy, orange, 282
tamale pie, 260
tarts: cookie, 201; pastry, 119-120, 201
tea, brewing of, 295; iced, 295
tortillas, 87
turnips O'Brien, 31

veal: cutlets, 215; stuffed, 215

waffles, 91-93; homemade mix, 92
yogurt, 144
zucchini Romano, 39